Standing into the Storm

A journey from industry into
100 percent grassfed bison ranching
and a call to reclaim our
agrarian heritage

Kathy Margaret Lindner
with
Kenneth Robert Lindner, Jr.

Lindner Bison Publishing
27060 Victoria Lane, Valencia CA 91355

Copyright © 2011 by Kathy Margaret Lindner and Kenneth Robert Lindner, Jr.

All rights reserved.

LIBRARY OF CONGRESS CATALOGING IN PUBLICATION DATA.
Lindner, Kathy Margaret; Lindner, Kenneth Robert, Jr.
Standing into the Storm, a journey from industry into grassfed bison ranching and a
call to reclaim our agrarian heritage/Kathy Margaret Lindner with
Kenneth Robert Lindner, Jr.

ISBN 978-0-9838574-0-2

Printed in the United States of America

10 9 8 7 6 5 4 3 2 1

LINDNER BISON PHOTOGRAPHY BY KENNETH ROBERT LINDNER, JR.;
CATTLE QUEEN OF MONTANA PHOTO BY THE GIBSON STUDIO, BUTTE, MT

COVER AND DESIGN BY CONNIE JACOBS, CJ MEDIA, MONTCLAIR, CA

TITLE PAGE GRASS ART BY MIKE SIBLEY, WWW.SIBLEYFINEART.COM

"This courageous and triumphant story shows how returning to Mother Nature's model of raising animals results in healthier food, healthier animals, and a life that is more rewarding for ranchers. When bison eat grass, their native diet, everything begins to fall in place. Kathy and Ken Lindner's decision to walk away from convention and raise bison according to their convictions has lessons for all of us."

—Jo Robinson, author of *Pasture Perfect* (2011)
and founder/director of www.eatwild.com

FOR THE NEXT GENERATION OF
100% GRASSFED BISON PRODUCERS

CONTENTS

Introduction   1

Forward   3

Part I
THE BISURKEY® (bah ZUR key) YEARS
(1993-2002)

1   Legacy of the Cattle Queen of Montana®   9

2   Saving the Best for Last (1993)   15

3   Nothing Personal, Just Business (1994)   21

4   It's a Bisurkey World! (1996)   27

5   Lindner Bison is Born (1997)   35

6   Bisurkey in Georgia (1998)   53

7   Relocation to Pittsburgh (1999)   77

Part II
THE CALIFORNIA GRASSFED BISON® YEARS
(2002-2005)

8   Return to Southern California (2002)   95

9   The Last Layoff (2003)   111

10   Buying Heritage Ranch (2004)   121

11   Preparing Heritage Ranch (2005)   127

12   Bringing them Home!   133

13   Integration of the California and South Dakota herds   149

14   Miracle Hay Wagon   155

Part III

STANDING INTO THE STORM

(2006 to present)

15 The Valley of 2006 and the Resiliency of Passion   167
16 Rainbow Lodge (2007)   195
17 Running in Place   201
18 Margaret (2009)   207
19 Storm Standers   219

Part IV

WE'RE THE ONES WE'VE BEEN WAITING FOR

Disconnect/Reconnect – Introduction   229
20 – for Us   233
21 – for the Animals   255
22 – for the Earth   267

A Call to Action – Introduction   277
23 – for Individuals   279
24 – for Foodservice   287
25 – for Bison Producers   291
26 – Societal Call to Action   299

Summary   305
Acknowledgements   307
Appendix   313
Resources   315

INTRODUCTION

One hundred and twenty years ago, 90 percent of Americans were engaged in farming. Today, two percent of Americans are farmers. This means that up to 98 percent of us have no farming education or background.

Today in California alone aging farmers 65 years or older outnumber beginning farmers 25 years and older by a ratio of 60:1. Consequently, in another 10 years, the vast majority of those who currently grow our food will likely be either retired or dead.

Already efforts are underway by agri-business to fill this void. Tractor-like robotic machines guided by the Global Positioning System (GPS) are being developed to replace farm workers. With no pesky humans to breathe in or absorb industrial farm chemicals, the need to provide medical coverage and wages for farmers may soon be a thing of the past.

In the meantime, practicing sustainable agriculture and the ethical farming of multi-species of animals and plants, as opposed to monocrops of corn, soy, rice or grain, requires *more* committed people. The model pioneered by farmer-activist Joel Salatin shows us that it's possible, practical and profitable. As more Americans join the ethical food movement, however, a backlash has already begun in the form of raids on organic small farmers and audit of small farmers that result in the enforcement of laws created by and for big corporations against small farms that do not have the financial resources or people power to comply. There are also more farmers' markets exposés.

Unless we wake up, our only legal food sources may be from commercially run, chemically-laden, GMO-based farms or offshore food producers. The remaining local ranches and agricultural lands may be controlled by industrial farming corporations, land and housing developers, and farmland and rangeland trusts. (Interestingly, some of these non-profit trusts acknowledge multiple financial sponsorships and support from such agribusinesses and pharmaceutical giants as Monsanto,

Wyeth Laboratories, DuPont Chemical and others.)

For today's generation and those who follow, reasonable and even encouraging to consider that what we choose do for a living may no longer be limited or relegated to one career throughout our lives. A factory worker becomes a chef. An engineer becomes a doll maker. Yesterday's oilrig mechanic becomes today's organic farmer. A musician/composer partners with a secretary to become 100 percent grassfed bison ranchers.

The true nature of all living things is to expand and grow. Most humans fit this model. Like the land, which thrives from a variety of animals, insects, plants and trees performing different tasks in a complementary ballet, we humans seem to similarly respond diverse challenges. Even if uncomfortable, we seem to seek change and inner growth.

Key elements of our humanness, flexibility and diversity are what this book trumpets and calls forth. This is a book for individuals from all walks of life, who want to personally contribute to the basic tenets of any sustainable life cycle: ethical and humane production and consumption of chemically-free, non-cloned, non-GMO food produced by caring farmers and ranchers.

Standing into the Storm begs three questions: "If not now, when? If not here, where? If not me, who?"

FORWARD

Becoming a breast cancer survivor did one pivotal thing for my life. It forced me to get in touch with my mortality. Having a longer childhood than many, by the time I reached my mid-40's, I was unemployed, unmarried and had a lump in my breast. Then I had two lumps. By the time I found a job with medical insurance and waited 90 days for coverage to kick in, I had three lumps.

According to statistics, I am lucky. A Southern California surgeon removed my breast, replacing it with an implant I aptly dubbed "Grace." Six months of chemotherapy later, I had begun early menopause. Somewhere in there, I met, fell in love and became married to an incredible man. So while it was a mixed bag, it seems that in many ways the best part of my life has been saved for last.

This book is an extension of the love and caring I found late in life. It is anchored, in part, on a special promise that my husband and I included in our wedding vows. We promised simply that we would be willing to be teachable. As best friends, it reminded and encouraged us to remain open, flexible and to listen to our hearts. And this led us to finding our way out of corporate America into grassfed bison ranching and selling our meat in farmers' markets. Along the way, we learned many things that we share here. But most of all, we learned that it's about more than deciding to do something different. It's about *doing* something different.

We hope the book encourages and inspires you to join us in reclaiming our agrarian heritage and the gifts it bestows: a direct connection with the land, increased independence and self-sufficiency, a sense of identity and a feeling of belonging.

You are invited and you are welcome here.

I

THE BISURKEY® YEARS
(bah ZUR key)
(1993 – 2002)

*The true nature of all living things is to
expand and grow.*
—UNKNOWN—

There comes a moment when deep inside, you know it's time to move on. It may mean leaving the nest, abandoning the familiar, doing something different. You know that in order to grow, you must go. Recognizing that moment is the beginning of every great journey.

Within most lifetimes are multiple opportunities to expand, explore and grow. Sometimes I do this kicking and screaming all the way. Other times, exhausted or powerless, I allow myself to be carried by the current. Still other times are embraced and welcomed, sensing that wonders await that could not even be imagined.

This was all of those times.

CHAPTER 1

Legacy of the Cattle Queen of Montana®
(1871-1931)

You cannot lose your land and remain free.
If you keep your land, you cannot be enslaved.
—WENDELL BERRY—

We all have a legacy. It may come in the form of family history, influences of external events, accomplishments and experiences that shape and guide us. When Ken and I began our journey out of corporate America, to summon forth courage, we called forth the pioneering spirit of my great-grandmother. It is her legacy that repeatedly renewed us, offering strength and guidance as we entered uncharted waters. Because of the ongoing recession brought about largely by the greed-based decisions of Big Business and Big Money, we better understand any sense of betrayal, anger and desperation that she experienced.

Legacies are the fruit of what we decide to nurture, love and protect, and they can be a mixed bag—it's what we do with them that makes the difference. While you may not have a cattle queen in your family tree, you certainly have someone with a similar spirit and energy. We encourage you to find it, claim it and begin. There is work to be done.

I can only imagine how she must have felt as she watched her beautiful Delta home burn. A home she had built with the help of her now-absent husband. A home that had become the centerpiece, the heart, of the 3200 acre ranch that had prospered under her care for some 40 years.

Some people later speculated that she had struck the match herself. From what I've heard and read about her, she certainly seemed capable of this. It would have taken raw nerve, strength and courage—all things she knew how to summon in the days when most woman were expected only to prepare family meals, do the wash and attend church.

Sometimes I can see human outlines against a moonlit night, carrying things out of her home. From a nearby rise, she looks back one last time as the flames light up the night, knowing the insurance money was the only way to save her ranch.

For the most part, my great-grandmother remained a mystery to me. Though my middle name came from her, what little I knew was from hushed stories occasionally told. There were no photographs or keepsakes. A new story element arrived in my late teens when mom confessed there had been rumors about how her beautiful house had caught fire and burned.

"Some people thought she did it to collect the insurance money," mom said.

"Why would she do that?" I asked.

"It was during the Great Depression," she said. "If she did start the fire, it may have been to just survive. Everywhere banks were closing and people lost everything. She lost all her money too. In fact, the story goes that she had driven into town on a buckboard that day, all dressed up the way you did when going to town on business. There were people gathered outside the bank wanting their money but the bankers hiding inside wouldn't let them in. When they saw it was Grandma Carlston though, they opened the doors. They knew she had just been to the yearly auction. That day she deposited all the money she had made from the sale, about $68,000. How's your math? That was a lot of money back then. The next day the bankers were gone."

"But what about all her money?" I asked.

"It went with them," Mom said and waited for this fact to sink in. "There were no laws back then to protect people's savings if a bank closed. There are now, but at that time, there was nothing. Some people even committed suicide because of their losses, and everyone was poor. We sure were. We got rations of sugar and flour and us kids always wore hand-me-downs. I didn't have my first new pair of shoes until I started high school." The look on her face was resolute, remembering.

Usually about that time, mom launched into how good my sister and I had it. We each had two outfits a week to wear and shoes that fit, so I quickly lost interest. But the shock of learning about the betrayal by those who Great-Grandma had trusted stayed with me. Intuitively I sensed that the course of our family had been changed by the theft.

After Great-Grandma died, the ranch went to her four boys, and Archie, who had remained on the ranch with his wife Fanny, was in charge. When Archie died, the responsibility passed to Grandpa who by that time had moved back to the ranch from Elkhorn with Grandma and several children, Mom included. At some point, Grandpa began to buy up his brothers' shares of the ranch, sometimes paying as little as a dollar in exchange for paying their back taxes. Eventually he and Grandma sold the ranch and moved to Missoula. The ranch was lost to our family then. Mom and her siblings had grown up during the Depression and associated the ranch with poverty, so they had little interest in keeping it.

Though I wasn't raised on the ranch, Mom often told us about ranch life. Stories often described being poor, a concept that escaped me. There seemed to be plenty we didn't have and I heard the phrase, *we can't afford it,* often enough. In contrast, Mom told of swapping her rations of sugar with her brothers and sisters for things more meaningful to her. Another example occurred at an unusual outing with my aunt to see one of the popular Ma and Pa Kettle films. The good-natured Kettles always seemed to be barely scraping by on a dilapidated farm somewhere with a dozen or so kids to feed. Mom and her sister would burst out in laughter, identifying with the impoverished rural characters. People in the audience turned their heads to see who was laughing. When I later recovered from my embarrassment, I asked why they were laughing. They smiled briefly at each other before answering.

"Because it was funny," they said.

After mom passed, we buried her ashes up Paradise Valley, in the same plot as great-grandma Carlston. Shorthill Cemetery is reserved for farmers and ranchers who grew up in the valley. Since we had to cross private property to get there, we stopped at the closest house to ask for permission. The family there remembered my mother and the Carlston family.

"They were always dirt poor, but they were sure always happy," said the woman, a Pine Creek schoolteacher. Her kind recollections filled me with gratitude and for one last time I marveled at Mom's world as a child. Strangely, through her passing, my connection to ranching seemed to emerge. It's who my family was. It's where I came from.

With the main storyteller gone, I began reflecting on stories that included Great-Grandma Carlston. One of my favorites was about how she drove a buckboard through a blizzard one night to pick up Mom and Grandma from a community gathering at the old school. Whenever Mom told it, the story was just as vivid to me as the last time she told it.

"It was snowing like the dickens," she would say. "Grandma drove up in a buckboard and ordered us to get in the back and cover up with the old Indian blanket stored there. She told us to stay put and not to budge until we got back. And when she told us to do something, we did it. Hours later we got to the ranch and the buckboard finally pulled to a stop. We lifted the blanket off and there she was, solid white. She was completely covered with snow and ice, only her eyes showed through. We knew then it was a miracle that we made it home at all. She was tough."

But my first real spark of a connection had occurred when I read an article written in 1980. Dan Hollow, now editor of the *Great Falls Tribune*, worked for the *Livingston Enterprise* at the time. He interviewed Mom, her siblings and Paradise Valley residents who still remembered Great-Grandma Carlston. The article (reproduced on lindnerbison.com under *Pioneering Heroes)*, provides a collection of unique personal perspectives and a snapshot of the times.

One person recalled a kind-hearted, no-nonsense woman who had killed a rattlesnake to provide rattles to an orphan she was caring for. Another described a cold woman who thought nothing of stealing a calf as she drove her herd across open rangeland. While one story spoke of her generosity with those who worked at the ranch, another hinted that a man who had disappeared might have done so as a result of her defending herself during a time of lawlessness on a rugged frontier. Descriptions of lavish parties included tales of days of bootlegging and rumors of a romance with a politician. Some men said they just couldn't out-swear her.

So who was she really? I shared her name, but what did that mean? How could I ever really know? To complicate matters, we came across a 1982 magazine article that reported a different cattle queen of Montana with a completely different name. Ken and I had legally trademarked the unofficial title and after reading the article, were left wondering if our family had any right to such a claim.

Years passed. As the Internet grew and provided access to historical newspapers, a welcome clue emerged. In 2003, we conducted searches around the time of her death. News articles, one after the other, emerged. Statewide and out-of-state newspapers announced the death of the Cattle Queen of Montana. Hurriedly I scanned the articles for a name. It was there: Margaret Carlston. All the newspapers recognized Margaret Carlston as the Cattle Queen of Montana; no other name came up. For our family, finally, it was confirmed. She indeed was known and notable. More than a story, more than a family secret, she was real.

More research uncovered an unexpected treasure in a 1931 editorial of the local paper, the *Livingston Enterprise* at the time of her death. Someone who knew her strengths and frailties, assets and liabilities, acknowledged the mixed perceptions of others in a tribute to a Montana pioneer. She was loved, deeply respected and defended by one who knew her heart, her soul, her sacrifices and her spirit. This touching editorial provided an essential emotional connection and would resonate with what we would later experience on our new path.

Then in early 2011, the Internet bequeathed yet another gift in the way of perspective of the times. A book posted by the Montana Historical Society (montanahistoricalsociety.org) provided a timeline of state, national and world events which three generations of Carlstons experienced.

As Ken and I had struggled just to buy and homestead land for our bison, there were times when we couldn't help but wonder how a ranch that she had fought so hard to keep, could have been relinquished. Reading the timeline on montanahistoricalsociety.org, it became clear. While Ken and I have only experienced a three-year drought at our ranch, that paled in comparison to Montana's ten-year drought from 1917-1927. During this time half of all Montanans lost their land. The drought was followed by the 1929 stock market crash and the Great Depression that lasted until 1941. Then, as if that weren't enough, in 1930 the drought returned, worse than ever. It lasted seven years to 1937, the statewide economic impact of which was *in addition* to the impact of the Dust Bowl experienced by the nation as a whole.

Under such conditions, it was understandable how the family had come to associate ranching with 24 years of unrelenting abject poverty. On a personal level the information helped provide a deeper acceptance and appreciation. While I grieve the loss of the ranch and community in a valley that I've always loved, I came to appreciate the legacy of Great-Grandma Carlston fiercely pioneering what she believed in and of my ancestors having the fortitude to persevere and survive over 24 years of drought, economic depression and a level of poverty usually associated with third-world countries. And their neighbors remembered them as happy. This was the heritage we reclaimed in 1997 when we started Lindner Bison.

Because of our own small ranch, we understand the connection Great Grandma had with her ranch, no doubt the source of much of her strength. We see how working our land has changed us, creating an alliance and synergy of energies unlike anything we could have imagined or asked for. For us, as it was for her, the survival of our ranch has become of overriding importance. More than the greater sum of our novice efforts, it more closely reflects characteristics of an emergent structure.

Despite this, I still sometimes find that I miss the friends and family members who have fallen away. There is no time or money for social outings, vacation trips, dinners or concerts. Priorities are reassigned for us based on the weather, animals and the seasons. Our ability to pay our bills depends on having meat to sell to the customer base we've worked hard to create. Fleeting personal exchanges are reminiscent of a life now past that surprisingly has little appeal. For each person who may express sympathy that we are "working so hard at our age," there are ten more who express envy, perhaps fantasizing versions of ranching life fabricated from various sources. Many will never know the passion that so consumes us now.

Part of the reason for sharing our story is to correct these fantasy perceptions of what life is like for individuals today who are ethically and sustainably producing meat on small farms and ranches. But mostly our hope is that by sharing our journey, we may identify roadblocks, obstacles and challenges that need to be addressed in order to inspire and empower those who follow.

It was only after finding Ken that ranching and other miracles seemed possible. But before we could begin, we had first to meet.

CHAPTER 2

Saving the Best for Last
(1993)

Opportunities for new beginnings often happen with the most unlikely collisions of tragedy and joy. When brought to my knees by uncontrollable events, I embraced what some call "the sweet willingness of the dying." Through that willingness, another door opened and my life would change forever in a wondrous way.

———— • ————

I heard about Ken before I met him. Byron, our general manager, had worked with him in Reno and was eagerly waiting his arrival in San Diego to head up the newly created Quality Assurance (QA) department of American Innovision (AI). Byron who was in his mid-fifties, about my height at 5-foot 7-inches, smiled fondly as he described Ken, saying only, "He's a tall guy."

This conversation stands out because around this time, I had a few things going on. During the previous year, I'd found a small lump in my breast. Then two. X-rays revealed suspicious calcium deposits sometimes indicative of breast cancer. Afraid and while waiting for health insurance to kick in with my new job, I found myself in a bookstore in Old Encinitas one night after work. They allowed psychic readings there and I hadn't had one for quite a while, so for $25, I waited. A middle-aged woman appeared and led me into a reading room. More like a fishbowl, it had a simple yet welcoming wood table, wood chairs, and windows on four sides looking out into the bookstore.

Calmly she laid out her cards and studied them. Almost immediately she talked about a tall man coming into my life. I knew no tall men, but remembered Byron's comment about his new hire, which I mentioned to her. Quietly she laid out more cards and scanned them. Suddenly her eyes grew wide.

"This could be him," she said, studying the cards, then glancing up at me. "This could be the one. "

Her energy had changed and she was excited, but I elected not to join in. *It sure would be nice*, I told myself. But I had hoped before. Still single at forty-two years old, I was unwilling to get my hopes up. In fact, it had been so long since I'd had a meaningful relationship, it was hard to imagine one would now magically appear.

Yet when I saw Ken for the first time, I couldn't help but be drawn to him. A tall man at 6-foot 5-inches, he had dark, naturally curly hair, which was beginning to thin slightly. He was clean cut, which I liked. His manner and energy were clear and deliberate. Talking to others in the open office corridor, papers in hand, he was waiting for Byron to come out of a meeting. I walked over and introduced myself. Looking up into his hazel eyes, as we shook hands I felt a solid, strong presence, a different kind of depth that I hadn't experienced before. In the moment of that handshake and brief exchange, I sensed an innate goodness, clarity and then more goodness. My heart raced a little as I returned to my cubicle.

My job sent me to a New York tradeshow to help market our company's product. While there, I found a third lump in my breast. Having just qualified for health insurance, I had a doctor's appointment a week after coming back, and had invited Ken to lunch.

We enjoyed our lunch and the next week, he invited me for a sports car rally. Somewhere in between I had an inconclusive needle biopsy and a conclusive breast biopsy. It was cancer.

With the reality of scheduling surgery, my fear and anxiety levels reached new heights in a roller coaster fashion. I had felt alone before, but nothing like this. In this journey, I really was alone and had no one to turn to. I couldn't pretend everything was okay because it wasn't. If I was to survive, innately I knew I needed support but where would I find it? One day at the office, it suddenly struck me there were plenty of people around me right there. With that realization and unable to cope, I made a deal with God. Rather than be falsely stoic, I agreed to accept any and all help that came my way. For the first time there were no bargaining chips, because I had none. It didn't matter who offered help or what form it took. If help was offered, I'd regard it as heaven sent and I'd accept it. It was then that a sense of calm and peace returned.

Deal made, I decided to keep my date with Ken. Even if we couldn't stand each other after a day, at the least it would be a good distraction and that would be helpful. As it turned out, it was the first real date either one of us had had in years and it was great.

Early Saturday morning he picked me up in his dark green Miata convertible. Fifteen minutes later, we pulled into a parking lot joining about forty Miata sports car convertibles of every imaginable color. Miata buffs of all shapes and sizes were happily greeting each other, swapping stories and comparing cars. There was an air of excitement and fun. A woman with a clipboard came over as soon as we arrived.

"Good morning," she cheerfully greeted us. "Let's see who you are."

"Lindner," said Ken and we waited while she studied her clipboard.

"Yup, Ken and Kathy. Okay, here's your number. You're all set. We're scheduled to leave . . . " and her voice faded as she gave instructions and directions to Ken about the day. As soon as she said our names, I heard nothing else. It flowed so easily off her tongue, *Ken and Kathy*. It sounded so natural. She had no way of knowing it was our first date and I was embarrassed by the impact of hearing our names together for the first time.

The rally started from Pea Soup Anderson's in Carlsbad and ended at Fallbrook. The fast pace and twisty mountain roads quickly gave me a queasy stomach, for which Ken later apologized. As we would learn at our first designated stop, he had inadvertently placed us toward the front of the rally, a position that means you prefer to drive fast. I had thought that going at top speed was Ken's preference. What I learned was that he was just trying to keep up. If we went too slowly, we lost sight of the car in front and were tailgated by the car in back. For novices, it was quite a balancing act, but it was a fun, comfortable time and the hours went by quickly.

That day we got to know each other. His father was a retired Army Colonel, so he had gone to several schools growing up, including France and Germany. He had a younger brother and sister who lived on the east coast. His parents spent part of their time in Florida and New Hampshire. I learned that as a child, he had asthma, so instead of playing sports, he learned to play the trombone. Discovering that he had a natural talent, as a teenager he was invited to play in the Honolulu symphony while his family was stationed there. He received a partial scholarship to attend the Oberlin College and Conservatory, where he graduated with a teaching degree. After graduating he taught at Hamilton High School in upstate New York where his underdog kids proudly won awards in their statewide band competitions. After a few years though, he left and became a computer tech which paid more money. Over the years, he'd taught himself reliability engineering and began being promoted into managerial positions as head of quality assurance for various high tech companies and then medical device companies. Divorced for seven years, his teenage son lived with his mother in Phoenix. He loved *Star Wars* movies and classical music, which he also composed. He had a passion for reading a variety of genres, mostly science magazines, biographies, history as well as general fiction and non-fiction.

He learned that I attended the University of Montana, majoring in Liberal Arts. Feeling out of place there, within a few years I moved to Seattle with friends and got a job with the railroad. After several years, I took a job in Japan working for a fashion and textile executive and traveling internationally with him. Though I'd had a few serious relationships, I had not married. My father retired from the highway department and lived in Montana and my mom died seven years ago. They were divorced when I was three. My sister was recently divorced and lived in Solana Beach. For the last 20 years, I'd lived in San Diego though I had worked a few years in Los Angeles and Salt Lake before returning. The extent of my musical abilities was singing in the shower. We shared a preference for classical music and I confessed to enjoying country music. I liked science fiction movies too, but was rarely drawn to reading fiction, preferring nonfiction instead. We both liked to cook and considered ourselves non-denominational Christians; we both chose to give a wide berth to political and religious zealots. All in all, it was a comfortable day.

Finally, the rally was over and it was time for everyone to leave. Back at my apartment, we visited for awhile before I walked him back outside to his car. Extending my hand, I thanked him for a fun day and said how much I enjoyed it. As he took it, he agreed that he had a good time too.

"Well, see you on Monday, " he said.

It's my practice to wait until visitors drive away before going in, so I stood and watched as Ken got out his car keys and walked over to his car. He stopped. Instead of opening the door, he turned around and walked back to where I was standing, put both hands on my shoulders, leaned over and gently kissed me. As we said goodbye a second time, as ridiculous as I knew it was at my age, I suddenly felt light-headed. He liked me and he wanted me to know it. I was so out of practice at being liked by someone who I liked too, I hoped my neighbors didn't notice that I nearly floated back to my apartment.

Our initial courtship period was interrupted by my being gone from work for two weeks for breast cancer surgery. A generous neighbor drove me to the hospital and Mary, who I'd known for twenty years, decided my recovery should include a week with her and her boyfriend Dan in Long Beach. I was grateful and happy to be distracted by their cheerful and practical expressions of caring.

During this time, I heard nothing from Ken. I had given him Mary and Dan's phone number and told them he may call. He didn't. Knowing about our date, when no call came, as good friends do, they said nothing.

At first I was disappointed. Then on further reflection, I considered the reasonable likelihood that he had decided he wasn't willing to take a chance on someone with cancer. It was certainly understandable. There was no guarantee. If it wasn't that, there were other elements. Though surgery included reconstruction, depending on an individual's perspective, I might now be regarded as less than whole, even if my prognosis was excellent. I found this possibility a little sad, yet still understandable. With that last thought, I let go and acceptance came.

The first week back at work, coworkers warmly welcomed me with good wishes and said to let them know if there was anything they could do to help. Mindful of my deal with God, I immediately accepted their offer. Men and women alike were drafted to help with a five-minute exercise to help stretch my arm muscles, which had been cut during surgery. The exercise was so painful that I hadn't done them. The lack of progress hadn't escaped my surgeon, who was now threatening another surgery to correct the tightening muscles if I didn't step up to the plate. His comment produced the desired effect. Thanks to him and the kindness of co-workers, today I enjoy full use and strength of that arm.

Toward the end of my first week back, to my surprise, Ken invited me for a second Miata ride. It was on Easter Sunday. We agreed to an early brunch in Encinitas overlooking the ocean, and then to an Easter parade in La Jolla. He was warm and considerate and explained he hadn't called because he didn't know Mary and Dan and he didn't want to intrude.

Months later, he confessed that while I was away, as I suspected, he had become concerned that he may become involved with someone whom he liked a lot and who had cancer. Though he was optimistic and leaning toward furthering our relationship, if it developed as he hoped, there was no guarantee that I would survive in the long term.

It was during this time that Ken had a series of email exchanges with his sister Jill. He outlined the situation and confided that he was leaning toward becoming more serious, but wanted to use her as a sounding board.

"So what do you think?" Ken asked in an email. The next message from Jill read, *Go for it*, commenting that I could be hit by a bus too. On hearing this, I immediately fell in love with Jill.

"What if she had said *No?*" I asked.

"Oh, I had pretty much already made up my mind," he smiled gently. "I was optimistic that you would be fine. And you will be. It was just nice to have her input."

From that Easter Sunday on, we became inseparable. One night he proposed and I accepted. We picked out my engagement ring and finally let others at work know. They were surprised and happy for us.

Reluctantly, Ken agreed to a one-year engagement. I didn't know what to expect from the chemotherapy regime and rightfully decided that planning a wedding may be more than I could handle. Also, I felt time was still needed for us to get to know each other better. I confess that in spite of the miracle of finding him, inside I was riddled with doubt and fear. During our first few years of marriage, he would help me work through these fears, which teetered somewhere between fear of commitment and fear of abandonment. Actually I had to totally learn the commitment part. Previous relationships had lasted a year or two and then ended. I had no experience or track record with anything longer than that. With us, it didn't matter. Ken proved himself an able teacher by example and I, a willing student. He is still the best example of commitment to a partner I've ever known. His loyalty extends not only to me, but to others too. And as I learned about the give-and-take elements of commitment, over time my fear of abandonment was replaced by a sense of grace and deep joy.

When I think back to that time of meeting and falling in love with him, it takes on a surreal tone. I had been diagnosed with breast cancer and was lining up surgery and postoperative help. As may sometimes be the case during a life-threatening event or crisis, I had no bargaining chips in my deal with God. I simply promised to accept the help from any and all who offered it. I would deny no one. With absolute clarity, the promise was unconditional.

Thinking back to the very moment I made that promise and the universe accepted it, I could see that the doors and windows to my soul flew open and stayed open. And in walked Ken, along with caring coworkers and friends. In time, as often happens, my coworkers and friends would change but Ken, my love, my soul mate, remained. With him beside me, the best part of my life had begun.

CHAPTER 3

Nothing Personal, Just Business
(1994)

Now you know how Ken and I got together, but nothing about our background or skills that could relate to running a business. All of life's lessons are valuable when they are harnessed and applied to new uses. We believe that our years in the corporate world were of great help to us.

Here's a little exposé of the kinds of things we experienced before deciding to jump ship and strike out on our own. It helped to mold our thoughts about our own business and how it would be different.

Some of this may sound familiar.

———◆———

With each passing day, it was becoming clear that neither one of us would have a job much longer.

Ken and I had met, fallen in love and become engaged while working for an exciting new startup company in San Diego. Conditioned by decades of the profit driven model of doing business, we were convinced that "getting in on the ground floor" would provide a great opportunity for us, a strong motivation for joining any start-up company. Working long hours and wearing several hats to keep the company lean and mean was the norm and expected. Though risk is often associated with startups, the carrot is a greater reward for hard work and taking that risk. We were all for it.

The company, American Innovision (AI), designed and manufactured optical recognition products, which used video cameras to do automatic inspection of pharmaceutical capsules. Product offerings had been expanded to include a special new "cooled" camera, used to image chromosomes in cells to detect a predisposition to certain cancers. The new camera captured the interest of a company called Oncor. Soon Oncor purchased AI in order to acquire this state-of-the-art process, making AI's founders, Susie and Jose, millionaires almost overnight.

Oncor was based in Gaithersburg, Maryland, but the integration of systems was to remain in San Diego. However, shortly after the initial introduction of the two cultures, the acquiring company's healthy ego surfaced. Meeting after meeting, those of us in San Diego felt that we were considered merely the technical, operational and manufacturing pawns—the grunts—while Oncor's personnel, from the lofty positions of their advanced degrees, were the scientists, the brains. Ken and I agreed we didn't care how we were labeled, as long as the opportunity was there.

I was the company's marketing assistant. Ken was tapped to create and head the San Diego Quality Department, establishing the necessary ISO 9001 regulatory policies and systems that would lead to critical registrations that are traditionally the precursor to selling into European and other markets.

I was not included in management meetings, but I had the benefit of hearing about them first-hand from Ken. During a meeting with the visiting new president, Ken learned that the company had decided to hand-select certain management positions to relocate to the East Coast and then shut down production in San Diego.

"I think we need to be looking for another job," he said reluctantly. After less than a year at his current position, he disliked the idea of starting over again somewhere else.

"They can replace me, " I said, "but if Byron brought you here, I would think they'd want to keep you." It didn't seem to make him feel any better. He had been to meetings on the east coast and had experience with the people there. He was not impressed.

"The people from San Diego are treated like hicks from the sticks," he said. Normally patient, reasonable and likely to give others the benefit of the doubt, it was unusual to see him angry. When he's angry, I've learned there's usually a good reason.

"Why do you say that?" I asked.

"Let's just say their mouths match their egos," he replied. Then he outlined other fundamental and practical downsides to moving to the East Coast such as high heat, humidity and the Maryland traffic. He didn't want to live there.

"We may have no choice but to start looking, honey," he said. "The Oncor president was very clear when they first received the financing to buy AI. He told us 'It's an exciting time, an exciting place to be. We have the technology, we have the backing, and we have the right people. If this thing fails, it will only be because we (management) screwed it up. '"

Unfortunately, we had already begun to see signs of mismanagement. Sales were not going well and ethical questions about potential misuse of the new technology were beginning to surface. For example, if our technology indicated a patient was predisposed to cancer, what were the ramifications when he or she needed medical insurance? This type of unanswered concern was becoming prevalent as advances in technology outpaced the creation of ethical guidelines for its use.

Finally, we agreed. Ken would contact headhunters and see what was available on the west coast. In spite of just starting a six-month regime of chemotherapy, I would start looking around too. We had to beat them to the punch. This wasn't the first time we'd seen this kind of handwriting on the wall. We couldn't sit back and hope things would improve because in our experience, they wouldn't.

As it turned out, within two months, I unexpectedly submitted my resignation. Following my mastectomy, and in my third month of chemotherapy, my boss, without warning, wrote a job review citing degradation of my work performance. Verbally he explained that he couldn't make allowances for my cancer any more than he could for someone who had a common cold. I was devastated, and Ken, from a human management perspective, was outraged.

"You don't hit someone when they're down," he said. "If he had a problem, there are a lot of things he could've done. He could've said something, he could've shown support by hiring a temp to back you up, he could've given you time until you could recover." With Ken's support, but without a job to go to, I submitted a resignation letter.

Gratefully, a company where I had done temporary work before, needed help in their marketing and advertising department. Almost immediately I contracted for the summer. The company was called Kelco and their main business was manufacturing commercial food fillers/ stabilizing agents such as xanthan gum and gellan gum. They developed formulas and provided ingredients for products such as low-calorie syrups, clear dressings, bakery products and other food applications. They paid well.

After I left Oncor, Ken interviewed locally but saw nothing as a fit until he was offered a job in Santa Barbara. Neither one of us knew anything about Santa Barbara, but when he gave notice, a co-worker voiced his approval.

"Everyone wants to live there," laughed Steve on hearing Ken's news. "But no one can find a job. Here you come along and get a job there right off the bat. How did you do it?"

Initially we puzzled over our new envy-worthy status. After moving there, though, we quickly understood. An upscale established community, nestled along the coast with the mountains on one side and ocean on another, Santa Barbara had somehow managed to protect itself from the urban sprawl experienced by so many coastal towns. It had retained a comfortable, small town feel making it easy to fall in love with everything about it.

Housing, though, was expensive. While I finished out my contract and planned a June wedding long distance, Ken took a small, temporary apartment near the university. Our San Diego house wouldn't sell in the down real estate market of 1994, so we became reluctant landlords and rented it out after owning it for only eight months. Without a down payment, this meant also renting in Santa Barbara. We found the lower part of an older duplex that wonderfully backed up to soothing and historic Mission Creek. Except for tiny tree frogs croaking their evening lullaby, it was quiet, spacious and affordable.

After the wedding, we settled into married life. I began working a few temporary and contract jobs before getting a full time job as Assistant to the Vice President of Investor Relations for Tenet Healthcare, a company that planning to set up headquarters in Santa Barbara.

Tenet, a hospital management firm, was the phoenix from the ashes of National Medical Enterprises (NME) of Santa Monica, which had crashed and burned after a scandal. The board of directors brought in two young investment banking executives from the movie industry to head the company as CEO and CFO. After restructuring, it was determined the executive offices would be located in Santa Barbara and the company moved there, where the CEO currently lived. Following two months of training in Santa Monica, the new building was finally ready. I helped pack up the department and settled into my new job back home.

And I loved it! There was a great energy to the place, people were positive and I was well paid. Here I would learn about investor relations – that is, relations with stockbrokers, the stock market, stockholders and quarterly reporting to Wall Street. My boss encouraged rather than micro managed. I was 46 years old and happy with my life, which seemed to synergistically work on all levels – wonderful husband, great boss and co-workers, charming new town and dear friends within a few hours drive.

We both had good paying jobs and benefits, terrific location, we were hiking and biking on weekends. The future looked bright on all fronts.

Ken's new job, which had taken us to Santa Barbara, was with a company called Circon. Circon was among the emerging medical manufacturing facilities at the time, seemingly awash in investment capital.

Looking back, medical was a big deal in the '90s, the way computers were in the '70s. Money began shifting over into healthcare, medical devices and biotechnology, so companies like Oncor, Circon and Tenet were all riding high when we were with them.

As is true in most industries, when there's money to be made, empire-building is the norm. *Takeover or be taken over* are the watchwords and people, being human, may become greedy. Tenet and Circon were both affected by this dog-eat-dog mentality, as were we.

Chief competitors for Circon included U.S. Surgical and for Tenet, Healthcare South. Following the failed takeover attempt of their competitor, rumors about Tenet began surfacing. These rumors created a chronic public relations migraine and its ripple effects were felt in the Investor Relations Department where I worked.

One of the rumors accused a doctor of performing unnecessary surgery to bump up the hospital's profits. Fiercely loyal, I was shocked. Working daily with the top executives, I knew them as talented, fine people and, I was sure, of the highest moral fiber. The rumors persisted. Almost in proportion to their acquisition of new hospitals, Tenet was accused of taking shortcuts. The press began to portray the company as valuing profits over caring for people.

In those days, Tenet's CEO and CFO were uncharacteristically young and inexperienced in the health care industry. A few years later, an even younger financial whiz kid was brought in from Wall Street and seemed out of place in a new department created for him. Most of us couldn't figure out why he was there. He in turn, hired even younger financial assistants, clearly eager to make their mark in a Fortune 500 company. They kept to themselves and it was rumored that they had all known each other previously.

One evening I was working late and as I walked by a cubicle where the group had gathered, I inadvertently head a low voice say, "All I know is that if anyone asks, just lie like a rug." I never did learn the context of that remark, which I now surmise had to do with strategizing a hostile takeover attempt of a competitor. At the time, I was shocked at what I perceived as a partnership of entitlement and deceit within the halls of a company I had come to admire and respect for its integrity.

Was I naïve? Ken didn't seem surprised when I told him about the comment I wished I hadn't overheard. Maybe he was right to distance himself at every opportunity.

Eventually the CEO was asked to resign with a golden parachute worth millions of dollars. The CFO, whiz kid in tow, relocated as CEO to Texas. According to early 2011 online resources, they are currently dealing with a hostile take over attempt. This kind of corporate dynamics and history are all too common in America today.

In Circon's case, it turned out that they had no stock watch program in place. As a result, one morning they woke to find their chief competitor, U.S. Surgical, had purchased a large block of stock, making Circon the object of a hostile takeover. It would be the longest recorded hostile takeover battle in U.S. history. After spending extensive legal sums, Circon put itself on the market and was sold to a company called Maxxim. Within a short time it was dismantled and Circon employees were either brought on board at Maxxim or left to fend for themselves.

As seasoned veterans of buyouts and takeovers, Ken and I share different perspectives on these or similar events. Ken believes that often corporations lock horns, based on the egos of those running them, though activities may be couched it in the guise of what's good for stockholders. Being close to the source, he believes it's the personalities, not the principles, that drive a corporation's demise.

I view these events as often being the result of the deceit of good people by those given positions of power without ethical grounding or life experience. Without life experience, how can integrity and ethics be invoked, when the model for success is profit at any cost?

Nothing personal, just business.

CHAPTER 4

It's a Bisurkey World!
(1996)

When something isn't working, what do you replace it with and how? Ken and I had experienced decades of downsizing, reorganizing, layoffs and firings, all of which were outside of our control. We felt like intelligent ping-pong balls. No sooner did we set out in one direction, than we were bounced into another. It was time to consider breaking loose from this cycle. As we began to explore alternatives, another world emerged. For us it was bison ranching and the way there was through Bisurkeyland.

———————————————

Shortly after becoming engaged and before moving to Santa Barbara, we began thinking about what we wanted from the next stage of our lives. We were fully in love and had a seasoned perspective that grounded discussions about our future together.

My life had been full of personal struggles, highs and lows, victories and defeats and hard won emotional progress, as I found answers by seeking, finding and applying widely accepted spiritual principles. For me, finding Ken was a loving completion and gift.

For Ken, having been married before, it was a second chance and a new beginning. We shared information about our previous relationships with others. Our weaknesses, our failings, our sorrows, strengths and joys were all laid out. We discussed how and why our marriage would be successful and what we would do differently to ensure its survival. We had few illusions left about who we were and what we wanted. The love and excitement at finding each other was tempered in practicality and maturity. For all intents and purposes, we were entering the final stage of our lives. Together, we were partners in its planning and execution. We both sensed it held promise for the most joyous chapter yet.

One night over dinner, I broached the subject of retirement.

"I'm wondering about where we want to be or what we want to do when we retire," I said tentatively, gently pulling a piece of bread apart. "When you think back, is there anything you've always wanted to do? Anything you always dreamed of doing, but never did?"

Ken thought for a moment, carefully considering the question.

"I've always wanted to live on the land," he said.

I was touched. He said it in a way that was sheepish, almost apologetic that he would want something so simple as that.

"When I was in Reno," he continued, referring to where he lived as a newly single man for seven years. "I had a garden there. I loved it. When I got home at night, I was tired, but somehow I always had enough energy for that garden. It was a retreat for me. And it produced such good food. I grew the best potatoes I've ever had in my entire life." He paused, reliving the experience. "I've always liked growing things," he added.

I saw that it meant a lot to him and was exactly what I was hoping for. To find out more about him, to find out what he loved and enjoyed. While he was pleasantly lost in thought, remembering his garden, my mind began racing. What he wanted was so close to what I had always wanted to do. How could we do what he wanted to do and what I wanted, too?

"That's interesting," I said. "I've always wanted to live on a ranch."

"Oh. A ranch? What would we do on a ranch?" he asked.

"Well, I wonder what you'd think about raising bison," I said. "The meat is really good and very easy to digest. I had it in Montana years ago."

As he considered the shift in focus, I began to feel guilty. Ranching wasn't exactly farming, which is what he had described.

"If we could find a way to live on the land and have the land pay for itself, maybe we could do something like that," I said. "The animals could be raised for meat and it would help make the payments. It could be a kind of active retirement. And we could have a garden too."

"I don't know," he said. "Maybe. I've never had the meat, so I don't know what it tastes like. I don't know anything about bison. But I guess it wouldn't hurt to take a look."

As we cleared the table, we talked about how we could learn more. I described my experience eating the meat years ago. In Livingston for mom's memorial service, my sister and I had gone to a local restaurant for lunch. Without thinking, I agreed to try a buffalo burger. [Technical note: American bison, aka bison bison, is a member of the Bovidae family.

Bison may sometimes incorrectly be called "buffalo," though buffalo is actually a different species originating outside North America.] Almost immediately I had buyer's remorse.

It'll probably taste like bear, I thought, annoyed at myself. *Not that I've ever had bear. But what ever bear tastes like, that's probably what buffalo tastes like.*

The waitress brought our order and instead of it tasting like bear, it was absolutely delicious! Slightly sweeter than a regular beef burger and fuller flavored.

"Gee, this is good," I said as sister smiled. My enthusiasm quickly waned as I then remembered that digesting red meat was something I'd had problems with for years. Any beef I ate seemed to take two to three days to digest. I chalked this up to being a child of the '60s and practicing the "I'm-going-to-live-forever" self-destructive behavior, which included drugs, alcohol, smoking and excessive dieting. For years I had deduced that my body had been permanently affected and was no longer able to digest red meat.

I prepared myself for the inevitable discomfort that never came. Instead I was hungry by dinnertime. Thinking it was a fluke, the next day I made a point of going back to the same restaurant to have the exact same thing. Once again, it tasted great and once again, I was hungry later that day.

Having the experience of easily digesting red meat was a welcome surprise and relief. And it tasted so good. It actually had flavor. A new thought came that this would be a good business. Unfortunately, though, it was totally impractical. Even if I had the money to buy an animal, what would I do with it? I didn't know any ranchers who would want to keep one for me and I sure had no place to put such an animal. The idea was dismissed as quickly as it arrived but I still wanted access to the meat.

I can't be the only one who knows how great this meat is. If I just wait, other people with money and resources will certainly get this into the marketplace. In fact, many new things often start in California, so I shouldn't have long to wait.

Armed with the logic of letting someone else do it, my version of the trickle down theory, I congratulated myself and returned to San Diego. Within a few days I found I was unwilling to wait for the trickle and made a call to the Livingston restaurant to see where my burger had come from. Maybe the meat was already being sold in southern California and I just didn't know. I tracked the meat to a ranch near Missoula in the Flathead area. They said they didn't ship outside the state.

Nearly 10 years later, I still remembered the incredible burger that I was describing to Ken. After dinner, I called a few health food stores to see if they had any bison meat. Finally calling one in Pacific Beach, the man in the meat department said he'd order it but it would take two weeks. To his surprise, I agreed and he wrote down my name and phone number. Two weeks later, we drove across town and paid $20 for what I remember to be one very small steak.

Back at the apartment, Ken studied it as it cooked in the fry pan. Once it was done, he quickly found that he loved the meat too.

"Okay," he said, "so what we do now is see what we can find out about doing this for a living. There must be a trade association of some kind that we can find online." I knew little about the internet back then and dutifully followed him into the den where he turned on his computer.

It wasn't long before we found and joined the American Bison Association (ABA). We also bought a book on bison production and visited a local university library to research industry databases. With the limited and dated information in the library, our focus returned to the ABA.

After the ABA merged with another group called the National Buffalo Association and formed a new organization called the National Bison Association (NBA), online information seemed to become more available. Old and new members alike were active on a new e-listserv called the *Bison Digest*. Here we learned about bison's money-making potential and most agreed there was more demand for the meat than there was supply. It was a good start.

Research and learning continued with our move to Santa Barbara. For the next two years, we read the listserv daily and asked plenty of questions. Enthusiastic information was exchanged and here we learned about the industry, the animals and about the people across the country who raised them. It was the first thing we read in the morning and the last thing at night. It provided hope and a welcome porthole into what our new life might look like.

Searching unsuccessfully in the online forum for answers concerning meat production and sales to private individuals, I became aware of a rancher in Minnesota named Mike. He seemed to be one of a few producers who shipped meat to customers. He had no email, so unlike the online exchanges with other bison producers, contact with him was by phone only and with a two-hour time difference factored in.

One morning, I called and introduced myself. It was clear he was busy, but once he learned we hoped to become bison producers, he was generous with his time, opinions and information. Once he let it slip that he usually was up by 5:00 a.m., (7:00 a.m. California time). After that, I became a regular pest, calling early and often, catching him before we all started our respective days. I always had just one more question. And as busy as he was, he always made time. His focus was building the meat market and he told us about his experience doing that. He said that's where we needed to focus too, if we were going to raise bison.

"Some producers just want to make money selling live animals," he said. "But if everyone did that without building a market for the meat, guess what? Pretty soon, they'll be out of business."

Later, Ken and I talked about this, and agreed. It sounded too much like the ostrich industry years earlier. Back then, ostrich eggs climbed as high as $3000 each, after which the industry crashed because no one had worked on developing a market for ostrich meat. To us, it was a typical get-rich-quick pyramid scheme. We hoped that the bison industry wasn't headed in the same direction.

"People want the meat," Mike said one Saturday over the phone. "So that's not the problem. In fact, the biggest problem you'll have is that there is more demand than there is supply. I can't keep up with orders. Those folks who just want to sell the animals for breeding are doing the industry a big disservice."

When we heard him say that there was more demand than there was supply, our alarm bells went off in a different direction.

"Well, this isn't good," Ken said after we hung up. "If there's more demand than there is supply, then what? The animals can't be manufactured like widgets."

It was strange to hear bison compared to widgets, but he made his point. It was the first serious concern we had. Having worked in manufacturing for years, Ken was even more sensitive to an out of balance system.

"Not having a supply for the demand you've created is almost as bad as having no demand at all. Even if it's the best product in the world, it won't matter. If people want it and find out they can't have it, it will just make them mad."

We fell silent.

"Maybe we can find a way to extend the ground meat," I said, thinking of the burger. "But we don't want to add breadcrumbs, or anything like that. That won't work."

We were standing in our kitchen in Santa Barbara on a Saturday morning, sun streaming through the windows. Suddenly Ken looked at me.

"Turkey!" he said, "Turkey doesn't have much flavor, so it shouldn't change the flavor of the meat much. We'll add ground turkey to the ground bison."

"Can you do that?" I asked.

"Why not?" he said. "People do it with sausage all the time."

On that note, my marketing brain kicked in.

"Bisurkey!" I said pronouncing it bah-ZUR-key after the word berserk. "We'll call it Bisurkey. "And the patties will be heart-shaped."

We looked at each other, waiting to see if either one of us could come up with a reason why not. Ken broke the silence first.

"OK, so what we need now is to figure out the best proportions of the mix," he said.

We ordered burger from Mike and bought ground turkey at a local store. On the fourth of July we made our first Bisurkey burgers for friends using three different recipes. When the votes were in, one blend was the unanimous winner. Bisurkey was born.

Meanwhile, new situations were developing at work. A co-worker of Ken's had accepted a new job in Atlanta and was hinting that the company, another medical startup, needed help.

"They're going to need a Quality guy," said Todd. "It could be a good opportunity. I'm hoping I'll be able to retire after this one," he laughed.

It was unexpected. We both loved Santa Barbara and I loved my job. Media rumors continued about Tenet though and management had started moving internal people around. Our department of two had received approval to add a third person, a manager.

After interviewing outside candidates, my boss was ready to make an offer. Then he learned internal applicants wanted to apply. A few days later he announced who would be joining us. To my surprise, it was someone without investor relations or stock market experience.

Seeing the look of surprise on my face, he chuckled.

"They're called *Puts*," he offered.

When I asked what a put was, he explained that puts are people who are put into jobs based on who they knew, rather than what they knew.

"Sometimes you get some really good puts," he said, and

authenticated his statement by naming a few people and connecting them with who they knew inside the company. Gracious to the end, he was conveying to me that he had no say in the matter.

I wasn't looking forward to it. Once the put joined us, I was expected to help train and support the inexperienced person. Any hopes I had of expanding my role in the department evaporated. It was the beginning of my wanting to leave.

At Circon, Ken was uneasy with the hostile takeover situation. He had begun to feel that working there was like was working in a place under siege. The already stressful high tech, medical device environment had become even more tense and uncomfortable. Upper management delivered unconvincing reassurances, while maneuvering to change corporate by-laws and create a poison pill for U.S. Surgical.

"This is exactly why we need to have our own business," we said after exchanging work stories. "There's no guarantee of security anywhere. And as we get older, it won't get better."

This truth kept moving us forward. A paycheck, the vacations, the health insurance, the perks just weren't enough any more. As employees become older and more experienced, we also become more expensive. Because health insurance companies categorize various age groups, with each passing year we represent more of a liability than an asset for any company. It meant we were increasingly becoming expendable.

With over 30 years at various companies, we had each accumulated an enormous amount of experience and business acumen. What we wanted was a sense of control over our destiny and security, rather than having to rely on the fluctuating good will of management, board members or investors.

Other factors had to be considered. When considering obstacles which our small business could reasonably expect to encounter, we compared our experience with the life cycles of technology companies and boom and bust cycles of the U.S. economy. We agreed that once we developed our customer base, if we were careful, Lindner Bison should be able to weather most economic fluctuations.

"Meat is a staple," Ken said one day. "People will always need to eat."

A few months later, we incorporated Lindner Bison. Once a talented graphic artist had completed the Bisurkey and Lindner Bison logos, we filed the necessary papers to register Bisurkey as a protected trademark.

CHAPTER 5

Lindner Bison is Born
(1997)

Two events unfolded in the first half of 1997 that would lead to the first tangible proof of our journey out of corporate America. First, we got word that our house in Carlsbad sold and escrow would close in the fall.

Second, Ken accepted a job in Atlanta, Georgia and would be needed there by Thanksgiving.

◆─◆◆─◆

1. THE FIRST FOUR

That summer, a check arrived from the sale of the house and we mulled over how to invest it. We had previously wanted to buy a house in Santa Barbara, but with our job situations, now we weren't so sure.

"Maybe we should see what prices are for bison," I said. Ken was lying on the bed on a lazy Saturday morning, reading. When I heard him agree, I went into the office, found the latest NBA newsletter and opened it to the classified ads. There I noticed an ad with the Montana area code 406 and the prefix the same as my hometown. Prices had been high and seemed to be going higher each year. The ad said "priced to sell," so I called. Maybe this would be a bargain.

"Well, they're not cheap," said Pete over the phone. "For a cow-calf pair, yer talking around $3500. That's for a proven cow."

"What's a proven cow?" I asked.

"Oh, that just means they've bred and have produced calves before," he said. "These were owned by some lady up near Glacier. She had 'em for a while, as pets I guess. Then she got tired of 'em so now I have 'em. They're good quality and they're sisters. You need to have at least four so they recognize themselves as a herd. That's what I got, plus their babies.

They're good quality and I just got 'em in this week," he added. "They won't last long."

He was a good salesman, and I bit.

"Let me talk to my husband," I said. "I'll call you back."

The way I remember that Saturday morning was this: Ken was lying on the bed enjoying his leisure time reading, as he often does. I was back and forth from the master bedroom to the spare bedroom/office/exercise room like a ping-pong ball. I would talk to Pete, then hang up and tell Ken what he said. Ken would come up with a question, so I would call Pete back, get the answer, and hang up and relay it to Ken. Finally, we agreed it might be worth asking someone who's already a bison producer about it.

"Let's call your friend Mike and see if he's even heard of this guy," Ken said. "Then ask him what he thinks of the price." Ken stopped, "But then what would we do with them? We don't have any land, so who could take them? Mike?"

It was the same thing that stopped me years before. We knew from the listserv that some ranchers took animals with an arrangement called an Absentee Owner Program or AOP. The absentee owner pays a fee to the rancher to keep them. Since we didn't know anything about ranching and still needed income from our jobs, it seemed like the best way for us as beginners.

"Maybe," I said. "Let me call him." Mike picked up the phone, and I told him about our conversation with Pete. "Yah, I've heard of Pete. He's an old buffalo trader who's been around for years. That sounds about right," he said when I asked what he thought of the price. "I'm surprised he has any. You should grab 'em."

"We thought we might, but we don't have any place for them. Would you be interested?" I asked.

"Well, I'm not set up for that here," said Mike. "But there's a guy over in South Dakota I've known a long time. He runs buffalo with his cattle and has for about thirty years. He might take 'em."

I was getting excited. "Really?" I said, "That would be great."

"I have to tell you, though, Art don't like people much," he said. "And he don't have much use for folks at the association, so I wouldn't mention that. So, I don't know if he'd even do it. But I'll tell you one thing. If you can get Art to take your animals, I'll garr-an-tee 'ya that you'll be successful. Here's his number. Give him a call and let me know."

I noted his Midwestern pronunciation of the word guarantee. It was unassuming and comforting.

Hanging up, I rejoined Ken, who had abandoned all hope of a leisurely Saturday morning. Putting the phone on speaker, we called the number Mike gave us. If we couldn't find a place to keep the bison, there was no need to buy them and that would be that. Still, we made a pact to be on our best behavior ever. We would be agreeable and respectful, so Art would like us and want to take our animals.

When Art picked up the phone, we introduced ourselves and gave him the short version of our conversation with Pete and the animals he had for sale.

"What kind of quality are we talking?" he asked with an equally respectful and measured tone.

"Um, well, to tell you the truth, we don't know, but Pete says they're first-rate animals."

We felt more than a little foolish, hearing our answer. Spending this kind of money without knowing the quality, from someone we'd never met, based on the say so of someone else we'd only met over the phone. Seeing the animals wouldn't have made much difference anyway, since we couldn't tell a good quality animal from a poor quality animal. We felt we had no choice but to trust that we were being told the truth.

Over the phone, Art had an easy way about him and seemed reasonable enough. With the kinds of questions he asked, it became quickly apparent it would be hard for anyone to pull the wool over his eyes for long.

"Yah, I've known Mike for a long time," Art said. "We go back probably twenty years or so. Where'd these animals come from, did this guy say?" he asked.

"Pete said from some lady in Montana who had them as pets, but now they're four years old and she wanted to get rid of them. Pete said there aren't any papers, but he thinks she said they're out of the Larry Byrd herd in South Dakota."

"Byrd, huh. Where are they?"

We told him.

"Do you have his number?"

We gave it to him.

"Well I can't make any promises, but I'll give him a call. Let me see what I can find out. What's your number and I'll call you back if I can get a hold of him."

We gave him our phone number and went into the living room to digest the morning's rapid series of unfolding of events. Suddenly, I was exhausted. When I had gotten up that morning, the last thing I expected was to be potentially buying bison. We were taking a huge risk, based on Mike's advice. And who the heck was Mike, anyway? At least he had a business selling and shipping meat, so he had to be real.

For me, it was scary to think about spending that kind of money, so I immediately began developing a few escape routes in case things didn't add up. Pete lived not far from my hometown of Livingston, so I could call on my dad or a few friends who still lived there, to verify there were actually bison where Pete said they were. Then, if anything funny came up, like they were skinny or unhealthy, we could always back out of the deal. Even if everything seemed fine and we mailed the check, we could always put a stop payment on the check if either of us got cold feet for any reason. If they were good quality, they would have no problem finding another buyer.

Looking back, I can gratefully say that we've never done anything quite like that before or since. It was an unusual moment in time and as I now like to counsel others who experience unexpected events: "It's not life's moments that define us. It's what we do with the moments, how we use them."

At the time, though I wasn't thinking that. I was asking myself, *how else can people like us get a start?* There weren't any nearby bison producers that we could drive to and see in person. And even if there were, we work during the week so we still wouldn't be able to take care of the animals ourselves. This whole deal was a risk and a gamble, but we both agreed this leap of faith looked like the only way we were going to get started.

Art called back within the hour.

"Well," he said, "it sounds like he's got 'em. If you're interested, I've got some numbers penciled out. I can tell you what it'll cost for me to keep 'em if you want to know."

We drew a deep breath and agreed.

"Now, there's no way to know the quality for sure until I see 'em. But if you want me to pick 'em up, I can get over there the middle of next week. I'll charge you for the gas over and back, that's it."

To our surprise, Art's rate for absentee ownership was less than the going rate. We reasoned it was probably because he had plenty of land that was paid for. It turned out we were right. Art told us he pays cash, or he goes without. Being a shrewd businessman, we would later learn he prides himself on not being greedy either. "It'll come back to bite you," he said.

"The calves don't eat much, so I won't charge anything until January when they're weaned. Depending on hay prices and the kind of winter we have, the rate could go up or down. Won't know until we get there, but I'm just letting 'ya know."

Ken and I told him we'd call him back. A half hour later, we called him back, agreeing to the deal. The three of us talked about the timing of the arrival of our check and when Pete could reasonably be expected to release the animals to Art. Since we were getting ready to go on vacation back east to see Ken's parents, we needed to get this taken care of right away.

We called Pete next and agreed on the price, saying the check would be sent and a rancher named Art would pick them up. They could make arrangements between themselves.

As promised, we called Mike back and told him the news. He sounded pleased and said we'd be glad about Art taking them. Mike had played such an instrumental role in coaching us through this whole process we asked if we could stop off at his place on the way to New Hampshire to visit Ken's parents. He seemed flattered and agreed. Perhaps being able to meet him and see his operation would help us understand that we hadn't imagined what had just happened. Just in case, we wouldn't say anything to anyone else until we got back.

The next week our check was mailed, received, and we were on a plane to spend part of our vacation with Ken's parents. Art said he'd call us once he had picked up the animals and got them to his ranch. Recovering from our initial shock, we were beginning to get more excited. Maybe this wasn't just a figment of our imagination after all! Maybe we really could eventually leave our jobs. At least we'd made a start. We had given Art the phone numbers where we would be. There wasn't anything more we could do, so we turned our attention to our vacation.

2. SMALL RANCHER'S RULE

Leaving Santa Barbara early, we got into Chicago in the afternoon. We rented a car and got to Mike's place by about 4 p.m. Storm clouds were gathering. We followed the signs and, seeing a sign that said "Money Creek Buffalo," we wondered if that was Mike's place. We stopped the car and looked past the sign. Two hundred feet away, sitting in a draw was a tired, weathered house that had clearly seen better days. A cheerful, young woman with giant, pink sponge-type curlers in her blond hair emerged from the house.

"You the folks from California?" she yelled.

"That's us," Ken yelled back.

"Mike's working the animals. There's a storm comin' in tonight, but he's expecting you."

As if on cue, Mike drove up and got out of his truck.

After brief introductions, he said, "There's a storm coming and we've got to work them animals. They're sold and need their shots. So you're helpin'. Hope you don't mind."

Dumbfounded, we looked at each other.

"Well, okay," we said, "but we need to change our clothes."

"Sure, I'll tell Robin," he said, and left us to pull from our suitcase in the trunk. In the house, we changed quickly from travel clothes into jeans, t-shirts and tennis shoes. Then we joined Mike in his truck. The house disappeared behind us as we drove up a nearby grassy hill. Cresting the hill, I caught my breath. We had entered another world.

Stretched out before us were several large corrals, made from a mix of wood and steel pipes. The grass had disappeared and the dirt had turned to mud covered with hoof-sized holes, most with pools of water inside.

What a mess, I thought. We had gotten out of the truck and I was trying to navigate through the mud toward the corral fence without falling down. In the distance, at the furthest point of the largest corral, were about 40 restless bison.

It was our first experience seeing them. For me, it was certainly the first time since visiting Yellowstone National Park as a child, and never in the context of a corral or handling system. For Ken, it was the first time ever.

"Wow," was all we could say.

While Ken and I waited, Mike went over to briefly talk with his son, a young man sitting on an ATV who looked to be in his late twenties. Mike came back after a few minutes.

"He's about to go get 'em," he said. "We'll wait down there," he said, pointing to another building. Mike turned and started walking toward the truck. "They were worked yesterday, so they're skittish now, but we've got to run 'em through again to vaccinate 'em."

We got back into the truck, and quickly arrived at a building that abutted a corral made of steel pipes. Inside the building, Mike grabbed a bucket that held needles, syringes, and small vials filled with light yellow liquid. He handed them to Ken, walking through the building and out the other side into a smaller corral system. We hurried to keep up.

"Ken, you give them their shots. Kathy, you keep track with this pad," he said handing me a tiny spiral notebook and pencil. "When he's ready, my son'll bring em down."

Walking as he was talking, he gave us a brief tour of his handling set up.

"Robin and me'll move 'em into the tub, and bring 'em through one at a time. After they hit the crash gate, I'll close the squeeze chute and you give 'em a shot through here."

He grabbed an unseen part of the steel fence, which opened like a small door.

"Just give 'em a shot in the rump and get yer arm back out quick. Don't stay in there any longer than you need to, to give 'em their shot. They can break your arm in an instant."

I looked to see if he was kidding. He wasn't.

Ken's reaction to all this astonished me. He's always been an extremely quick study, and was taking in the change of venue and priorities with a calm demeanor. I couldn't detect any outward sign of fear, insecurity or surprise. He seemed sure of himself, commenting that the syringes looked similar to some of the medical equipment he'd quality inspected in the past.

How do guys do that? I wondered, noting my own growing sense of panic. Neither one of us expected this. I wasn't sure Ken had ever been on a ranch, other than the dairy farm he used to live next door to in upstate New York. Even I had never worked cattle, which are large animals. But these were bison.

Hey, I'm the one from Montana, I told myself in an effort to bolster my nerve and recapture my confidence. Yet in spite of all the Montana ranches I had visited growing up, I had never been invited to help with large, moving animals.

What I did know about, though, was the *rancher's rule* about visitors. It didn't matter why you were there. Anyone visiting a ranch is fair game for free, badly needed help. There's always plenty to do and this is especially true when there are sudden changes in weather, equipment or fencing. These events will always crowd out social niceties, which are a luxury enjoyed by those who live in the city. If a visitor doesn't want to help, they are welcome to come back another time. The joke is, there is never a time when ranchers and farmers aren't busy.

"Here, make yourself useful," was one of Mom's favorite post-ranch phrases for drafting help.

Watching Ken fill a syringe from the vial, I was grateful to be assigned the job of scribe, though it wasn't clear what I was supposed to be writing down. Ear-tag number is all I could remember. Before I could ask for clarification, we heard a whoop from Robin in the distance.

"Here they come!" she yelled.

Briefly we looked her direction and then ran to our assigned spots.

My panic was replaced by excitement, followed by a surge of adrenaline. Above us, cresting the hill, running bison appeared. They were all heading in our direction.

Moments later we heard an engine and saw Mike's son on his ATV. He was driving quickly back and forth behind the herd in a ribbon-candy like design, to keep them moving toward the corrals.

"They're splittin'!" hollered Mike, "Don't let 'em split!" Immediately, the ATV engine got quieter as his son backed off, allowing more distance between himself and the bison.

In response, a smaller, separate wave of bison rejoined the main herd, forming one river of bison streaming down the hill. They rounded the corner of the building where we had just been. Miraculously, within moments, they had funneled into the large corral where we waited.

Mike quickly closed the gate. The animals milled around, no doubt looking for the exit. While he moved toward the tub, Robin was on foot in the corral, separating three and four off at a time, moving them into the crowding tub. The crowding tub is a large round, solid steel enclosure, with walls about seven feet high. It's considered especially valuable in handling bison, since the nature of bison is that when they discover there's no exit, they want to go back the way they came in. The theory is, that in following the curve of the tub, they believe that is what is happening. In reality, they are being steered into another alleyway where they must uncharacteristically enter single file. When they see the crash gate at the end of the alleyway, because they can see through the steel pipes, they think they can go through it. This natural instinct draws them forward.

Once each animal reaches the crash gate, they are in a narrow area called the squeeze chute. A steel collar is closed behind their heads to hold them in place and the squeeze chute is narrowed to hold their bodies in place. Now an injection may be given, or ear-tag affixed. Only after that, is the chute widened and the gate opened to release them back into the outer pasture or a corral, depending on the setup.

For us, it was baptism by fire.

At Robin's coaxing, one by one, individual bison entered the alleyway. From outside, Mike would guide them and when each one reached the crash gate, he closed the steel collar around their neck. Ken had each syringe filled and ready. He quickly opened the small door, injected the exposed rump, and got his arm back out as fast as he could. Over the loud clanging of the bison against the steel pipes, Ken would yell out the ear-tag numbers, which I wrote down. When Mike heard Ken yell out the numbers, he released the bison back into the larger corral.

What Ken remembers most vividly about the whole experience was seeing the steel squeeze chute, which weighed over a ton, bounce as the bison entered and were secured with the collar. This was particularly the case when a larger bull entered. Though bison strength is legendary, he was unprepared to see the entire chute lurch inches off the ground, depending on the shifting weight and speed of each animal. He remembered Mike's warning not to let them break his arm. Right.

The whole process which took about an hour seemed to pass in seconds. As quickly as it began, we were done.

"Looks like that's it. How 'ya doing Ken?" Mike asked, walking over. It was the first sign of a smile we'd seen.

"Well, I've never done anything like that before, that's for sure," Ken said.

"Yah, well, sorry about that. But we had to get them animals ready to be delivered in the morning. And do it before it rains again and this place turns into a muddy mess."

We looked around following his gaze. It clearly had rained earlier and the wet ground was still holding puddles of water where the bison's hooves had been. It also explained the slipping we had seen from a few of the animals coming down the hill as they rounded the corner of the building. If it had been raining, the exercise would've been impossible.

The four of us walked back to the house together. Mike and Robin were visibly more relaxed. Mike was a likable character. Probably mid-forties, full, wooly head of blond, curly hair, totally uncombed and unkempt. His manner was casual and business-like at the same time. He was unassuming, but I elements of the marketer that I had met over the phone were there.

Entering the house, he ushered us into his living room and insisted we watch a video clip of the movie "Dances with Wolves." This featured Cody, his famous buffalo bull, which he had hand-raised as an orphan calf. We hadn't heard of Cody, but we complimented him on the animal's cooperation for the movie. When Mike told us how much they were paid, we realized this wasn't a simple case of wanting to be in the movies. He was well compensated for Cody's participation and we were impressed.

Then he proudly showed us a huge, tanned bison robe, which was draped across a well used, brown leather couch. Dutifully we examined it, noting how especially heavy it was.

"It's a winter robe," he said. "Depending on size and quality, you can usually get between $1,500 to $3,000. You don't often see one this size."

I found myself doing a reality check about every five or ten minutes. What a shift in worlds. One moment being in Santa Barbara, then stepping off a plane a few hours later, interacting with bison and steel handling equipment. What a sheltered, convenient life we had been living. Mike's ranch provided a stark contrast to California, while somehow being more tangible and real. Unlike corporate environments, where things are often done by committee, here there was an immediate response to events. There was no guessing, wondering, waiting, or asking for permission.

I found myself hoping the contrast of our worlds wasn't too obvious, yet feeling every bit the greenhorn, tenderfoot – completely out of our element. Yet Mike and Robin made us feel welcome. We joined them for dinner, and afterward, wandered back outside so they could show us around before we left. For fun, Robin took me on a short ATV ride, up the side of a steep hill and down. Then Mike introduced us to Cody, who hammed it up nicely for our camera. We learned that Cody loved Oreo cookies, so Mike gave us some to feed him. We had a friend for life.

Afterward, we all climbed in the truck for a general tour of the ranch. Ken and I got in the back with their big, friendly ranch dog. As we entered one of the pastures where the main herd was, a big bull about 100 feet from the truck turned and stood facing us, tail raised. We heard a kind of growling coming from the bull and as we got closer, it got louder. Even as greenhorns, it was clear to us that this was not bison talk for, "I'm glad to see you."

While Mike nonchalantly explained that the bull was just displaying dominance, Robin became alarmed that he was getting ready to charge the truck. She looked back at us to see what had the bull riled up. Spotting the dog, she immediately ordered, "Cover the dog! Cover the dog!"

Good grief, cover him with what? I wondered anxiously, looking at this large affable dog sitting next to me, tongue happily hanging out. But the sense of urgency in her voice was real. With nothing to cover him, I lifted my t-shirt and quickly pulled him underneath next to my chest. My new best friend.

It worked. The dog disappeared from view, the bull stopped growling and everyone relaxed again.

Before we left for the hotel, Mike surprised us by inviting us to meet him at his meat processor's place in the morning so we could see that part of the business. Then he said we could all go to lunch and still be able to catch our afternoon flight. Though tired, we didn't know when we would have another chance like this to learn. We agreed.

3. SOONER, RATHER THAN LATER

The next morning we found our way to the meat processor. As we pulled into the parking lot, almost immediately we spotted Mike near his pickup. He was talking with a man outside the building. Attached to his truck, was a large livestock trailer backed up to a chute that was connected to the building.

Mike introduced us to the owner. Then Mike said we wanted to see his place and see how they do things. In response to his hesitation, Mike added, "They're producers."

"Go around the front and in through the store area," he said. "Tell 'em I said it's okay."

Before we knew it, the three of us were inside the small processing plant being shown around. We had entered through the store area where they had meat for sale under glass counters. Then we were led through the cutting room, full of stainless steel sinks and tables. Attached to that was a chill room with large meat hooks hanging down. Huge sides of bison hung from large rails near the ceiling.

"This is where we age the meat," said our tour guide. He was wearing a white, medical looking light cotton coat that extended to his knees.

"And this is the kill floor."

We had just entered a large room with a tall ceiling and cement floor. Almost as soon as he said it, we heard noise on the ramp to the truck. In seconds, a bison trotted into a nearby chute-like chamber with cement walls extending up a good seven feet. Overhead and behind the chamber was a station for the shooter. At this point, Mike said to wait here and left to talk to the owner about getting on his schedule for his next delivery. He exited through a nearby side door.

Waiting alone for few uncomfortable moments near the waiting animal was enough. Ken and I opened the same door Mike had used and joined him outside.

He looked over as we approached.

"What are you doing out here?" he asked accusingly.

"We just thought we'd come out," I said.

"You get back in there," he ordered, pointing to the door.

Like scolded children, we obeyed. We knew he was right. Looking back, Mike had made it his business to make sure we saw all aspects of raising bison. If we were going to raise the animals for meat, it was better that we learn about this part of the business sooner rather than later.

Back inside, we found a man with a rifle now in the room. Briefly we talked with him about the various things we were seeing for the first time. Then from an overhead position, he took skilled aim and fired his rifle. Blam! Instantly, the animal collapsed. My own tension turned to relief as we watched the rapid sequence of events that followed.

One of the walls fell away and the carcass slid to the floor. The jugular vein in the neck was quickly cut to bleed the animal. With the help of a single pulley, the carcass was hoisted above a drain in the floor. Workers moved swiftly, skillfully cutting the length of the under belly. The stomach, intestines and offal spilled out and were guided into waiting containers.

While one man worked with a pressure hose to immediately clean the inside of the carcass and cement floor, two other workers fastened corners of the hide to a machine. With the whir of a motor, the machine began to uniformly pull the hide from the carcass. In what seemed to be about fifteen or twenty minutes, with three people working quickly, the carcass was transferred into the cooler for aging. We thanked the nearest person and went back outside.

This time, Mike could tell by the look on our faces that we had seen the kill.

"So what d'ya think?" he asked.

"It's interesting," we said with mixed feelings. We decided to focus on the technical aspects following the kill and asked him a few other questions. Later, all Ken and I could say to each other is that we never thought that this was something we would ever be doing or considering doing for a living, and left it at that. We knew it was an inescapable part of the business. That's all we knew. For now, it was enough.

As promised, Mike took us to an early lunch at a nearby roadhouse. Old wooden floor planks creaked as we walked through a large dimly lit room and sat down at a table. They had recently bought his burger, so while he was coaching the cook on how to prepare it, Ken and I relaxed a bit. Faded, dirty posters adorned the dark walls and everything pretty well reeked of stale cigarettes and spilled beer.

Plenty of honky tonk nights and weekends are had here, I mused. *And no doubt more to come.*

Though light years from our life in Santa Barbara, as strange and awkward as it felt, it also felt good to be exploring and pursuing an alternative for ourselves. A door had partially opened. What we saw gave us a sense of hope for a more secure future, and a new beginning. That afternoon, we climbed back on an airplane headed for New Hampshire to give Ken's seventy-five-year-old parents the news.

4. The Surprise
Your children are not your children.
They are the sons and daughters of Life's longing for itself.
—Khalil Gibran—

You could have heard a pin drop.

"What?"

"We just bought some bison and we think we're going to be bison ranchers," Ken repeated.

My very gracious seventy-five-year-old in-laws just looked at him. Then they looked at each other. Then they looked back at him.

Ken continued, "Just before we left to come visit you, we bought four cow-calf pairs. A rancher is picking them up this week and is going to keep them for us. Right now, they're actually near Kathy's home town, so we asked her dad if he would drive over and see if there are any bison there. In fact, on the way here, we stopped off in Chicago and worked some animals with a rancher named Mike. We took pictures to show you."

In retrospect, they had to be flabbergasted. It was only my third time with them in person, so I was still getting to know them, and they were getting to know me. All I knew about them was what Ken had described using family photos. His dad, a retired Army colonel, had accepted assignments around the world, fought in World War II, and had even acted as an advisor to Chiang Kai-shek during the conflict between the Nationalist Chinese and Red Chinese armies in the late 1940s. With the exception of China and a few other hardship tours, the family traveled with him most of the time. Because of the many moves, they were all extremely close. It hadn't always been smooth sailing, but there had always been a sense of security and closeness.

When we were first engaged, Ken's descriptions of his parents had me envisioning the kind of family depicted on TV programs in the '60s like *The Donna Reed Show* and *Father Knows Best*. He said that compared to his college classmates' descriptions of their parents, his parents had always been loving and supportive. They continued to be so in Ken's adulthood. He said he couldn't have done better for parents if he had picked them out himself.

Coming from a divorced family, my experience didn't support what Ken described, though I knew both my parents loved my sister and me. At the time, I was sure that Ken's purity of spirit included a little harmless exaggeration that was based on an over-developed sense of commitment and loyalty.

I was glad to be wrong. Watching them react to this new information, I was learning why he felt the way he did about them. They had lovingly supported him through a difficult time as he healed from his divorce. Before that, they watched as he and his first wife relocated from the East Coast to the West Coast. And even before that, supporting his childhood love for music, they proudly saw him obtain a teaching degree from Oberlin, then exchange his chosen profession for a computer technician position in order to earn a living. Now, here he was, with a new wife, saying we were going to raise bison.

I said nothing. Studying their reaction, they were as Ken had predicted they would be. They were supportive.

His mother, Betty, was the first to recover. "Well," she said slowly. "What's a cow-calf pair?"

"Yeah," his dad said. "I mean, we don't know."

I was moved. Their interest was genuine and, as always, their manner gracious. They leaned in now as Ken began telling them about the four bison cows and their calves, and about the research we'd been doing for the past three years.

"We're going to proceed slowly," he said. "We're not quitting our jobs. We want to see if we can do this while we still have other jobs. If we can sell the meat and it makes sense, then we'll see what happens."

They were relieved and agreed.

Ken continued. "Neither one of us feels secure with any company any more. They merge, they downsize, they upsize, they move – and who knows if social security will be around by the time we retire. We thought it would be better to have a plan of some kind."

They said they understood and then asked to see the pictures he had taken. My mother-in-law is a huge fan of photos, religiously bringing her camera to outings and events. It seems she loves to take pictures as much as seeing the pictures others have taken too. So these were especially welcome as a visual tool.

As Ken laid the pictures on the table, they leaned in even closer and asked him to describe what they were seeing. As he predicted, they were especially astonished to see the photo showing Ken with a hypodermic needle, getting ready to use it on big, brown bison rumps from outside a steel cage. I was glad they couldn't hear Mike saying to be sure to get his arm right back out so it didn't get broken.

"So you say you have four bison now?" mom Lindner asked.

"Right. And their calves, so it's actually eight. Art is picking them up this week sometime. They're about twenty miles from where Kathy's dad lives. We gave Art your phone number so he can call and tell us when they arrive and unload at his place."

"Where's his place?" Dad Lindner asked.

"South Dakota."

Finally, Ken showed them the last photo and leaned back in his chair. "That's it," he said.

"Well for goodness sakes, you two," mom finally said.

"That's something," said dad.

Ken smiled, "Yeah, kinda fun, huh?" He knew it would take awhile for it all to sink in. It was taking awhile for it to sink in with us, so we could only imagine how it must be for them.

I was grateful for their support and graciousness. If they had their doubts, they didn't express them and that was nice. I had my own doubts and hoped we weren't making a mistake. Neither one of us had an agricultural background or had dealt with livestock, except to ride horses. If it ended up to be a mistake, I secretly felt that it would be my fault. I had been the one to bring up bison in the first place.

Despite these thoughts, it was exciting too. It was something we could do on our own that may provide a sense of security and allow us to work for ourselves. Though we had a lot to learn, we were both willing to try.

With this last thought, I felt closer than ever to Ken. It would be a chance to build something from scratch together. We were both achievers. Ken has a wonderful quality of stubbornness tempered with self-confidence, education and integrity. He presses on when many would hesitate and stop. Dissatisfied with mediocrity on any level, once he decides on a reasonable and appropriate course of action, nothing less is acceptable.

I've always had a rebellious streak along with tenacity and a strong work ethic. In my twenties, I was in the big city, out to prove myself. Through my thirties, I was re-evaluating and by my early forties, I realized I had plateaued. Though gleaning plenty from industry and executives over the years, increasingly the work was stifling, unsatisfying and dehumanizing. And I was always in the position of reporting to and helping others get ahead.

Until finding Ken, my life reflected only nuances and variations of this same theme.

With the bold purchase of our bison, new hope emerged. And like a dessert responding to a spring rain, my heart responded.

Who knows, I thought, snuggling up to Ken that night. *We'll see. We can try. At least we can try.*

5. LEAVING SOUTHERN CALIFORNIA

The send-offs from our respective companies was warm and friendly. I had loved my job with Tenet. They treated me well and paid me well. I enjoyed the work and the people. In many ways, it was one of the best jobs I had, which is saying a lot since I've had plenty over the years.

But loving my job didn't change the telltale signs that, once again, things were shifting and changing. Knowing myself, my foibles and frailties, I was afraid I just wouldn't last long with the new people being brought in and the inevitable culture shift to follow. I had seen and experienced it many times. With Tenet, I was glad to leave gracefully, on good terms, with wonderful memories of challenges met and expectations exceeded.

As it turned out, my replacement was vice president of a local bank that was downsizing. When my boss told me her background, I said, "So you mean all this time, I've been doing the work of a vice president?"

He chuckled without looking up and said "Yes, but we just don't call it that."

As a boss and a human being, he had been great. One of the most gratifying things about him was that he respected my intelligence and allowed me to exercise and expand my contributions. I would miss him.

As always, when Ken left a position his people were sorry to see him go. He often heard "You've been the best boss I've ever had." He knew they meant it and that he deserved it. He prided himself in treating people reasonably and fairly. He rejected the autocratic style of management and often chose to stand alone, outside the corporate trappings of "management" culture. He treated others the way he would expect to be treated; he treated them like human beings.

Together, we left Santa Barbara and spent the first night in Long Beach with Mary and Dan. Saying goodbye the next morning was more difficult than I expected. For twenty years I had never been more than a few hours away from Mary. In my twenties and thirties, I had found moving and changing environments exciting. Now I was forty-nine. This time it was different.

Raised in a military family that never lived more than a few years in any one place, Ken was sympathetic to my tears, but couldn't relate. To console myself, I shifted my focus to the big, roomy house waiting for us in Alpharetta, Georgia. When that didn't work, I reminded myself of what I had heard years ago about change: *If I keep doing what I'm doing, I'll have what I have.* We wanted something different, so this meant we had to do something different.

Our bison were somewhere in South Dakota with a man named Art. And we were going somewhere we had never been before in an effort to find a way to join them.

As we began the cross-country drive, the changing landscape confirmed our first visible step away from and out of corporate America.

CHAPTER 6

Bisurkey in Georgia
(1998)

With only eight animals, four of them calves, we obviously couldn't start a meat business using only our tiny herd. But it was important to learn the meat business before we got any deeper into ranching. We agreed that Ken's new job would provide steady income, while I developed our infant business. This provided leeway for us to make mistakes and relieved our new company of the immediate need to show a profit. The arrangement also allowed me to work full time on business development. As it turned out, it was hardly enough. We were about to learn about the commercial meat industry and its connections to restaurants and food stores.

---

1. Bisurkey Starts Up

Arriving in the beautiful Windward community near Alpharetta, Georgia we settled in quickly. Our house was third from the end of a cul de sac in a quiet and stately neighborhood. The homes all had large, wooded lots and neighbors seemed to be about our age or younger. Ours was a two-story, grey stucco house with a steeply pitched roof and black shutters on French style white trimmed windows. On the backside, the daylight basement made it a third story facing a wooded back yard. The front yard was accented by a single magnolia tree off to one side. I had only dreamed of living in such a house. Yet here it was and here we were.

We arrived over a weekend. On Monday, while Ken started his new job I continued the unpacking. The house had instantly swallowed up our furniture and wanted more, but it would have to wait. Instead, I focused on setting up my office in the basement. Like the house, the huge basement featured floor to ceiling bay windows opening to a fenced back yard. Just beyond the fence was a small creek and bordering that were tall trees and thick under-growth, through which glimpses of deer could be seen making their way quietly and effortlessly. At night, familiar tree frogs croaking their lullaby provided a feeling of home.

We were there because of a company called Biofield, another small biotech firm that was going to set the world on fire. They were following the popular entrepreneurial business model of developing a product using new technology and other people's money. The new technology was designed to detect cancer using non-invasive methods.

While he was busy acclimating and establishing procedures for their Quality System, I was working on my own transition. Initially uneasy about not earning a paycheck, I registered with some local temporary agencies and took some assignments. Within a few short months, I was motivated to re-shift full time to Lindner Bison and Bisurkey. Ken's salary was good and it seemed that as long as we were frugal and kept the business and ourselves on a shoestring, we would be fine.

There was plenty to do. The website, the trademark, the label and logo, the meat sources, tooling, the meat processor, the distribution channels, and the marketing materials all demanded my attention. During my years with various companies, I had either worked for executives overseeing this type of work or had performed the tasks personally, so I knew what had to be done. It was time to put that experience to work for Lindner Bison. Before long, the effort took on a life of its own. It was a huge undertaking for one person and my days were long and full.

Soon, I was tackling specifications for the patty plate to fit a commercial burger machine. Initially, I explored existing heart shaped molds offered by the meat industry, but to me they looked more like plump apples rather than hearts. The salesmen insisted the apple shape was necessary so the meat would fall from the plate. This was the best they had, they said and I wouldn't find anything better. Unconvinced and annoyed with their take-it-or-leave-it attitude, I left it. I was unwilling to compromise my vision for the heart-shaped patty, but now what?

Over the phone, I told Ken what had happened. That night after work, he made drawings the machinists could understand in order to create the shape that we wanted. For the first time, a design was specifically created to fit *our* vision and specifications. It felt good.

After calling around for quotes, I was referred to a local machinist who had a reputation for good quality, provided a competitive quote and had reasonable turn-around time. When I picked up the plate, I was thrilled to see that it looked just like the drawing.

Now the question was, *Would it work?* Would the meat fall from the plate or would the tip of the heart get stuck and tear, as I was told by industry experts? There was only one way to find out.

I began calling commercial meat processors to have samples made. No one did samples. Days later I found a Minneapolis meat processor who was willing to make small batches of the heart-shaped patties for us. His name was Frank.

"I suppose you have your own labels?" Frank asked.

"Labels?" I echoed.

"Yes, we're a USDA plant, so all labels have to be approved by USDA before we can use them," he said. "You'll have to get a form from them. This sample run won't be for sale, so it should be okay initially."

And with that, he scheduled a date for a small run of samples to be made.

Over the next week, I filled out a label application form and drafted a computer-generated heart-shaped label to fit the patty shape and size. Then I faxed both and eagerly awaited USDA approval. Instead it was rejected. The heart-shaped label represented an implied health claim they said. In disbelief, I called and talked to label reviewer who advised they had an appeal process. The rest of the day was spent writing an appeal and resubmitting it. Eventually, the heart-shaped label was approved for use with Bisurkey.

Next, a label manufacturer was found and I ordered the smallest quantity possible of their cheapest label. These were made and shipped to us. The labels were placed into the same box as the heavy patty plate and shipped to the meat processor who promised that he would let us know whether or not it actually fit on his machine. Two days later, he called. The patty plate fit.

The minimum amount of organic turkey meat was sourced from a small producer on the east coast, along with organic grassfed bison meat from an organic grassfed bison producer in Nebraska who we'd only talked to by phone. Both meats were drop-shipped to Minneapolis.

Finally, the day arrived when the sample patties were to be made. Would the meat mix together and fall out okay? Would the patties stack up okay? Had we overlooked anything? I wanted to be there for the test run, but instead waited hundreds of miles away. Finally the call came. Yes, the patty fell out and stacked up just fine. Yes, the heart shape was intact. The plate worked!

The processor immediately froze a few samples and shipped them to us the next day. As soon as the packages arrived, I transferred them to our freezer until Ken got off work.

At each step of the product development phase, there had always been technical and design considerations. Now there were new questions: *Would it cook up and taste the same as when we made it in our Santa Barbara kitchen? Did they get the recipe right? Would it be different somehow?*

Ken got home early that day and like expectant parents we hovered over three heart-shaped patties in a frying pan—watching the clock, watching the meat cook, watching for signs of anything that might tip us off that something was different.

It looked the same as we remembered. It sure smelled good. Ken turned off the heat and transferred one patty to a plate. Then he cut off a few pieces and added a dash of salt.

"Okay," he said, handing me a fork. "This is it."

We each took a bite and looked at each other. The Bisurkey burger tasted great.

"Well, the experts were wrong," Ken smiled. Commercial meat professionals, on hearing what we were planning to do, told us that the two lean meats just wouldn't hold together.

"You gotta have the extra fat," they knowingly had cautioned. It wasn't true. Bisurkey held together fine.

The next day, I donned my recently abandoned business attire—a dress, jacket, nylons, earrings, the works. Carefully organizing the frozen meat for transport, I made cold calls all day to area restaurants with free samples of Bisurkey. The chefs greeted me warmly and were delighted to get the free meat sample. They all loved the name and assured me they would cook it up that day. Providing cooking tips for the lean meat, I got their names and promised to call for their reactions.

The next day, all reports were great. It cooked up fine and they loved the flavor. From each of the eight or so chefs, comments were positive. They all loved it, but no one ordered. Reasons given: (1) the menu was already set for the season, call back later; (2) they had no freezer space; (3) customers wouldn't know what it was, so they wouldn't be able to sell it (4) waiters and waitresses are too busy to take time to tell them about it.

With each phone call, my heart continued to sink. After all the work and hurdles overcome and money spent, I never dreamed we wouldn't get at least one order so people could try it. We had field-tested the flavor and mix and everyone loved it. They loved the name. The meat processor in Minneapolis primarily distributed to restaurants and had even said he thought chefs would love it.

Wondering what I was doing wrong in my sales approach, I called and asked if I could fly up for a visit and accompany him when he called on chefs. He agreed. So in January, instead of celebrating my 50th birthday with Ken, I was on an airplane to Minneapolis.

Arriving late in the afternoon, the processor welcomed me and gave me a tour of his big facility. Everything was clean, shiny and highly automated. Employees all wore white cotton coats, hair nets and many had plastic gloves.

The one thing, which especially stood out during the tour, was the discovery of a huge, automated tenderizing machine. From an overhead industrial arm, forty or fifty tiny, long stainless steel needles went in and out of thickly sized steaks which were lined up on a slow moving conveyor belt. The processor noticed my fascination.

"Chefs won't take a chance on the steaks being anything less than tender for their customers," he explained, "so this is how we provide that assurance to them. We'd be out of business if we started shipping tough steaks." At the time it seemed reasonable, but I just had no idea this kind of industrial meat tenderizing was done.

That same evening, we left the plant to call on one of his larger customers, the head chef at a renowned five-star hotel chain. If the chef liked the Bisurkey, perhaps the chain would want to include it on their menu.

Accessing the hotel from a commercial entrance in back, we made our way to the kitchen, navigating past shelves of dry goods and numerous stainless steel doors that hid the frozen and refrigerated foods. Frank pushed through a set of double doors. The chef turned, wiping his hands, when he heard Frank's greeting. Frank made the introductions and gestured to me to open the cooler containing the Bisurkey sample. The chef took the sample, turning it over in his hands while I described it.

"Can it be cooked from a frozen state?" he asked, eyeing me cautiously.

"Frozen state?" I echoed looking blankly at Frank. Frank laughed and clarified, "Can he cook it up while it's still frozen?"

"Oh," I said, "I don't know, I guess so. We haven't cooked it that way, but I don't know why not. You tell us."

The chef seemed mildly annoyed and involuntarily intrigued. Dismissing me as the inexperienced layperson that I was, he told Frank that he looked forward to trying it and would let him know what he thought.

Flying back to Alpharetta early the next day, I was encouraged that, with Frank's help, Bisurkey would have a start. By the end of the week, the chef had reported to Frank that he enjoyed the meat and that it cooked up great. But he too did not order.

Ken and I were puzzled and frustrated. We knew the product was good. Everyone who tried it had said they liked it or loved it. Why wasn't anyone ordering? Again I called Frank, who shared an axiom known to those in foodservice.

"Chefs are a strange breed," he said. "They all want the newest, latest and greatest thing; something that will be unique and help distinguish them from everyone else. But no one wants to be first."

If this insight was meant to be amusing or bring comfort, it did neither. It only deepened our sense of isolation and reconfirmed that we were strangers in a strange land.

Back in my basement office, I reviewed our accomplishments to make myself feel better. As novices, we had succeeded in clearing several major hurdles. The Bisurkey patty plate had been designed, made and successfully used as intended. We had identified the best bison and turkey meat sources. The heart-shaped patties dropped cleanly from the plate and stacked up evenly as intended. The lean meat combination held up to cooking in a commercial setting. After an unexpected rejection of the heart shaped label, a written appeal had been submitted to USDA and won. The trademark application for the Bisurkey name had been submitted and filed.

All of these elements had taken a significant amount of time and money from our personal savings. If restaurants didn't want to be first with a new product, perhaps demand by consumers at traditional supermarkets would change their minds.

I shifted gears. Using the yellow pages of the phonebook, I began calling supermarkets in the area. Rejection was immediate. "We just don't have the freezer space." "All our buying is handled by our home office. Talk to them." "You have a specialty product. You want a health food store."

Opening the yellow pages again, I searched for area health food stores. Within a ten mile radius of any major city in California, I could easily expect to find at least ten or more health food stores with organic food, vitamins, ready-to-eat preparations and juice bars. Upscale Alpharetta, I quickly learned, was different. In that same ten-mile radius, I found one store that sold a huge assortment of international foods and two stores that sold vitamins. That was it.

After a neighbor confirmed the international food market might be our best bet, Ken and I drove there one night with a frozen Bisurkey sample. We located the manager who was stocking fruit in the produce section and he listened with interest as we described Bisurkey to him. Seeing the now familiar smile on hearing the name Bisurkey, I asked if he would be interested in trying it in the store.

"It has a wonderful flavor," I said, "with less fat and cholesterol than even turkey."

He looked down for a moment, turning over a piece of fruit in his hand. As he placed it in the display with the others, he politely said that they had multiple relationships with large commercial meat brokers and placed orders solely with companies that could provide volume pricing.

"What kind of volume can you do?" he asked, looking finally up at us. "Can you match truckload pricing?"

"How much is in a truckload?" I asked.

"Depending on the truck, usually about 40,000 pounds," he said

We admitted we couldn't initially do that kind of volume.

"But Bisurkey has less cholesterol than any of the meat you have here," I pointed out, unwilling to accept another rejection. "And it has less fat."

A faint smile of amusement crossed the man's face as he picked up an unopened fruit box and placed it on a nearby table.

"Folks around here like their fat," he said.

We thanked him for his time and left.

"Ya ain't in California any more," said Ken as we walked to the car.

2. TAKING THE CORPORATION OUT OF THE PERSON

Okay, we weren't in California anymore, but we were in Atlanta and Ted Turner lives here. Recently, he had made headlines by acquiring large ranches in the Midwest. It was reported that he loved bison and had started raising them.

After reading authorized and unauthorized biographies of his life, I felt I had a sense of the man. Clearly he was shrewd and the fact that he had turned his attention to bison was an endorsement. With his deep pockets, it's doubtful he would have problems filling the 40,000 pound truckload requirement.

Shortly after the international store visit and after talking it over with Ken, we decided I should call Ted Turner's office and introduce Bisurkey. The worst thing that could happen is he could say 'No,' to which the correct response is 'Next' and we just keep going. But even with this pep talk, it took another few days of considerable self-dialogue before I had built up enough nerve to call.

His assistant was pleasant and the familiarity of her role immediately put me at ease. I described what we wanted to do with Bisurkey and asked if she thought he might be interested. She didn't know and encouraged me to send a letter. By the end of the day, it had been written and faxed and I showed a copy of it to Ken when he got home. We agreed Turner could be intrigued and began discussing elements of our presentation to him, which would need to be kept short and to the point.

The next morning, I began assembling demographic data. Even if Mr. Turner didn't invest, when Biofield made its stock offering in a year or two, we'd be able to use that money and leave the corporate world behind. Either way, it seemed plausible that Bisurkey was the vehicle that would finance our ranch. All we had to do is secure the money to make and market Bisurkey in volume. That night Ken asked if I had called Turner's office.

"I thought I'd give it another day," I said.

In the regular scheme of things, after an introductory letter is sent, what is supposed to happen is a follow up call by the sender a few days later to make sure it was received and request an appointment. The next evening after work, again Ken asked if I had called Turner's office yet.

"It's too soon," I said.

A few more days came and went. Finally Ken stopped asking. We had agreed we wanted to leave corporate America, yet this approach increasingly felt in conflict with that goal. What was bothering me? Why was I now hesitating? We needed the money and this might be a way to get it.

Unexpectedly, I had begun to experience a recurring sense of threat which I struggled, to no avail, to make sense of. Lacking clarity on the issue, I considered hypothetical outcomes: (1) because we were vulnerable to an offer of money, we'd be asked to relinquish control or compromise the quality of our product in some way; (2) doing either of these things might result in our acting as a supplier and getting into ranching sooner, which was the real goal anyway; or (3) failing either, we'd have met a powerful person who might eventually help us get where we wanted to go. All of these scenarios felt awful. Trusting my gut instinct, I didn't call or follow-up. And I couldn't find a way to justify it to either myself or to Ken.

Twelve years later while writing this book, the Ted Turner episode nearly refused to be written. Days were spent drafting, revising, adding, deleting and rewriting while trying to understand, explain and justify my lack of follow up. Then came the harsh feedback that the chapter didn't ring true. The editor said he just wasn't buying it, that I was just too savvy for it to be believable. Ken agreed. I didn't know what to say. I had done my best. If it wasn't believable, what do I do with that? How do I explain something I don't understand myself?

Early one morning on our way to the ranch, while Ken drove, I decided to take one last look at the chapter on my laptop.

"Do you think the book would miss anything if this chapter was just left out?" I asked.

"Well the way it's currently written, it probably wouldn't be a great loss," he said dryly. We were both tired.

"It just made no sense," Ken continued. "Even to me, not to have followed up."

With the tone of his comment and exhausted from the internal struggle, words began to pour out of me. I blurted out the agonizing and subsequent guilt because I knew he wanted to be free too.

"I thought I had explained to you how I felt," I said. "I felt awful, but I hated the way I'd been treated in so many jobs. I was told I wasn't being paid to think. There were blatant sexual advances, innuendoes, and harassment. Then there was the fist smashed down on my desk by the guy who fired me and later killed his fiancé. The deliberate stack of heavy manila files dropped from two feet above so they made a sudden loud noise just inches from my nose. Other times I was stepping and fetching, serving coffee and sandwiches. It was awful."

The closer we had gotten to following up with Turner and possibly re-entering that corporate world, the worse I had felt. Now, remembering, old feelings of worthlessness began to re-emerge and piggyback onto my work misadventures.

"In fact I sometimes wondered why you would even marry someone without a degree. Don't people usually try to marry at their own educational level? Isn't that important?"

"Not to me," he said adjusting to my unexpected outburst. "When I met you I sensed a depth," he said. "I could see you were intelligent, competent. That's what mattered to me." He paused before continuing.

"You know," he said, "it's easier to control those with low self esteem. And there will always be those who will knowingly work that to their advantage. You were encouraged. For that reason alone, you need to include this chapter. Now it all makes sense. It was a pivotal moment in time for us. If we had gotten financing, maybe it would've put us on a completely different path and we wouldn't be doing this."

I had worked hard to avoid the pain that came with remembering some of the abusive individuals, how I'd felt, how I'd been treated over the years. Forgiven childhood echoes had again whispered that I was ugly and stupid and that was the real reason I hadn't followed up. Though maturity, experience and logic dictated otherwise, astonishingly, even now I was afraid it was true. And the tagline was that if Ken ever found out, then I would lose him too.

Instead his voice reached through like a balm and I indeed saw that many doubts and insecurities had been fostered by others for a sense of power, control or personal gain.

"Now it all makes sense," he repeated. "Write what you just told me." He was driving and since I couldn't hug him, I just cried it out and made him promise to help. I marveled at how empowering it is *at any age* when there's someone who completely supports and believes in you. And how important it is to recognize that the after-effects of compartmentalizing emotions on the job may linger long after the job had been left behind.

I found it was perhaps a rite of passage signaling a disconnect from a conditioned, measured response environment and reconnect with a more natural cycle of life. All in all, a good thing.

3. WHEN THE STUDENT IS READY, THE TEACHER WILL APPEAR
(1998)

When we had talked by phone with Art, he had said he hoped we wouldn't be like someone else he'd had before in an Absentee Ownership Program (AOP). The man apparently had plenty of money. He bought the animals and paid Art to keep them. Once every year or so he would fly up from Florida, rent an airplane and fly over Art's property to "see" his bison. Art never did meet him.

We were happy to assure him that our intentions were quite the opposite. Contrary to his experience, we wanted to learn hands on and if okay with him, we'd like to visit at least once a year. We wanted to see if it made sense for us to buy land of our own and raise the animals for meat.

The late-1997 job relocation to Georgia had prevented us from visiting our small herd that year and meeting Art, so as soon as we could after the holidays, we flew to Rapid City. Arriving late in the afternoon, we rented a car and drove another hour to the motel where Art and his wife, Jackie would meet us.

As we entered the lobby the next morning, Art and Jackie were easy to spot. Art was spiffed up pretty good with what seemed to me to be his best western hat. Standing 5'10" with a full salt & pepper beard, he appeared to be our age. Jackie was the same height, with thick, reddish brown wavy hair and infectious smile. They were good naturedly bundled up for the cold and I immediately noticed that both had on western boots.

It seems silly now, but I had spent hours debating whether or not to pack our western fashion boots that had never seen a spec of dirt. Wardrobe choices may be the ultimate frivolous issue when country and city first meet. A carry-over from youth, the less I know about a destination, the more emphasis goes to looking good or at least blending in. In the end, my insecurities dictated that the bulky boots be packed.

Art and Jackie were down to earth and immediately likable. Over breakfast, we exchanged pleasantries and got to know each other. Jackie worked for a non-profit company helping the developmentally disabled. Art did the ranching which included haying and raising cattle and bison. He was the third generation to have bison. His great-grandfather had been one of the ranchers to bring a handful of bison onto their Wyoming ranch in an effort to save them at the turn of the century. This effort was shared by other ranchers and occurred well before any kind of Endangered Species Act or government action was in place. It worked. By the late 1800s, there were an estimated 600 to 1000 animals left. Today there are over 500,000 with an annual growth rate of around 20 to 25 percent.

As we were leaving, Jackie's casual observation endeared her to us for life. Looking down when we got up from the table, she chuckled saying, "She's the only one who wore practical shoes." That morning, I had looked outside and saw how icy the hotel parking lot looked. My sneakers had won the fashion debate. Ken changed his boots before we left while Art and Jackie laughed that they would change theirs too. It seems we all wanted to make a good first impression.

We followed their blue and silver pickup from the parking lot and after a few miles we turned off the freeway onto a two-lane road. It stretched for a good 10 miles and wound through rolling South Dakota hills covered with a few inches of snow. It had been a milder winter than normal and the roads were clear except for icy patches the morning sun hadn't yet reached. Finally we reached another highway, crossed it and entered a dirt road. Level farmland dusted lightly with snow on either side of the road now replaced the rolling hills, providing a broader vista. An occasional farmhouse was visible, but mostly it was open countryside. As I scanned the landscape, I took a deep breath. The clean air was familiar. It felt like home.

We saw Art's right turn signal blinking as he pulled onto an even smaller road. About 500 feet ahead was a modest yet distinguished looking log cabin home. The snow-packed road circled the house, providing easy access to and from the main road.

They parked in front and as Jackie walked into the house, Art gestured to pull behind his truck. At the front door, a big black dog slowly wagged its tail and with each friendly bark, emitted a brief white burst of mist. Following Art to the door, we stomped our feet and once inside, were immediately greeted by a toasty, pot-bellied stove. We would learn later, besides the oven in the kitchen, it was the only heating system in the house. It reminded me of my childhood in Montana when wood stoves were the heart of the house. And for some, they still are.

We looked around. The inside was like the outside—rounded log walls, darkened by time. The small living room was left of the entry, with a chair, sofa, TV and coffee table. Through the picture window was the rental car and Art's truck. Inside, about ten paces from the door was a round kitchen table where Jackie was serving hot coffee. We all sat down briefly and visited, talking politely about their house, the weather, our trip there. But Art could tell our minds were elsewhere.

"Well, I suppose you want to see your animals," he finally said.

Our spirits lifted. "Yes," said Ken.

"We sure do," I added, trying not to sound too anxious.

Art's understanding smile was my answer as he rose from the table and slid the chair back in.

"We'll go on out, then," he said to us as much as to Jackie who was already in the kitchen.

We all put our coats, gloves and hats back on and followed Art through the kitchen and out the back door. The dog, hearing the door, was immediately there, tail wagging. It seems I just can't resist dogs and this was no exception. Petting his heavy, matted fur, I asked his name.

"Oh, that's 'ol Bear," Art said with a hint of affection. "We'll take the red truck over here. Let me get 'er warmed up."

He climbed into the cab of an old Ford diesel pickup and started the engine. It had probably been red in its earlier years; now there was little finish left, but plenty of dents and scratches. The cab contained an old fashioned, three-person bench seat. Art hopped back out and with a few steps, was inside a weathered, three-sided shed. The shed was attached to a weather-beaten barn, which was attached to a corral system extending toward the house.

"We'll take some cake out to 'em," he said, leaning over and grabbing one of several big bags.

I was tickled, hoping it was a kind of a treat. At the same time, I admired how easily Art slung the bags into the back of the pickup. Wanting to be a good guest, I leaned over to grab hold and lift the nearest bag. When it barely budged, I looked again. The bottom of the bag read *Weight: 25 lbs.*

Art smiled, "Let me get that for you, Kathy. They can be a little heavy." He picked up my bag and tossed it into the back of the truck.

"That ought to do it."

It registered that he was doing what we may have to do on our own ranch. We needed to be able to lift heavy bags of things. I had just received my first reality check of my physical strength and hoped I hadn't pulled anything. Briefly I considered I may be older than Art, but actually we seemed about the same age.

OK, so he's a man and has muscles. With that thought, I looked at Ken, who seemed mildly amused at my even trying to pick up the bag. I ignored him.

"What's cake?" I asked.

"Oh, it's just a treat for 'em," he said. "A little mix of oats, wheat, some minerals. To them it's like candy. I've been putting it out the last few weeks to get 'em used to the truck before you got here."

I was grateful. We only had a few days. Without knowing much about his place, proximity to the animals, logistics or what to expect as an absentee owner, he was telling us that he had taken all this into consideration.

We climbed into the toasty cab of his pickup. Instantly, a potpourri of scents collided: dust, diesel fuel, dog hair and stale cigarettes. Again, it was familiar. Many of these same smells were in my grandpa's old pickup, various uncles' pickups and as a teenager, my girlfriend Jane's old pickup that she used in our high school years.

Art steered the truck down the short road we had just come in on and turned right at the fence at the main road. Driving at a measured pace, Art pointed out a few of his property lines and answered our questions about acreage, hay, rainfall and electric fencing. Shortly after another right turn, he pulled to a stop and switched into four-wheel drive. Slowly we began to make our way up a steep incline on a frozen and deeply rutted dirt road.

Art chuckled. "You know, people keep saying I need to get this graded. But I figure it's sometimes better than a fence to discourage unwanted visitors. Most people don't want to take a chance on messing up their cars on a road like this."

No kidding. Deeply rutted and with hard cement-like dirt, it occurred to me it would be fairly easy to get stuck or fishtail and roll over even in four-wheel drive. While I fantasized stopping and backing down the hill, Art chugged merrily along, familiar with every dip and rut.

"You ought to see this in the spring when the snow melts," he said cheerfully.

"Wow," I said, drawing a breath of relief when we crested the top of the hill. A minute later we had pulled up to a wide, green steel pipe gate with a metal sign wired in place that read: "Bison 6, Trespassers 0." He was pleased to see us reading the sign.

"That's just a reminder for those who don't know the score," he said. "Bison will always win."

He got out of the truck and opened the big gate. Getting back in he said, "It's okay to leave it open for now. They're not in this pasture."

We looked around. There were heavy scrub oak bushes and trees on either side of the truck. We drove through a small gulley and pulled up to another gate. This time it was a barbed wire gate, stretched to a post across the road as an extension of the barbed wire fence on either side. Ken got out, opened it and after Art drove through and the gate had been closed, Ken hopped back into the warm truck.

Sensing we were now closer to where the bison were, we grew quiet. Art stopped talking too, scanning the snowy landscape for signs. Rolling hills extended before us, coupled with open flat areas of winter grasses poking out from the snow cover.

"How do you know where they are?" I asked.

"Well, they've probably heard the truck by now," he said driving slowly across a flat pasture area. "They'll be here."

We moved forward another 200 feet and suddenly around a distant corner, a big brown bison emerged trotting toward the truck. Then there was a second and third. Two more appeared. It was like that, until we soon found ourselves surrounded by about twenty huge bison with full winter coats. We could see their breath, though they seemed oblivious to the cold. They were absolutely beautiful. Milling around, they jockeyed for position as each new bison joined the group. About eight had calves with them. It was thrilling.

Art had stopped the truck by now and was watching with a discerning eye.

"Which ones are ours?" Ken asked.

"Over there," Art pointed. To the left and in front of the truck, were four large bison cows and three calves. They were nonchalantly grazing nearby at tall stubbles of pale yellow grass through the snow.

"They're still getting used to their new home," he said. "They'll separate themselves off like that until they figure out the pecking order."

We looked to the right of the truck where about twelve other bison milled around, giving each other a wide berth. Art climbed out of the cab and we did too. Cautioning us to stay near the truck, we joined him at the tailgate.

"We'll put out some cake and then you can get a good look at 'em," he said, leaning in and opening up one of the bags. "Just hold the sack open like this and I'll drive slowly so you can spread it out on the ground. Otherwise, they'll just wander off."

Ken and I climbed into the back of the pickup and Art pulled the truck forward slowly in a wide circle. As we got within twenty feet of our animals, we tossed cake pellets to them. Art's bison crowded around wanting more and we gladly obliged. Then he stopped the truck again and joined us alongside the truck bed.

"You folks got some first class animals," Art said. "If it weren't for the ear tags, it'd be hard to tell 'em from mine. They're all like cookie cutters."

"That must be the cow that lost her calf," I said looking at the one calf-less female.

"Yeah." Art said. "That calf would've just been coyote bait. It's too bad, but there's nothing you can do in a case like that."

We grew silent as I recalled the unexpected phone call from Art six months before. He had picked our bison up in Montana and offloaded them at his place in South Dakota. Unbeknownst to us, one of the calves had broken a leg while being rounded up at the previous owner's farm. We had been led to believe the calf would be fine, but as soon as Art saw it, he knew differently.

Over the phone that day, he broke the news to us as gently as he could. "You have an injured calf," he said.

"Yes, we know," Ken said. "Pete told us, but he said she seems to be doing fine."

"Well, that's not the case," Art said. "It's broke clean through and is pretty much just hanging there. You can see bone. She'll just be predator bait. And I don't want her endangering my herd. When I saw her, I told Pete that was a dead calf. He knew what I meant."

"I brought her here because the cow wouldn't come otherwise, but once they get settled in, I'll have to shoot her."

In our Alpharetta kitchen, we could only stare at each other stunned silence. Ken's face mirrored my feelings. We had owned them less than a week and already we were losing a calf?

"I told Pete to give you folks your money back on that calf," he continued. "That's a dead calf," he repeated.

We didn't protest. There was no discussion. We certainly didn't want to endanger his animals. Though the AOP offered a chance to learn about raising bison from an experienced producer, we never dreamed this would be the first lesson.

Hanging up the phone. Ken and I hugged each other trying to absorb what he said.

"He knows what he's doing," Ken said quietly. "It's his place."

We knew we would have to learn how to deal with this part of it; the death losses, the attrition rate. It's part of the statistics we read about, but I hadn't understood how the statistics were arrived at in the first place. Now I knew one way.

I was angry at whoever had rounded them up. Later, when we talked to Pete on the phone, he put it on the bison cow for not being a good mom. When we asked Art how it could have happened, he had said they may have been in too much of a hurry. "It happens sometimes," he said. He promised to call us back in week or two, which he did.

"It's done," he said. "I'll leave the carcass there for a few days, so the mom will know her calf is dead and won't go looking for her. Then I'll move it out of the pasture so it doesn't draw in predators."

"Is there anything at all salvageable, Art?" I asked not wanting to let go.

"Nope," he said. "Pretty much that's it." With that, I did let go and accepted the calf's death. We had lost our first calf. It didn't have to happen, but it had.

Now, instead of seeing four calves with the four cows, there were three calves.

"Over here's the bull I have set aside for a hunt," Art said, jolting me back to the present.

We looked over to see a massive lone bison bull standing inside a fenced pasture, separate from the herd. Apparently a hunt is not exactly a hunt, but a contract between a hunter and a rancher to shoot a bison for meat and/or trophy.

"Mike's bringing over another bull this spring that he swears throws mostly heifers," he said.

"That's good," Ken said. "We sure want to grow the herd."

"They should all calve next spring, then we'll see," Art laughed and shook his head. "I don't know how he knows, but he swears that bull of his throws mostly heifers."

The thought of new calves in the spring lifted my spirits. Art saw me take another look at the lone bull.

"You know, the best way for a buffalo to leave the ranch is with a bullet," Art said. We both looked at him.

"It's the kindest way. They're wild. Bison aren't like cattle. Handling them isn't natural and things can happen," he said. "The best way is with a gun."

Saying nothing, I looked at the snowy ground. It was our first day with Art. We listened, as we would year after year. And year after year, Art grew to become a beloved mentor and friend. He taught us what he had been taught, what he had experienced and what he believed. We didn't always agree with him, but in time, we found his logic sound and his intentions humane. He always placed the animals' welfare first.

Emptying out the last of the cake, Ken pulled out his camera and took pictures. And Art captured the very first photo of us with our seven bison in the background.

Toward the end of our visit that afternoon, he volunteered one last thing.

"And I won't put 'em on feed neither," he said firmly. "Don't ask me, I won't do it."

"Okay," we agreed. We knew Mike finished his animals on grain, so this came as a surprise. We had been told that grain feeding was the traditional way.

"It's just not natural for them," he said. "Some people do, I don't."

And that was that. Within our first four months we had lost a calf, learned that Art preferred field harvest and felt strongly about not feeding grain to bison. We deferred to his experience and his judgment. We were glad to have it.

On the plane trip back to Atlanta, we recalled what Mike had said.

"If you can get Art to take your animals, I'll guarantee 'ya, you'll be successful."

4. KATHY'S THEME

Though we had minimized our risk, we weren't insulated from the unexpected. This story shows how vital family support is to a career or occupational change. Ken and I have met otherwise talented, bright, passionate people who long to ranch or farm, only to falter after the first few steps. They fail because one of the partners is not equally interested or supportive.

The lesson for newcomers to agriculture is this: ethical farming and ranching is inconvenient. It's hard work. The transitional period may in some ways be even more difficult. A stalwart and shared commitment is absolutely essential. We encourage others to start only when both individuals are 200 percent on board from the very beginning. While the challenges are real, the rewards are beyond measure. And you may find as we did, that sometimes Life's greatest treasures arrive on the wings of adversity.

A few weeks before Christmas, Ken called from the office. Biofield had announced they were out of money and a number of people would be laid off the next day.

It was déjà vu. We had hoped Biofield would reward Ken for establishing their quality system and ISO9001registration in record time. These components were critical to the government approval process that was required before any medical device manufactured in the U.S. and overseas could be marketed.

"Maybe this stock will be worth something," we said to each other. "Maybe this time, things will be different."

Yet here we were again. After creating the quality system from scratch and being there barely a year, Ken was packing up his office. Just four months earlier, he had hired and began training an inexperienced young man for the quality engineer position. Unwittingly he had been training his replacement. Ken received no warning and no severance. While our world came crashing down around us, the company was "sorry."

The first Tuesday after being laid off, Ken stopped me in the upstairs hall.

"I have to talk to you about something," he said. His tone was different. His eyes held mine as he told me that he just gone over our finances. Then he told me that he had ordered a painting I had admired for years in Santa Barbara. He knew I had never had a painting before and he'd been looking forward to surprising me with it for Christmas.

"I just don't know if it's a good idea," he said. "We don't know how long I'll be out of work."

The disappointment in his voice was uncharacteristic. It was another reality check and indicator of the fear and uncertainty we were both feeling. After a second of grieving for the painting that I wouldn't get, it was surprisingly easy to let it go. Growing up, our family never had the kind of money to be able to afford paintings. And it seemed silly to now grieve the loss of something I never had.

"I love you for it, but the painting will be always be there," I said. "Now is just not the time."

He studied me for a minute, then pulled me into his arms. "I so wanted to be the one to do that for you," he said. "I'm sorry."

I hugged him harder for a minute before pulling away so I could see his face.

"This is not your fault," I said evenly. "You did nothing wrong. It's the company that screwed up. This is exactly why we need to get out. We both know it's just going to keep happening. You did nothing wrong."

We hugged again and agreed how lucky we were to have each other.

"That's what Christmas is about anyway. We have each other," I said.

Ken held me for a minute longer. "I wish I could've gotten it for you," he said again.

"I know honey. But I don't need it. Just give me something hand made. I've always wanted you to write a song for me. You could do that, you know. Kind of like *Lara's Theme* from *Dr. Zhivago*."

"But I really wanted to get you something special," he said.

Suddenly I was angry.

"Don't you know that anything you make would be special?" I asked pushing him away. "If you don't know that, then I feel sorry for you."

He was shocked by my abrupt change in demeanor. I was equally surprised to hear myself. And even more surprised when I realized that I truly meant it.

"But writing music doesn't work like that," he protested. "I can't just sit down and force it. It's a creative process. It comes when it wants to. I never know."

"So, then, just start," I snapped. "If nothing comes or you don't get it finished, just put a note inside a box that says, it's not done yet, but it's coming. It's still a gift."

And with that I turned and walked down the stairs. I was so angry that he didn't know how special I thought he was. And how cherished a hand-written note would be from him or just the effort to create such a gift. I didn't *need* an expensive painting. I needed him.

Immediate remorse followed. How could I treat him that way? I agonized that I had just placed another unreasonable demand on him as he was dealing with the shock of losing his job. He wanted, he needed, he deserved nurturing and reassurance from me and asked for it in the only way he knew. Dealing with my own fear, I was unwilling and unable to give more. I saw continued lament about the painting as a potentially dangerous black hole that could suck us both in if we let it.

Sometimes unexpected anger has a way of jarring us into more productive behavior and thinking. I know my fear often masquerades as anger. Maybe a kind of survival instinct had kicked in. The rest of the morning I struggled to reconcile my behavior and find a way to support him. *At least, writing music would get his mind off the job loss. It might keep him preoccupied with something he loves and feels good about while waiting to hear about interviews.* I didn't feel any better. Quietly we went about our day. The order for the painting was cancelled. Though we were kind to each other, the energy was awkward and neither one of us seemed to know how to make it better.

Ken updated his resume and faxed it to headhunters. With Christmas in a few weeks, it wasn't surprising to learn that companies were closed until after the holidays. There was little he could do but wait.

Meanwhile, my Bisurkey efforts came to a screeching halt as I contacted temporary agencies telling them our situation and right away got a week's assignment at a medical glove manufacturing company. It wasn't where I wanted to be, but the work kept me busy, brought in a little money and helped bolster my self-esteem.

In the back our minds, too, was Art's comment about having new calves in the spring and the fact that our three original calves would be weaned next month. As the herd grew, it would add to our monthly AOP fees. Every penny we made had to count.

The next morning, after reassuring each other that we would be fine, we turned our attention to his parents' impending visit from Florida. For the first time, they and his aunt Anamae would be with us for Christmas, but we still didn't have end tables, lamps or a coffee table in the living room. Not even pictures for the walls. The house was much larger than anything we'd had in California and interior decorating had been low on the list of priorities.

We agreed not to tell his parents about being laid off. It would just worry them and they would want to help. Now nearly eighty years old, they deserved better than having to worry about their jobless adult children who wanted to be bison ranchers.

Early the next Saturday I was driving through a nearby industrial park and noticed a sign for a furniture liquidation sale. I stopped and found a warehouse full of used office furniture, over-sized pictures and an assortment of tables and lamps. They were inexpensive! Some of the large framed pictures were $10 and $15. I bought a few items for $20 and went home to show Ken. After I described all that I had seen, we agreed on a budget and I immediately returned. That afternoon I spent a few hundred dollars and brought home seven pictures, three end tables, one coffee table and three table lamps. Everything had nicks, scratches or dents, but by turning them a certain way, these imperfections were barely noticeable.

The next day, Ken glued a few loose pieces on the coffee table and we hung the pictures upstairs and downstairs. The house looked great. Once we got the tree and Christmas decorations up, the house would be ready for my in-laws.

A few days later I woke up early to find Ken in his office with the door closed. Sleepily knocking on the door, I turned the knob only to discover that it was locked. He came to the door.

"You can't come in," he smiled politely. To my blank look, he explained that on waking that morning he had 'heard' a melody and rushed to his desk to write it down before it faded. As he began composing, more notes came, so he kept going. He was still writing.

"Only Sam gets to hear it," he would tease, referring to our six-month-old Scottish Terrier. Day after day, he stayed in his office working on it. Only once did I see the self-doubt return. He said he didn't know if he'd be able to finish it in time for Christmas. I could see the sadness and stress in his face return.

I walked over and kissed him. "Then just put a note inside a box that says it's coming," I said. "That's fine." With that, I turned and left the room.

To me, it didn't matter. There was no rush, no deadline. I had the rest of my life to wait for him to finish that song. I had waited all my life for him. I could certainly wait the rest of it for his song. In fact, the anticipation would only make it sweeter. Heck, if he wanted to, he could get a lot of mileage from me during the whole creative process. But I knew that wasn't the way he was. Once he starts something, he can't seem to rest until he's finished.

The important thing was that he had started it, he had tried. To me, it was everything. The gift was in his effort. He is a perfectionist and therefore hard on himself. I knew I couldn't change that. He would just have to learn that, as far as I'm concerned, *he* is enough. Not the painting, or the music or a Christmas present, but *him*.

Two days before his parents arrived, he emerged from his office upstairs.

"It's done," he said triumphantly. His face was radiant and he beamed victoriously.

I was surprised. He had prepared me that it might not happen. In three steps, I was in his arms. We hugged, we kissed and then just looked at each other.

"I can hardly wait," I said. He smiled back at me with Sam dutifully looking on.

"Me too," he said. "I think you'll like it. Sam likes it, don't you Sam?"

The two of us are pretty big on frequent hugs and kisses and this particular holiday season there was abundance between us, lasting well into the new year and beyond.

Christmas morning, Ken waited until everyone had opened their presents. Then he quietly got up and retrieved the last package under the tree. Walking over, he presented me with a box wrapped with mismatched Christmas paper and Christmas bow. There was no card or tag on the outside.

"And this is for you," he said, sitting down next to me on the couch. "Why don't you open it?"

"What's that?" asked Aunt Anamae. "Oh, another present?"

"Yes, one more," I said.

Trembling, I tore the paper off and took the lid off the box. A black three-ring binder with a cassette rested comfortably in the box. Opening the binder, I saw printed sheets of music and his name. At the top were the words *Kathy's Theme (for my love at Christmas)*. I was holding it and looking at it, but I couldn't believe it. My name was at the top of a sheet of music. It was music composed for me. It was written by someone I love and who loves me. It was written by the person I had waited my whole life to find. It was written by my husband, my best friend.

And even though all this time we had been trying to pretend that everything was fine, I suddenly realized that we really *were* fine. We were more than fine. No matter what, we had each other. I couldn't hold back my tears.

"And here's the cassette," he said, gently removing the cassette from the notebook in my lap. Keeping his composure, he asked, "Would you like to hear it?"

While his parents and aunt struggled to see what was in my lap and why I was crying, he rose and inserted the cassette into the tape player. He explained to them he had written a song for me. Expertly adjusting the volume and balance on the speakers, he rejoined me on the couch, bringing a box of tissues with him.

Hearing the music for the first time with his parents and aunt there, all I could do was cry. How could I be so blessed to have found this incredible human being so late in life? From time to time, I still ask this same question, knowing the answer remains one of Life's better held secrets. And whenever I tell him how lucky I am, as I often like to do, he always replies, "We both are, honey." Perhaps the best part of these short conversations is that we both know it's true. And just knowing that each remaining stage of my life now is with him, is enough.

As for *Kathy's Theme*, it remains the gift of a lifetime. For those who may be curious, it is available as a somewhat dated midi file at the url below, placed here for safekeeping and sharing with others by Oberlin classmate Kerry R. Scott. We hope you enjoy it.

http://scottopus.org/kenLindnerMusic/theconcerthall1_library2.htm

(Note: Allow for a seventeen second lead in.)

CHAPTER 7

Relocation to Pittsburgh
(1999)

Sometimes it seems changes or obstacles can make strategies obsolete before they can even be applied. I'd been working to establish Bisurkey in Georgia. Now I had to continue with demographics in another state and learn a completely different culture. As we dealt with the impact of our second job relocation in just over a year's time, this one presented us with the additional opportunity to see how committed we were to our goal.

———•———

By mid-January, Ken had interviewed for two jobs. In February, he accepted a position as Vice President of Quality Systems for a company called Alstom Automation, located in the South Pointe Industrial Park near Pittsburgh, Pennsylvania. The fact that the company was not in the medical field and was not a startup appealed to both of us. In the back of our minds, too, was the fact that I was a breast cancer survivor, so resumed health benefits were welcome.

As usual, the new job and relocation meant Ken had to go on ahead. The large Georgia home felt empty and I was lonely without him there. While I kept myself busy cleaning, sorting and getting the house ready to sell, Sam did a good job of distracting me with his frequent chase-the-squirrels routine off our back deck. Almost daily, squirrels would rob the bird feeder, a feat I soon found both annoying and expensive.

In retaliation, Sam and I formed a squirrel conspiracy. He was too short to see them through the window, so when I spotted them, I tiptoed quietly over to the back door. In order to not tip off the squirrels, I whispered a few times, "Sam, squirrel," until he came to me. Very quickly, he knew what it meant and was ready.

The element of surprise was always in our favor. Silently I opened the door, Sam scurried out onto the deck and mayhem followed. Squirrels scattered every direction, up, down, sideways, kitty-corner. Many launched themselves off the railing, which was a good twenty feet above the back yard, landing below with a sickening thud.

From the deck above, I watched the drama unfold. For a few seconds, they were dazed and couldn't move. Meanwhile Sam was yipping and running down the stairs as fast as his little legs would carry him. Reaching the yard, the flying squirrel recovery process was considerably shortened by his arrival. Time and again at the last instant, they dashed away, sometimes bouncing repeatedly against the garden's chicken wire fence. Always and thankfully escaping just before Sam reached them.

Meanwhile in Pennsylvania, the company offered Ken a modest, one bedroom furnished apartment close to work in an area called Bridgeville. In our daily phone calls, he would tell me about neighbors he met and I reported on Sam's squirrel disbursements and house showings, which seemed to have a slow and uneven start. Every other weekend, he flew back to Georgia, and a few times, I traveled to Pittsburgh to house hunt.

With no offers and few showings, in July we finally changed realtors. Almost immediately an offer was received and the house was sold. Eager to join Ken and with a short escrow, the next stages of the move were scheduled with a truck and crew, followed by the familiar packing, sorting and cleaning. We still hadn't found a house to buy in Pittsburgh, so rather than add more stress to our situation, we put our entire household belongings into storage.

By mid-August, Sam and I joined Ken in the small one bedroom apartment. The new Lindner Bison office was now in a closet-sized space with a relatively unobtrusive water heater off our small kitchen. No more bay windows looking out onto a back yard and green forest. No more watching my playful Scottie puppy blast in and out of his dog door to and from his back yard, where frogs, squirrels and rabbits lurked. The beautiful 3000 square foot, triple story dream home was a now a memory, gratefully traded for a job with health benefits, a new city and a sense of renewed hope.

For now we were okay, but we knew that any lasting security would have to be created by us. More than ever, our experience with Biofield confirmed that we were absolutely on the right track. With a new resolve, I began exploring the area to learn what I could about Pittsburgh culture and demographics.

1. Food Show Award

We are often asked, "Why isn't your product in stores or restaurants?"
As we learned more about the commercial food business, we learned that
there were barriers for small producers trying to enter the market, even when
they have an award-winning product that people love. Let this story serve
as a partial answer to why Lindner Bison products are not more commonly
available and an object lesson for beginning small food producers who believe
that entering the U.S. food system is a simple proposition.

Shortly after unpacking and bringing my computer, printer and
email back to life, I got wind of a food show in Los Angeles via a foodservice
listserv, i.e., an internet bulletin vehicle serving a community of like-
minded people. Foodservice industry newcomers were being offered a
significant discount on booth space to encourage food entrepreneurs to
showcase their new food products.

With Ken's agreement, Lindner Bison was registered and Bisurkey
samples were shipped. Almost immediately Bisurkey won their Innovator
Award in the healthy food category. We were congratulated and told that
Bisurkey would be featured in the show's daily newspaper. This exposure
would help drive traffic to our booth and create visibility for Bisurkey and
Lindner Bison.

Flight reservations were made, and we were excited to be going back
to southern California. We would stay with Mary and Dan, who had since
moved from Long Beach to Pasadena. They also volunteered to help us
introduce Bisurkey at the food show.

Mary had been my maid of honor when Ken and I got married. By
that time, I had known her a little over twenty years. A beautiful woman,
and about ten years my senior, Mary wore her thick black hair cut neatly
to shoulder length. Standing 6-feet tall, with an absolutely winning smile,
she has a natural ease about her and a great sense of the absurd.

Known to mock her professors' podium lectures by standing behind
them and miming out the words "Who cares?" there is nothing shy about
Mary. And those who know her wouldn't have it any other way. She is
warm and unobtrusively hysterical, if that's possible. On a regular basis,
she leaves the rest of us unable to catch our breath for the involuntary and
uncontrollable laughter she evokes. Most people quickly fall under her spell.

Mary and I had coincidentally arrived in San Diego the same year and
met at a holiday gathering. I was single and she was newly and tragically
widowed. Sadly her husband, who worked for the State Department, was

shot and killed in front of her as they left a movie theatre in Washington DC. With four kids entering high school, she returned to California for family support. Two years after that, she went back to school for a masters degree in social services. This is where she met Dan, whom she would later marry at age 65.

Initially viewing Dan as an inappropriate suitor, I soon found him to be a warm, intelligent and sensitive man with a quick laugh and wonderful sense of humor. The physical contrast between them however is stark. She is 6-foot, he is 5-foot 6-inches; she has black hair, always gets a great tan, he has red hair and freckles. She has 20/20 vision, he wears wire rimmed glasses. Other than that and his being ten years younger, they are two peas in a pod and completely devoted to each other. After graduation they had moved to the Los Angeles area where job opportunities placed them in non-profit organizations and teaching.

Ken took a few days off and we flew to L.A. but not before we shipped hurriedly made banners and marketing materials to the convention center. Bisurkey was shipped separately. Miraculously, everything arrived without a hitch.

The night before the show, in Mary and Dan's dining room, we constructed ridiculous Bisurkey hats out of dyed neon yellow feathers. I had picked neon yellow to match the magic marker I had used to add color to our black and white printed labels. The plain labels hadn't been our first choice, but we couldn't afford full color labels so this did the job just fine.

For three days at the fair, Ken cooked Bisurkey and the four of us, decked in our silly neon feathered hats, handed out samples to hundreds of people. The response was terrific. The media interviewed us and restaurants said they would buy. We rented lead-tracking equipment, collected business cards and handed out hundreds of fliers that I had printed on the inkjet printer in our closet office.

At the end of the show, exhausted, we said good-bye again to our friends and boarded the plane for our trip home. Based on the interest shown and leads generated, we felt it had all been worth the effort and expense. We were finally going to launch Bisurkey and our dream of working for ourselves and living on our own bison ranch seemed closer. All I had to do was follow up the leads when we got back and get orders going.

Late Sunday we arrived back to our small apartment to find remnants of a toilet plunger scattered about, obviously the work of a bored little eight-month-old Sam. The next morning after Ken left for work, I got up, fed Sam, and got ready to follow up on the leads generated in California. Rather than wanting his food, however, Sam wanted to go outside. Taking him out, I discovered that he had bloody diarrhea.

I called the teenage pet-sitter that we had left him with and she confirmed that he had gotten into things after she left each day. I had mistakenly told her it was okay to leave him out instead of keeping him cooped up in his crate. Now it seemed likely he may have swallowed some of the toilet plunger bits. All he could do is look at me in a sad and forlorn way, and pass runny, bloody stools every 10–15 minutes.

The vet's office told me to bring him in, so I bundled him up and drove to the clinic. Immediately they put him on an IV for dehydration and said he needed to be kept there overnight for tests and observation. Driving back in the empty car, I felt guilty. I had been too involved in the trip to think clearly about Sam's care and the fact that innocent puppies left alone need to be protected.

The day there was little change in Sam's condition. They said his tests and the vet would be available by 1pm, so I made arrangements to be there and spent the morning calling the sales leads generated at the show.

After several calls, an unexpected pattern began to emerge. Customers wanted to order Bisurkey, but not without our having a representative in L.A. Rather than accept direct shipments, it seemed that it was standard practice for food producers to hire a broker/distributor who would coordinate the receipt, storage, distribution and delivery of the product to restaurants.

A few names were suggested, so I began calling them to see what kind of costs were involved. It was a moot point. The brokers I talked to insisted that we didn't have the local cold storage facility they needed to make it work, nor did we have the volume to make it worth their while. In addition, Bisurkey was unproven. Even though it had won a food show award and I said we would provide the sales leads, they insisted it would take too much of their time to explain what it was.

After hours of phone calls and repeatedly hearing the same thing, I drove to the vet's. Perhaps there I would at least have more to show for my time.

The clinic allowed me to take him into a spare room, and for hours I just sat there next to him on the floor, with an IV needle taped to his front leg for the drip. Being there with him, my guilt returned at having put him in danger just because I didn't want to confine him to a dog crate. Now he certainly was confined in a wire kennel with a wire floor, and 20 or 30 other dogs in similar kennels surrounding him in the same room. Sam was clearly miserable.

By the end of the second day, there was still no consensus between two vets as to Sam's condition. One doctor seemed new and had less influence; she believed an operation was unnecessary. The senior vet thought that Sam had swallowed a foreign object that was perhaps not showing up in the X-rays. I was told to leave him overnight again. If the foreign object was there and it moved, perhaps they would see it on the next round of X-rays.

Early the next morning, before leaving to check on Sam, a call came in from U.S. Foodservice, a big food distribution company. They had sampled Bisurkey at the show and believed it had potential. They were hosting a food show in Denver in another month and the woman caller had been authorized to invite us to attend. Sysco, another food distribution giant would also be there, and other companies would be introducing competing new food products along with us.

"This is by invitation only," she said. "Of course there are no guarantees for orders," she added quickly. "Just to be invited, though, is a good sign."

"How much is the booth fee?" I asked.

"Three thousand dollars," she replied.

Before I even told her I would talk to Ken and get back to her, I had done the math in my head. Total costs would be closer to $10,000 by the time airfare, hotel, meals, artwork, literature and marketing materials were added, along with the meat and processing for Bisurkey samples that we would provide for free. On top of that, there would be rentals required by the Food Expo show people for standardized carpeting, drapes, trash pickup, electricity and on site storage. If we wanted to rent a telephone line, or equipment to scan business cards, this would be extra as well.

Even if we could afford the show, there weren't enough bison in the world for the kind of volume demanded by these commercial foodservice broker-distributors. The last thing I wanted was to see Bisurkey launch once, then fizzle out because production couldn't be reasonably and steadily ramped up as more animals became available. The invitation may be a good sign, but a good sign for who?

Again, we couldn't figure out how any small food business could ever get started. Did everyone but us have financing, investors and an endless supply of operating capital? How does any small food entrepreneur begin? How do small bison producers survive? If you aren't independently wealthy, where does the money come from? Banks, investors, benevolent friends, relatives? Do only heavily financed food companies survive? It was certainly beginning to seem that way.

Exhausted and discouraged and worried about Sam, Ken and I talked. He immediately agreed that Denver may sound like a great opportunity, but we didn't have the money to go on what may be a national food show circuit, only to come back with no brokers in place to distribute. Or to set up distribution, but not have the volume they demanded. Even if a company like U.S. Foodservice was willing to take it on, without enough volume, Bisurkey at best would be a short-lived one shot wonder.

"It's not the right venue," Ken said. "We'll keep looking."

Relieved, I agreed and called the woman back. She seemed genuinely surprised when I thanked them for their kind invitation but declined to attend.

That afternoon at the vet's, I gave them permission to perform surgery on Sam. Nothing was found. A few days later, he was back home recovering and, between doting on him and promising to be a better dog-mom, I settled back in the office/laundry room.

Now I had to figure out where to go next with Bisurkey.

Springtime came and with it, the purchase of a charming three bedroom home in the suburbs on one acre. With a back yard and tall trees toward the back, Sam quickly adjusted to chasing deer instead of squirrels. The community was quiet and friendly and we were all happy be in a house again.

After organizing the office, my focus turned to finding an outlet for Bisurkey. By this time, the food show award had helped us gain access to a large commercial bison producer called Durham Meats. Durham had a sizable bison ranch in Wyoming and were active members of the National Bison Association. Processing several hundred head annually, they commercially distributed the meat from their USDA plant in San Jose, California.

Arrangements were made for us to fly to California where we were warmly greeted by the owner's family and crew, and given a tour the facility. That afternoon, we discussed specifics for processing Bisurkey and flew back with high hopes to Pennsylvania. Though their bison were grainfed, their willingness to process Bisurkey solved our biggest hurdle of having to source the meat from several producers and have it shipped to a single processor. Durham had the people power and money to source and process the two meats, were intrigued with the concept and offered affordable processing terms. After getting the heart-shaped patty plate to them, labels were made, shipped and the first run lined up. Once we received the meat, local marketing was next.

I phoned some restaurants and a health food co-op, and dropped off product samples and literature. Eventually the food co-op enthusiastically introduced Bisurkey to their customers. Their customers loved it and were especially happy to support small producers. Although the co-op was a 45-mile round trip, we provided free delivery of Bisurkey for well over a year. It was a great start, but unfortunately it was only one outlet. The profits barely covered the gas for the delivery.

Finally, three restaurants placed orders. The first restaurant wanted only bison tenderloin and New York steaks, not Bisurkey.

"We just want to see how our customers like it," the owner said. "If they like it, maybe we'll order more."

Sourcing the meat from Durham, I delivered the tenderloin and New York steaks. Once they tasted it, we knew they would be glad to add Bisurkey. The following week, they had sold everything and said everyone loved the meat. Several follow-up calls later, there was always a new reason why they couldn't order Bisurkey. Finally, I stopped calling.

The second restaurant was located on a golf course in the industrial park near Ken's office. They catered to the business lunch crowd during the week and to golfers on the weekend. Bisurkey was featured as a fun, low-fat meat alternative for those concerned with their health. It sold well for a few months with regular reorders, before the orders abruptly stopped. When I visited in person, at first the owner repeated that they didn't need any. Finally, he said they got a better margin on commercial meats supplied by an area food broker.

A third restaurant in the nearby town of Washington placed several weekly orders for a good four months. When they asked for free table toppers for thirty tables, within a few days, I proudly delivered them to the restaurant. Before I'd even left they'd quickly put them out on all the tables and in the adjoining sports bar. By the next week's delivery, Bisurkey Burgers had been added at the top of the menu board facing the main dining area. Each week, their Bisurkey orders were growing.

"It's a big hit," the manager said. "It's outselling our other burgers three to one. We want to order more in time for the big football game in the sports bar."

We were thrilled. Finally, a restaurant that was willing to be first and proving that people loved Bisurkey. It was the proof we needed to show other local restaurants.

But after four months, orders abruptly stopped. Suddenly the restaurant didn't need any. Calling back each week the answer was the same. Looking for an answer, I made a social call to the restaurant. Immediately I noticed that Bisurkey had been removed from the blackboard and that all the expensive table toppers that had been asked for and provided were gone.

I asked the manager why they were no longer ordering when Bisurkey had been doing so well. He replied that no one was asking for it. Since he had been the one to ask for the table toppers months before, I reasonably pointed out that the table toppers were gone and Bisurkey wasn't listed on their menu board.

"It's hard to sell an invisible product," I said.

If he was uncomfortable with the logic, he said nothing. No apologies, no explanation. Not a word.

When I asked for the expensive table toppers back, he disappeared for a minute and came back. He couldn't find them, he said. No one knew what happened to them. He guessed they had been thrown away.

In each case, without explanation, Ken and I were left to draw our own reasonable conclusions. We surmised that while customers wanted Bisurkey, the restaurants may have received a higher margin for high volume, commercial meat items. Perhaps the area broker/distributor noticed his orders had dropped and had issued an ultimatum that he wouldn't supply anything unless orders remained at a certain level and was bought from him only.

We'll never know for sure. What we do know is that people loved and wanted Bisurkey. And it didn't matter. What mattered is what the system allowed them to have.

2. Proving the Market
"The little guy proves the market and the big guy takes it away.
It's a sad fact, but true."
—Bob Messenger, Publisher-Editor, *The Morning Cup*,
food and beverage industry digest—

Because of our experience working in mainstream corporate America, we had seen examples of where, based on new product strength and ingenuity, the little guy could still occasionally win. Even when competing with established, commercial companies, innovation and quality could out-compete tired, inferior products. Believing in this premise, we continued to search for ways to get Bisurkey into the marketplace.

Unable to retain restaurant accounts for more than a few months or fill orders in L.A. without an agent, I turned to the internet for ideas. It seemed reasonable that Bisurkey needed to be championed by a commercial food company. Such a company would have resources we lacked to distribute it. Once they learned how good it was and experienced the same customer interest and demand we had, naturally they would want manufacturing and distribution rights. We just had to find a way to let them know that Bisurkey existed.

The internet led me to an online foodservice newsletter written by a consultant to the commercial food and beverage industry. He posted daily news bites from national and global media sources and provided commentary on selected topics. Registration was free. Soon I was exploring what the food industry wanted, what they valued, where their focus was. Reading his daily newsletter, I accessed and read source urls and links containing meat and health-related food news.

The emerging theme seemed to be flavor and nutrition, two elements that fit Bisurkey. Then I noticed the newsletter author reviewed new food products for those who dared send him samples. He could be scathing. "If you know you have a marginal or inferior product, don't send it in for me to try. If you don't know it's bad, you need to be told."

I hesitated. Then remembering our Innovator Award, I dialed his number. I described Bisurkey to him over the phone and he agreed to sample it—but not before reminding me of his brutal honesty when it came to new products and giving me one last chance to reconsider. Instead, I immediately shipped a pound to him along with cooking instructions. For days, there was no response and no review online. I was almost ready to give up, when a heading caught my eye. It was entitled "Bisurkey—A Love Story."

Giving Bisurkey about three inches of written text, it couldn't have been better. He ended by writing, "What I liked was the juicy, big beefy taste of this product. Better than traditional beef burger – better for you at least. I have no qualms, this is a four star rollout!"

We began getting calls from food editors, cooking magazines and newspapers. I talked with all of them. The local newspapers interviewed us. All wanted samples, which we provided and shipped for free.

Encouraged by the award and the endorsement, I pushed myself even harder. I began calling some of the largest names in commercial food, including Con-Agra, Wal-mart, and Trader Joe's. All asked about the ratio of turkey to bison. If we believed there was a reasonable likelihood for a business relationship, we agreed to tell them, providing they were comfortable signing a simple non-disclosure, non-compete agreement. In the business world, non-disclosures are generally regarded as a practical matter. At a minimum, they represent a show of good faith and integrity; in a worst-case scenario they make legal recourse possible should a similar name or product be offered without financial compensation to the originators. Most business people understand and accept the practice.

Con-Agra, though, was different. The man I talked with seemed genuinely amused when I mentioned our non-disclosure agreement. He said *we'd* have to sign an agreement with them before submitting a sample. He casually added that most people didn't want to sign it.

Though surprised, I assured him it was probably fine and asked what kind of an agreement it was. He explained. He said that when it came to proprietary food mixes or recipes, it would be unusual for anyone to have created something that Con-Agra's many food scientists hadn't already thought of.

I wondered if he believed what he was saying. Undaunted, I asked him to fax it anyway. Then I faxed him ours.

Neither one of us ever signed the other's agreement. When we got the Con-Agra fax, it was as he had described. It was short and said in plain English, without legalese, that it was highly unlikely that any proprietary recipe hadn't already been thought of and tried in their test kitchen and by signing the agreement, we willingly acknowledged that they already owned it.

As we learned later, this really meant that whatever it was, they had the ability to reverse engineer it to determine the recipe

Boy, are we out of our league, I thought and quickly moved on.

Wal-mart was friendly enough and the product development man didn't seem to mind that we were small, new or that he would need to sign a non-compete agreement first. What he was politely adamant about was that they preferred the product be in a box. This was for their stacking and storing in store freezers, and to reduce handling by stockers. He told us that when we had a box mock-up we should send that to him along with the product and they'd be glad to consider it for their stores.

When Ken got home from work that night, we discussed it. From a marketing standpoint, it meant the meat wouldn't be visible. Bisurkey's beautiful deep red meat color and low fat, we believed was a key selling point. Ken seemed intrigued and said it shouldn't be too hard to make a mockup of a box with a window. Over the next few days while he designed and engineered a box with the dimensions needed, I labored over the artwork, design and layout, which included a small window so the meat could be seen.

Ten days later we abandoned our efforts. Estimates from box manufacturers were exorbitant and required high minimum orders. Though Wal-Mart was willing to see the product with only a mock-up, if they decided they wanted it, then what? Sooner or later, the cost of the box would have to be dealt with and factored into the cost of goods. And we didn't know anything about the meat processor's capability to handle such a custom box.

For the umpteenth time, we asked ourselves, *How does anyone just starting out in the meat or food business survive?* We couldn't figure it out. They all had to start somewhere, how did they do it?

Trader Joe's. Customers who bought Bisurkey at the health food coop or directly from us told us we needed to get into Trader Joe's. We heard the suggestion so many times that one day I finally called and talked to a buyer there. After a week of discussion, I concluded that he was overworked and/or unavailable. We later learned that Trader Joe's buyers have a reputation as shrewd and tough negotiators. They have to be in order to keep the costs so low for their customers. The bottom line for us was that they needed a 40,000 pound minimum order, no exceptions. And the highest price they would pay amounted to about five cents/lb. over our actual costs.

3. Leaving Pennsylvania

Within two years of relocating to Pennsylvania, Alstom Automation was sold. A venture capitalist changed the company's name and promptly began to dismantle it. As the Pittsburgh plant began to close down, Ken and a few others were invited to work at the Long Island, New York headquarters.

Now his job involved a weekly round-trip commute to New York, coming home on weekends. Rather than stay in a hotel, the venture capitalist insisted that he and the other employees share a guesthouse that he owned. Under these unique conditions, Ken was unable to get a good night's sleep or have any privacy. From here the situation degraded rapidly for both of us. Then the venture capitalist offered Ken a job and we began to discuss relocating yet again, this time to Long Island.

We were tired of moving. Certainly, we weren't getting any younger and had yet to find a way to finance the ranch. The herd was growing and each year was more expensive to keep them on Art's place. Still, we couldn't envision ourselves raising bison on the East Coast.

"I've always liked the western states," said Ken. "That's why I moved there years ago, much to my parents' dismay. There are just too many people here and too much humidity. I love the West Coast."

We both did.

And I began to see the telltale signs of stress return. The same headhunters were contacted once again and interviews were set up. The first one was in Los Angeles.

Thursday night I met Ken at the Pittsburgh airport to hand him his interview suit and change of clothes. We talked for a few hours in the airport before he caught a red-eye to L.A. Friday evening he called. The process had been exhausting. With little sleep on the plane, he had interviewed with five people in one day. Late Saturday I picked him up from the airport. He spent Sunday at home, repacked his suitcase, and on Monday morning flew back to Long Island for the week.

About the interviews he said only, "It's going to be difficult. They're trying to do a lot in a short period of time."

But it was in California. Selfishly, I hoped he'd get the offer. Mary and Dan would be nearby again and it was a culture I knew. I felt more at home there with the value most people placed on healthy food and lifestyle. Ken, however, was dubious from the tone of the interviews and he disliked freeway driving.

But we both sensed that California may be better for marketing Bisurkey and selling our bison meat. In fact, months before, we had thrown a wide exploratory net over the United States to determine acreage costs and feasibility for a ranch. Though we yearned to live in a rural area, we reluctantly agreed if we lived in the country, but couldn't sell the meat to pay our bills, it made no sense to have the either a ranch or the animals.

Art had been instrumental in grounding us to this basic approach. Remarking once how beautiful it was in Montana and South Dakota and how nice it would be to live someplace like that, Art smiled. "You can't eat the scenery," he said.

We got his point. Wherever the ranch was, we needed to be able to earn a living. And not just during summer months, but year-round since our bills are year-round.

We were well familiar with the higher cost of California housing.

Also, we knew about the population density in L.A. Without knowing how we would ever be able to afford a ranch there, we agreed that California offered our best chance for success. Somehow, some way, somewhere in California is where the ranch would be. And if Ken got this job, we would only be living in the huge city for a few years.

When the position was offered, with mixed feelings, Ken accepted. The offer included a full relocation package home.

II

THE CALIFORNIA GRASSFED BISON YEARS

(2002 – 2005)

What this power is I cannot say. All I know is that it exists and it becomes available only when a person is in that state of mind in which they know exactly what they want and are fully determined not to quit until they find it.

—ALEXANDER GRAHAM BELL—

During these years, we tested the endurance and stamina of our hearts and souls. The passion that had ignited from our experiences was being kilned, refined, reformed and redirected. With marginal and short-lived success on the East Coast, we plotted our course and set sail for home.

CHAPTER 8

Return to Southern California
(2002)

Lessons about leasing land and searching for a small meat processor.

———◆———

Again Ken started work at his new job while I stayed behind to sell our house. We said goodbye to our wonderful neighbors and moved into a temporary apartment north of L.A. The company, based 25 minutes away in San Fernando, had plans to relocate to Valencia in a year, so this was the area where we would look to buy.

As before, our things went into storage and Ken settled into his new job as head of Quality Assurance. The company was aggressive, ambitious and poised to do an initial stock offering. The carrot of potential riches again dangled before us. Maybe *this* would be the job that would help finance the ranch. As for job security, we now understood that the most we could reasonably expect from any company was relocation expenses and uninterrupted income for a year or so. I got to work.

During this same time, Durham Meats, the company that had been making Bisurkey, decided to discontinue processing it. This was a blow. Los Angeles was where we had received the food award and had been unable to fill orders because we had no brokers or distributors. Now that we had moved here, we could be our own distributors.

We consoled ourselves that L.A. was a major city with millions of people who all had to eat. Surely there were many other meat processors here. All we needed was to find one who was interested in processing Bisurkey.

While Ken figured how to minimize his freeway commute, I was with our realtor looking at places within our price range. Determined to scale back and buy something more modest, we wanted to have a down payment ready for land once we found it. After seeing the small houses and locations for the price we had set, my confidence waned. The modest homes were okay, but the locations were questionable. Finally we began looking at condos and found a two-bedroom model under construction that would be finished late that fall. It was small, had a one-car garage instead of two, but as Mary pointed out, we wouldn't be there that long. Two years, max.

"Heck," she said, "you can do anything for a couple of years."

We agreed. It was reasonably priced for the area and showed promise as a good investment.

While waiting for the builder to finish and escrow to close, we turned our attention to identifying California ranchland. Our herd was growing almost exponentially now and with a fixed cost per head, we were fast approaching a number that would be too expensive for us to maintain under an absentee ownership program. We had to either find land quickly and move them, or sell some of the herd.

First we looked just outside our immediate area. Theoretically this made sense while we built the business. If we could establish the business here and a ranch not too far away, the transition later would be easier.

The search was short. We soon learned that Southern California acreage was too expensive, didn't have water, and was prone to seasonal brush fires. Land that wasn't zoned for building and development was dominated by irrigated agricultural orchards and cropland. Purchase prices were $5,000–$10,000 per acre, while monthly lease costs, excluding water, averaged $3,000–$4,000 per acre. We turned our search northward.

A local realtor gave us the name of a banker who owned property in the San Francisco Bay area where he wanted to graze livestock to help keep his land in good shape and the weeds down. We were also told that the owner would be intrigued with having bison on his land and might even be willing to help with fencing costs. Before calling, we asked for and were given an estimate of what the owner would consider a reasonable lease fee.

But when we talked with the banker over the phone, he quoted us a monthly lease fee that was double this amount—and that was before we even talked about fencing

"Why is it so high?" I asked.

"Because it's bison," he said.

"But bison are more efficient grazers than cattle," I replied.

"They drink a third less water than cattle and they're a heritage animal for the state," Ken added.

"You can get more money for bison," he said.

"Because it takes longer to get them to harvestable weight," I explained.

The silence that followed told us his pricing wasn't about fairness, reason or logic. It was about money. He didn't care about bison healing his land, or being a heritage animal that he could help restore to California. What he understood was that bison meat costs more than beef and he wanted a piece of that action.

1. SEARCH FOR A SMALL MEAT PROCESSOR

In the meantime, while Ken was at his already stressful new job, I worked to find a meat processor for Bisurkey, and perhaps eventually our bison. Days turned into weeks. The few small, affordable USDA-licensed processors had no openings in their schedules and the larger commercial processors were available for high volume, truckload orders only.

Over the years we'd heard about an international meat processing and distribution company in California. Similar to Durham Meats, the owner sold bison meat by sourcing it from Canadian suppliers and processors. We were told he insisted that producers grain-feed their bison, which he imported and distributed from his base in Los Angeles.

What we had heard about him from five or six sources was cautionary. Those who had done business with him believed that he liked to be regarded as difficult because he felt it was the best way to protect himself from people taking advantage of him. We were also told he made it common knowledge that he had placed himself on the fast track to become a multi-millionaire by a certain age and that it seemed clear that he didn't care how he got there. They all said that if they could avoid doing business with him they did, and encouraged us to consider doing the same.

Desperate times call for desperate measures. Here we were in L.A. where we thought Bisurkey could do well, but even in this large city could not find anyone who would process less than full truckload orders. If this owner we had heard about was as ambitious as he said and had access to bison meat, it may be worth looking into. Other people's experience didn't mean it would be our experience. Perhaps he had been misjudged.

I called and immediately got through. Describing Bisurkey and food show award, I asked if he might be interested in processing it for us. He was. He said he had heard about it some years earlier and thought the idea had merit. We agreed to meet when he returned from a trip. He said he'd sign the non-disclosure/non-compete agreement, which I faxed after we hung up. Our experience has been is that the form is often signed immediately and faxed right back. No fax came.

When I knew he should be back from his trip, I sent an email confirming the appointment and asking for the signed agreement. He responded that he was busy, but would get right to it.

The morning of the appointment I called to confirm. Again I asked to have the agreement faxed for our files. He was busy he said but said he would have it there when I arrived.

Radar now on full alert, I got ready to leave. I was reluctant to cancel the appointment after having arranged to meet with him. We needed a meat processor. Perhaps he really was busy and just not well organized. Allowing for morning traffic, I arrived early. The office was in a two-story building, located in a low rent industrial area of Los Angeles. A short stocky man came into the waiting room and introduced himself. As he led me into an open office area full of people, I asked if he'd had a chance to sign the non-disclosure yet.

Suddenly, he whirled around.

"Don't insult me," he hissed, his face turning bright red. "Who do you think you are, anyway? Do you own a multi-million dollar company? Do you? Do you?" he demanded.

I was stunned. Is this what others' experiences had been like? If the situation hadn't struck me as oddly comical, I might have been intimidated. Though a stretch, I considered he might be suffering from jet lag. By anyone's standards, his behavior was unreasonable.

"Of course not," I replied evenly.

"In fact, get out of here!" he bellowed, waving his arm toward the stairs. "You're wasting my time, coming in here and insulting me!" All eyes from the office were now on us and it occurred to me that was his real goal. Remaining calm, I convinced him to give us a chance to talk. Not that I particularly wanted to now. Still I was determined to have something to show for my efforts, even if it meant ignoring his irrational behavior and abusive manner.

He acquiesced, grudgingly leading the way into his office which was about 10-feet by 10-feet. Entirely cased in glass, it allowed him to keep a watchful eye on what I guessed to be about thirty-some employees in the adjoining area. The open office area reminded me of some newspaper offices I had seen. Everyone's desk abutted someone else's desk. Employees were on the phone or riveted to computer screens. Every few seconds, many nervously glanced over their shoulders; strangely, everyone seemed to be watching everyone else.

Now they were especially watching me. Relieved, no doubt. While he had me in his sights, they were safe, at least for the moment.

My curiosity began to surface. He obviously had some interest in Bisurkey or I wouldn't be there. More than ever, I resolved to learn what his interest was. Because there was no signed non-disclosure, there would be no exchange concerning the mix or value-added properties. If he wanted to somehow reverse-engineer it, the information wouldn't come from me. Now I just needed to know what he hoped to accomplish by agreeing to a meeting. I settled in and waited.

I showed him the sample he had requested. Shifting gears temporarily, he voiced approval of the packaging. Then avoiding my gaze, he slumped into his swivel chair and morphed into a measured casual demeanor.

For the next several minutes he asked empty questions, i.e., answers to which were easily available online and in our literature. Finally, the question came, though it was asked in such a muffled low tone, I almost didn't catch it. Gazing out one of his windows, he said "So, I suppose that with a name like Bisurkey, you have a trademark for it, eh?"

"Oh, of course," I said. If he had done his homework, he would've seen the small R with a circle around it on the label and literature. The name was registered and therefore protected. So that's what he wanted. I felt his confidence level drop as mine rose.

Soon the meeting concluded and I was relieved to be going. We had both learned what we needed to know. He said he'd cook up the sample and get back to me. I thanked him for his time and left. This was no one we would want to do business with. Ever.

Continuing our search, the very next week I was excited to find a small meat processor located just 30 minutes away. Over the phone the man was down-to-earth and receptive. Their processing fee and turnaround time was competitive and they were happy to provide business references. He told me they needed the business and were glad to have it. That's great, I said, because we would sure like to work with them and we believed Bisurkey would do well.

After checking their references, we made arrangements for them to make a test batch of Bisurkey. Immediately I began looking for sources for a minimum amount of bison and turkey, got shipping quotes, and began making arrangements to get the plates to the processor. When I called a week later to get their labeling machine specifications, I was told that they had to raise their processing price. I wasn't concerned since it's not unusual for a rate to occasionally shift by a few cents. The problem was, their new processing rate was *triple* their original quote.

When I asked what had changed in a week and why the rate was now so high, I was educated again. They had been struggling, they said. Someone had just given them a large order and the promise of a contract. In fact, at first they turned the man down saying they didn't have the equipment. The next thing they knew, the man delivered the equipment to their place, free of charge. They were grateful and couldn't believe anyone would be so nice. Unfortunately though, now they couldn't fit me in. When I asked who was so generous, I was told. It was the same man I had met with two weeks before.

This is just one example of how a small company may be slowed down, squeezed out, or stopped before even starting. Agreements change overnight, costs arbitrarily and dramatically change, equipment or tools may become mysteriously damaged or missing, new requirements or regulations may become part of the quote, or the supplier or manufacturer is suddenly too busy.

We had experienced all of this before and would experience it again. If you don't like it, take your business elsewhere. The problem was that when it comes to small meat processors or low volume meat processing for resale to the public, there often is no "elsewhere."

People still ask when we'll have Bisurkey available again. We wonder too.

2. Background: *E. coli* and the Shortage of Small Meat Processors

The shortage of small meat processors makes it exceptionally difficult and often impossible for small ranchers and farmers to have their meat animals processed for resale to the public. It is said that the shortage began after the 1993 Jack-in-the-Box tragedy in which three children died and over 400 people were sickened by a strain of *E. coli* bacteria known as O157:H7.

The deadly strain is often incorrectly lumped together with the naturally occurring *E. coli* bacteria O157. One is naturally occurring and friendly (O157) and the other (O157:*H7*), is unnaturally occurring and unfriendly. (Note: To keep them straight, just remember H = Hazard.) The friendly *E. coli* O157 bacteria is part of the normal flora of the gut, and can provide some benefits to their hosts (specifically by producing vitamin

K_2 and preventing the establishment of pathogenic bacteria within the intestine). But the H7 version loves acidic environments, having evolved there in order to survive in the rumen of a grainfed ruminant. (The rumen is the first and largest division of their stomach in which most food collects immediately after being swallowed.) When humans ingest the meat, the H7 version of *E. coli* is not killed by our stomach acid, so it can pass through our intestine and cause illness or worse.

Bison, like cattle, sheep, goats, and other ruminants, are designed to eat and digest grass. Grain—which they receive in feedlots in order to fatten them up—is not a normal part of their diets and makes them sick. The hazardous type of *E. coli* is reportedly higher in *grain-fed* cattle because it has mutated in order to survive in the hostile acidic environment that develops in their gut due to their unnatural diet. When grain-fed ruminants are being processed for meat, this *E. coli* can be transmitted when sloppy processing exposes the contents of the intestine, including feces, to other areas of the carcass being processed for human consumption.

E. coli strains may also be transmitted via non-meat foods such as lettuce, spinach, etc. This may happen when the product has been exposed to runoff from a contaminated feedlot that enters a shared water source. Another way that the bacteria may be transferred is by birds or flying insects that have visited the feedlot or water runoff before visiting the crop located some miles away. The consistent element or origin seems to be feedlots for ruminants. It's our belief that if ruminants had not been confined and fed an unnaturally rich diet of corn or grain, *E. coli* 0157:H7 may not exist today. Knowing what we know about evolutionary biology, there would be no reason for it to exist. It's that simple.

3. The Birth of HACCP for the Food Industry

The origin of the 1993 Jack-in-the-Box Ecoli O157:H7 contamination was found to be the multi-million dollar San Diego-based Foodmaker Corporation. As a result of this tragedy, new safety regulations were quickly passed to deal with the problem at processing plants; however the feedlot diets, which we believe is the source of the problem, were left intact.

The mother, or precursor to all safety standards requirements, was born to the food industry called HACCP, acronym for Hazard Analysis and Critical Control Point. The original concept was developed in the 1960s to assure that food transported into space would not cause food-borne illness for astronauts.

In March 1994, the HACCP Alliance was formed as a preventative program to assure safer meat and poultry processing. It was housed within Texas A&M University's Department of Animal Sciences. The Alliance's 1995 annual report stated that "Developing HACCP programs for on-farm, feedlot and other pre-harvest operations is more complicated and less understood than in-plant and post-harvest HACCP systems. The development of pre-harvest HACCP systems is a priority of the Alliance." It seems this priority may have never become fully activated and instead, efforts were directed to post-harvest systems.

In 1999, new HACCP standards became mandatory for all U.S. meat and poultry processors. The HACCP for Meat and Poultry program was designed by and for large food processors, such as the Foodmaker Corporation that had processed the Jack-in-the-Box meat tied to the *E. coli* outbreak. Unfortunately, small meat processors also had to conform to the new regulations, or be shut down. Compliance often meant developing and implementing new procedures, acquiring new equipment, hiring additional employees or consultants, as well as increased testing and inspection costs.

Unable to bear the financial burden, many small processors were shut down or closed. In the aftermath, rumors of small meat processor suicides surfaced. In one reported incident, a USDA inspector was shot and killed attempting to close down a family-owned processing operation that had been in business for over 20 years.

When the regulatory dust finally cleared, only a few small meat processors were still standing amidst the medium and large commercial and foodservice meat processing companies. As small meat processors became unavailable, medium and large processors expanded to fill the void. Some small meat processors may have even survived as the result of a sub-contract here and there from larger processors who were unable or unwilling to completely shoulder increased demand and pressure on their resources. In some cases, the few remaining small processors may have been controlled by larger ones that were *helping* them meet new regulatory requirements by providing equipment and/or personnel.

Today, 18 years after the Jack-in-the-Box outbreak, *E. coli* O157:H7 recalls continue, and new *E. coli* strains are emerging. Thirteen new strains were identified for the first time in 2010 alone.

Upon learning this history and hearing the stories, my confidence plummeted. How could Ken and I, as a small fledgling company, deal with the shortage of small meat processors and the meat quality problems and recalls? At that time, we were sourcing grain-fed bison through Durham Meats. How could we insure our product was safe and remain in business?

Drawing on Ken's quality assurance background, and before any Bisurkey was processed and sold, we had established reasonable quality standards for the handling and processing of the product. Because of his experience with medical devices, computer technology and robotics, Ken was familiar with potential contamination issues, bio-burden, testing and product quarantine. He understood what was reasonable—as well as what was unreasonable—to expect from human beings and equipment at various stages of production. His experience with the national Food and Drug Administration (FDA) and the HACCP certification program also helped us create proactive testing standards. Even though the plant we were using was USDA inspected, we had each batch of Bisurkey sampled by an outside lab and paid for the test out-of-pocket. Always the teacher, he described the process that I, and other non-technical people like me, could understand.

"What I've learned over the years is that it's impossible to inspect-*in* quality to any product and expect to find errors much above around 80 percent. Quality has to be there from the beginning. Putting inspection in place after a product release is like closing the barn door after 20 percent of the horses have left," he said. "Whether the product is food, a medical device or a widget, the same quality principles apply. One may be more life threatening than another. That's the only difference."

"And companies may not always be motivated to proactively insure quality before product release. It takes extra time, planning and people which costs money. Some may be in too much of a hurry to beat their competitors to the marketplace to do the necessary testing before release. Unfortunately, products that are made by a larger company doesn't necessarily insure high quality. It may only mean they have deeper pockets and more insurance to offset potential liability issues that may arise."

In 2008, we learned of a massive recall in Los Angeles of 143 million pounds of beef from the USDA-inspected Westmark/Hallmark Meat Company plant. It was the largest recall ever in history. Frustrated, Ken tossed another gem my way.

"How many small meat processors can you think of who have had recalls in the past several years?" he asked. "Not many," he said before I could answer. "So what does that tell you about who may have a good quality-culture in the first place? *Small* meat processors. Many are simply more careful. They process smaller volumes of product, which allows them to take greater care. They can't afford to make mistakes that would drive them out of business. Their entire livelihood depends on their good quality."

4. Abandoning the Greed Model

When we bought our first four bison and incorporated Lindner Bison, we had been clueless about the food industry. All we knew is that we wanted to make and sell Bisurkey as a way of financing our dream to leave the corporate world, create our own business and our own destiny. Loving bison meat, we wanted to raise bison, sell the meat and live on the land. It was the only plan we had.

Having been willing capitalist soldiers in various corporate armies over a span of thirty years, the profit-driven model was the only one we knew. It was familiar and it seemed to work. But when it was our turn to start and run a business, we repeatedly tried to apply the same principles and at every turn, we failed miserably. Still, we were determined to find a way to survive and we had to do it while we were still healthy and solvent. Now in our fifties, the likelihood of our being able to financially recover from miscalculations or errors in judgment was low.

As we successfully found ways that didn't work, we discovered three valuable qualities in our character that had helped to get us this far. We found that (1) we were willing to do what most people weren't willing to do (2) we were willing to pioneer an unproven business model in exchange for being able to do what we wanted to do, and (3) we didn't know that we weren't supposed to want to do either. In other words, we were willing to do what it took in order to create a sense of purpose and security for ourselves, something our previous employers had been unable and/or unwilling to provide.

Five years later, we were back where we started in Southern California. Progress had been glacial and negligible. Our hopes of finding a small local processor for Bisurkey was quickly evaporating and we could think of no one we could go to for advice. In fact, we didn't know anyone who was trying to do what we were trying to do, that is, leave the corporate world for animal agriculture.

"We're not like other people," I lamented one day to Ken. Encountering another dead end, I was feeling sorry for myself and more isolated than usual. There were endless reminders that we had absolutely no one to counsel us about the seemingly endless brick walls we were encountering.

"I never have been," Ken replied quickly, then more firmly added, "You haven't been either."

He was right of course. It meant we were on our own. It meant we had come too far to turn back. It meant that all we could do was trust our gut instincts, align our actions with our core values and leave the familiar behind.

So we abandoned the only business model we had known—one that was based on commercial production and massive distribution channels. The high volume model just didn't fit no matter how hard we tried.

As we began to distance ourselves from this way of thinking, we almost immediately began to feel better. Rather than toss the baby out with the bath water, we decided to stay keenly aware of the strategies used by the commercial business model. It was then we realized that because of what we knew, we could position ourselves and navigate the waters in new ways. We redialed our compass and adjusted our target settings. As farmer-author-activist Joel Salatin suggested, we would "fly under the radar."

The shift was surprisingly easy and some things became immediately clear. We began by embracing what worked for the greater good. This meant that if it didn't work for the earth, it wouldn't work for our bison. If it didn't work for our bison, it wouldn't work for us. If it didn't work for us, it wouldn't work for our customers.

What we didn't know, we would learn. What we couldn't afford, we would improvise or retrofit. But we wouldn't stop. We couldn't stop. Not now. We had a growing herd in South Dakota and we couldn't keep them there much longer.

5. REDISCOVERING FARMERS' MARKETS

While getting nowhere with my calls to area health food stores and food coops, picket lines appeared outside area supermarkets. Overnight, local supermarkets became devoid of shoppers. It was eerie. I couldn't figure out where people were buying their food.

One day a neighbor asked if we'd heard about the new farmers' market in Santa Clarita. We hadn't.

"It's wonderful," she exclaimed. "It just opened last Sunday. It's over by the college, you can't miss it."

Recalling the incredible farmers' market years before in Santa Barbara, we were excited. It was the best food we'd had in decades and it quickly become part of our Saturday morning ritual.

Early the very next Sunday, we arrived at the college. The parking lot was already jammed with cars. Nearby were at least thirty farmer canopies and there was a great energy to the place.

"So this is where everyone is!" I said. "Look at this, it's great!"

Ken agreed. Leisurely we wandered around, enjoying the morning and feeling suddenly more at home. We tried samples, bought bags of fresh fruit, vegetables and produce. It was a bonanza. Back at the condo, we prepared our Sunday dinner with anticipation. Consistently, the flavor was better. It was exciting and freeing to have an alternative to flavorless supermarket food, often with additives we didn't want.

Savoring every bite, during dinner I said to Ken, "Maybe this is where we should try selling. The people at the farmers' markets have got to have small volume too, that's probably why they're there."

This logic resonated. The next day, I went online and printed out the pages of Los Angeles area farmers' markets. There were so many! Overlaying the list on an L.A. city map, I highlighted the closest ones. The Santa Clarita farmers' market wasn't even listed yet, so I called the next closest one in Encino.

There was a recording. On it, a cheerful voice announced the market details, including hours and a brief description of products. One of the products was locally grown chicken.

I could hardly wait to tell Ken. For years, we had all but given up eating supermarket chicken because it had so little flavor. No matter where we bought, there was always something off with the flavor and texture. In fact, the last time had been memorable. When preparing it for the oven, rather than the bird standing firmly and proudly in the roasting pan, instead it collapsed nearly flat onto itself. I had never seen anything like it. No matter how I tried to reconcile it, I knew something was wrong. We cooked it anyway, hoping it would taste good. It didn't.

That Monday, I left messages with several farmers' markets. We raised bison, I said, and we wondered if they might be interested in having us sell meat at their market. No one returned my calls.

The next Sunday, we found our way to the Encino market and almost immediately located the chicken people we had read about. After they described how they raised and harvested their birds, we bought two of them. Then we explained our situation and asked them what kind of insurance they needed to sell their chickens. The lady told us what they did for poultry and suggested a few county agencies to call.

Thanking her, we continued our shopping, enthralled with all the choices. I found a table full of lettuce and greens. Customers were standing in line while the farmers quickly waited on them. Bags were weighed, money exchanged, and the farmer would yell "Next!"

In a moment of insight, I realized that while this was a leisurely outing for us, the farmers were far from casual. They were there to make money. This was how they paid their bills.

I felt a tap on my shoulder. It was the chicken lady we had just talked to. Beside her was another woman, who she introduced as Jane, the market manager. I shook her hand and introduced myself. Ken had stopped now, too, and introduced himself.

"So, I'm told you raise bison," she said.

"Well yes, as a matter of fact, we do," I replied.

"News sure travels fast," Ken said, and we all laughed cheerfully.

"If you have a minute, let's go where it's a little quieter," Jane said and we agreed.

We followed her into a nearby building and left the market din behind. After being comfortably seated in her office, Jane started the conversation.

"Well, I don't know if you've noticed, but we don't have any red meat here. In fact as far as I know, no farmers' markets in southern California have red meat."

"We were wondering about that," I said. "Why do you suppose that is?"

Jane shrugged and laughed, "Beats me," she said. "Most ranches are up north, that could be part of it. Maybe no one wants to come this far south. It's a long way."

Her manner immediately put us at ease.

"Right now our herd is in South Dakota," Ken said. "Our plan is to move them here in the next year or so and see if we can make a living selling meat. I want to leave my job and do this full time. In fact, the sooner, the better. This is our active retirement plan."

"Before we buy land and move them here, though, we want to first make sure there's a market for the meat," I said. "As you know, land in California isn't exactly inexpensive." Jane agreed and listened thoughtfully as Ken outlined our situation and our plan.

"We know of too many people who started raising bison because they loved them, then found out they hadn't developed a market for their meat so they had to quit. So, we're doing it a little backwards. Before we invest in land and move them here, we want to make sure there's a market. We don't have the deep pockets some bison producers seem to have. We're on the pay-as-you-go plan."

"Makes sense," she nodded.

"That's why we're here. We're now thinking of farmers' markets," I said. "To see if there's any interest."

"Oh, I'm sure there will be interest," Jane smiled reassuringly.

We spent the next forty minutes together as she explained the selling regulations and gave us the names of other market managers who might have space and may be interested. She also gave us the names of people to contact concerning approved coolers and storage.

Ken reiterated that we needed to be able to make an income from the markets. It was the only way we could see that would help us pay for the land for our bison and support us too so we didn't have to have other jobs.

Jane nodded, chuckled and said, "Well, other farmers here make it work and your plan sounds like a good one. I'm sure there are a lot of people out there who would like to do what you're doing, too."

On the way home, we talked excitedly that we finally may be on the right track. Jane's encouragement provided a stark contrast to the years of cold shoulders from restaurants, stores and large food companies.

"She seems genuinely interested," Ken said.

"What a nice change," I replied. "I think she really thinks it could work."

"Let's call the people she suggested and see what they say," he said. "If things go well, we'll start looking for land and get the herd here. Just think. No more absentee ownership payments!"

"And, finally, our own ranch!" I said. "We'll have to start getting some suggestions from realtors on where to look for land."

We were energized with a renewed sense of hope and purpose. That week, I was on the phone almost non-stop, researching what was needed, and creating an infrastructure of sorts so we could figure out what was needed to be able to sell at farmers' markets. I contacted the suggested market managers and we met many of them the following weekend. They told us they were very interested and asked us to let them know once we had things in place.

There were no other red meat producers at the markets, so once again we were on our own. There was no one to ask, no model to copy. In an email exchange with a Colorado grassfed bison producer who sold at seasonal farmer's markets up there, we at least got a lead on a small portable display freezer.

In the back of our minds, always were the unanswered questions: Would anyone even buy our meat? Or if they did, would they cook it right and want to buy it again? We thought so, we hoped so, but we just didn't know.

It seemed we may finally have a venue where we would be able to find out.

CHAPTER 9

The Last Layoff
(2003)

Sometimes when we're stuck, the universe gives us a gentle nudge to change directions. If we ignore it, a stronger nudge may follow. Finally, there comes a definite shove. The timing of may not always feel good, but in the long run, it usually works out for the best.

———————•—•———————

One Friday around noon, Ken called from work. He'd been laid off and was packing up his office. Bolstering up their financial picture to attract investors, part of the company's strategy included making their financial statement attractive by reducing overhead. The recaptured salaries and benefits dollars could then be added back into the corporate money pot. Those who were left would each get a larger share of the pot.

Once again, Ken's upper management position was filled by a younger, less experienced and therefore less expensive employee. Ken had set up and established the quality system needed to comply with the ISO 9001 standards and was no longer needed.

We had talked about it, saw it happening around us, experienced layoffs and even tried to prepare ourselves by expecting them. Even then, it came as a shock. The only good news was that this time Ken would receive severance pay and outplacement services.

The next day, Saturday, he had an appointment at the company offices with a representative of the human resources department. I went with him to help retrieve the rest of his things. We both needed the moral support and were glad to be together.

Ken led the way into the building where we looked for the empty boxes that he had left there yesterday. They were gone, apparently removed by the cleaning crew. The day before, Ken was paid and trusted to show up. A day later, we weren't supposed to be there unsupervised. With this new status, and feeling like unwelcome guests, we tentatively looked around the immediate area for cardboard boxes to pack his things in.

Within a few minutes, the HR representative arrived and Ken excused himself. The man glanced over at me briefly, then conducted Ken's exit interview in hushed tones in the nearby hallway. It was so familiar. There would be papers for Ken to sign to release the company from any liability. Details of the severance package would be verbalized and acknowledged.

Though I was some distance away, it was my impression from the low voice tones, the HR man's posture and lack of energy that he felt uncomfortable. In fact, I may be giving him too much credit, so let's just say I hoped he felt uncomfortable. And if my being there contributed to his lack of ease, all the better.

I was proud of Ken. As angry as I felt watching the two of them, the difference between the two men was noteworthy. The HR man was slumped forward, almost cowardly whispering the details of the severance package and outplacement. In contrast, Ken was standing erect, tall and his demeanor was non-accusing and somber. He occasionally nodded, saying nothing.

We all knew. This is the way it ends for many of us, perhaps especially as we get older. Even when in excellent health, age may place us in a higher insurance category. In Ken's case, by expertly doing his job and completing the priority early, he was expendable. Some people stay ahead of the cycle by requiring termination contracts before agreeing to employment, but Ken and I hadn't wanted to spend time and energy trying to outfox the fox. Instead we decided it was wiser to build our henhouse elsewhere.

I reflected briefly on the differences between Ken and me. Over the years, I had learned office politics with the best of them. I recognized and respected the verbal and non-verbal cues, nuances, innuendos, power struggles, manipulations, tangible and intangible rewards and punishments. When powerful allies left, those who intended to survive effectively nurtured new alliances. Yet while I knew how it was supposed to be done, I failed at executing any of these corporate cultural strategies for myself. Ken, on the other hand, had never been motivated to play the corporate politics games.

Watching him now, I felt enormously proud to be married to such a man. Because of him, in many ways I had become a better person. He deserved better. He knew it. They knew it. We all knew it.

The drive back to the condo was quiet. Unloading the boxes from the car, all he said was, "I'm glad to be out of there."

I was glad too, but uncertain what it meant. Mary and Dan were moving that weekend to Catalina, so it seemed as though our only two local support systems had simultaneously evaporated. The next day we went to a movie to distract ourselves.

On Monday, I watched for signs as to what Ken was thinking. He dropped his shirts and pants off at the dry cleaner and I had seen him looking over his expensive interview suit to make sure it was clean. As fastidious as he is about everything, it was.

Sometime during the day, he made an appointment with the outplacement service and on Tuesday he went for an interview. Several hours later, he was home.

Hanging up his suit jacket and tie, he said, "Ironically, it sounds like the parent company may want to use me." I felt an involuntary wave of relief. He stood waiting for my response.

"That's interesting," I said. "I guess they liked your work. What did they say?"

He mumbled a few indistinguishable words and wandered off. That afternoon we said little as unspoken emotional aftershocks continued. Silently I mused that we both had plenty of experience getting jobs, but our track record for keeping them was getting shorter. And we couldn't yet claim any experience at starting and keeping a business going either. It didn't matter. We had to survive.

A few more days passed. I watched for signs of Ken's get-back-in-there-and-fight mode. Nothing. I finally decided it would be better for both of us if I got back to work looking for a small meat processor and ranchland. As I was crossing our small living room, Ken came out of the bedroom.

"I don't want to go back," he said.

I stopped. The look on his face told me he'd had enough. He was waiting for my reaction.

"Okay," I said, swallowing my fear. I wasn't sure what it meant yet, and I also wasn't sure how much more I could do on my own anyway. There was little to show for my six-year effort to get Bisurkey going and it remained to be seen how we could proceed with farmers' markets. In two steps, I was in his arms. Hugging him tight, I said, "We'll find a way."

"Oh, I know we will," he said in a determined voice and solid demeanor. "I just don't want to go back."

"Good," I said.

And with that, we walked into the office together. His fighting spirit was back. This time, we would go forward, finally and fully together. That day, we reviewed the situation with potential California meat processors and confirmed our herd count in South Dakota. We reviewed the notes I had gathered from the various phone conversations I'd had concerning equipment and regulations for selling in farmers' markets.

The next three hours were strangely reminiscent of orienting a new employee, but this time it was my husband. How would we do working together? Would he, like others, want to control and dominate ideas, efforts and activities? Would I? Could we partner together, work together, eat, sleep and live together?

I was determined we would and I could see that Ken was equally determined. We had a new focus, a new energy, a new combined strength and a new imperative. The timing was not of our choosing, but we would make it work.

At long last, we were both out of corporate America. Together, we vowed we would stay out.

1. Pasadena Litmus Test

Two weeks before Ken's final layoff, we were accepted at the Pasadena Farmers' Market for Saturday mornings. Gretchen, the market manager, knew we were struggling to find land so we could bring our animals to California. She also knew that it had to make sense for us financially and she was willing to give us a chance. Since we weren't California producers yet, she placed us in the non-producer's section. Pasadena became our litmus test.

The costs to get the infrastructure of our business in place were staggering. To store the meat during the week, we needed a commercially approved cold storage facility. Most had high volume requirements and others had something called 'pick' charges. This meant that any time we wanted something from cold storage, they would charge a fee for them to pick it out for us. These fees were in addition to their incoming and outgoing charges, set up costs, computer fees and monthly rates. Most allowed no weekend access, which was exactly the time when we needed to pick up for the farmers' markets.

My head was swimming by the time I finished. The county health department agreed that there was a shortage of cold storage facilities. They were also clear that we would need to use one to be allowed to sell at the market. Since our meat wasn't coming directly from our ranch to the market, it needed to be kept in a commercially approved cold storage facility. Eventually, we did find a cold storage facility in Kern County. It was hours from the farmers' markets, but it was within our budget and they allowed 24/7 access.

For market use, we ordered a small commercial display freezer from Texas. There was no power available at the market, so Ken created a portable battery pack and AC inverter to run the freezer. Once built, it weighed over 160 pounds, but it worked and we were grateful. We bought a tent canopy and a red tablecloth, and dusted off an old folding table that his parents had formerly used for camping trips.

For $99, a simple banner was made with our logo and the words *Grassfed Bison!* We found plastic coolers on sale for transporting the frozen meat. Frozen non-toxic gel packs kept the carefully packed meat frozen inside the coolers.

I'll never forget that first Saturday. We got up early. Not knowing what to expect, we took three small coolers of mostly burger and a few steaks. I wore a cheerful turquoise summer dress, put on makeup and earrings and smiled at anyone who would look my way. Mostly people just wandered by and seemed surprised to see us there. They would look first at the banner across the front of our tent, then at the table with its red tablecloth. Then they would scan to the back of the SUV and the small freezer containing our meat. Finally they'd glance back at us standing between the SUV and the table.

"What's that you're selling?" they would ask.

When we smiled and answered bison, several people scrunched up their nose as if we had just said rattlesnake or bear and walked away.

A few customers stayed longer so we could describe our meat and how wonderful the flavor was. By the end of the market, we were glad to have made a few sales.

That first day in Pasadena, wanting to make a good first impression, I remained standing for five hours. By the end of the market, my legs were numb and feet were sore. But that wasn't the only physical challenge. Loading the SUV that morning, I was huffing and puffing after getting the three small coolers of meat in and out of the car. We struggled to put up and take down the simple tent that experienced vendors effortlessly erected and collapsed within seconds.

"How in the world are we going to make a living doing this?" I asked myself several times. By the end of the market, I had a new question.

"How do I tell Ken that I don't think I *can* do this?"

The simple truth was I couldn't say anything. I couldn't and wouldn't say that to him, not now, not yet. For years, we hadn't been able to sell Bisurkey or bison meat anywhere for any meaningful length of time. The farmers' market seemed to be the only place that offered any real hope. First we needed to know if people even wanted the meat. We needed to find out if they liked it, would cook it correctly and then if they would buy it again. Until we knew, any aches and pains would be kept to myself.

2. You do not Choose the Buffalo, the Buffalo Choose You.

It was during this time of self-doubt that I received support from an unexpected source and an answer to a long time, secretly held question. Our own connection with bison is one that has slowly unfolded. It is clear that many are also drawn to these magnificent heritage animals. Somehow bison seem to belong to all of us, though it hasn't always been that way.

Earlier that year, I read an article written by a Native American woman in Colorado who made drums. It beautifully described how individual drums are carefully hand-crafted with bison leather. Each drum has a special sound and she believes that each of them is uniquely destined to belong to a certain individual, a certain soul. The article also described the special relationship that Native Americans have with bison and the gifts that bison offer. I was especially struck when I saw the words:

"You do not choose the buffalo. The buffalo choose you."

I decided it was time to call her. As silly as it may sound to some, I needed to know that it was okay for Ken and me, a descendant of pioneers who settled the West, to raise bison. I wondered how she, as a Native American, felt about that and how I could claim the same strong connection to the animals that she described.

Over the phone, the drum maker was lively, gracious and warm. After a while, the conversation turned to bison, which she and her husband also raise. I finally got up my nerve to ask the question I had called her for.

"Because they are so special to Native Americans, is it okay for others to raise them?" I asked.

The drum maker stopped for a moment, surprised by the question. Slowly she replied, "You know, when ever I encounter those who bring up the past . . . " she paused and laughed, "and there are plenty on both sides believe me. I tell them to 'Put down that rock. We are all one now.' Of course it's okay for others to raise them. They are prophesied to return." She graciously and kindly added she could tell by the humbleness of the question, that there was no doubt we had been chosen.

After we hung up, I surprised myself by having a good cry. It wasn't the first time I've been moved to tears because of owning these animals and I knew it wouldn't be the last. She had, however, given me an answer that I needed to hear.

3. CATCH-22 PIONEERING

During our search for ranchland and small meat processors, we talked with a few bison producers. One rancher named Bob in northern California had his bison ranch for sale, but with an asking price of over $1 million, it was outside our price range. Unlike other producers who shipped their live animals out of state for grain feeding , processing and distribution, Bob's animals were completely grassfed, processed in-state and the meat delivered mostly to Bay area restaurants.

Because we wanted to learn about California meat processing facilities and test the regional grassfed bison flavor, he sold us a small herd and agreed to keep them for us until his ranch sold. His AOP fee was similar to Art's reasonable monthly rate, so it offered a way for us to test the California waters. Owning this small AOP herd also took an enormous amount of pressure off us. We no longer needed to take on substantial debt and prematurely move our larger herd here before we knew whether or not the farmers' markets would work for us. Also, we bought meat animals so we could sample the meat flavor produced by California grasses.

Another possible benefit to the arrangement was that once we paid for these animals we may request a producer's certificate be issued to be used when applying to farmers' markets. From the beginning, we had become aware of shared confusion and conflicting interpretations concerning regulations for selling meat at farmers' markets. Some markets said we couldn't sell there unless we were certified and others said meat was non-certifiable. Either way it seemed to disallow meat, but chicken and fish were already being sold there. It was confusing.

Jane, the Encino market manager, surmised the confusion stemmed partly from the fact that the original market rules had been written for produce and fruit which don't usually require processing. When any processing is involved—that is, if the product is changed from its original or natural state between the farm and the farmers' market—the product falls into a different regulatory category. As meat producers, it potentially provided a perfect catch-22 situation, since we couldn't offer our product for sale in its original state.

The confusion over the regulations lasted for years. At one point, out of frustration, we seriously considered mimicking a priceless April Fool's Day news spoof pulled off by the BBC decades earlier. In 1957, they ran a three-minute news piece showing a Swiss spaghetti tree farm near Lake Lugano at harvest time. There, for the whole world to see, were blossoming spaghetti trees. The spaghetti farmers were proudly pulling off strings of "ripe" strands of limp spaghetti ready to be dried to uniform length after years of careful tree nurturing and species selection. (For a treat, visit youtube.com and search "Swiss Spaghetti Harvest.")

In our case, rather than an orchard, we had one somewhat pitiful and precious volunteer tree. The spoof we envisioned was to proudly introduce the endangered cold-cut tree. We would hang small packages of frozen meat off various branches. Each branch would represent a certain cut, which we would then harvest, carefully pack and bring directly to our customers at the farmers' markets. Thankfully wiser minds prevailed, pointing out that those in charge of the regulations may not share our sense of humor. We heeded their advice and are glad we did. As much as we may have craved some comic relief, this was no time to endanger our fledgling new business while those in charge made a sincere effort to sort out policy guidelines.

In the meantime, we visited the county agricultural office where our bison were located. For several years, we were issued a producer's certificate to display in farmers' markets where we sold and this seemed to keep the occasional visiting agricultural and county health inspectors satisfied. Eventually this was replaced by a letter from the head of the California Department of Food and Agriculture that confirmed that non-certifiable meat could be sold without a producer's certificate in farmers' markets.

In the early days, pretty much everyone was trying 100 percent grassfed bison meat for the first time. This meant that at each and every market, we talked non-stop, educating and teaching people how we raised the animals, how to cook the meat and what to expect. By the end of the market, my throat was often sore and we would arrive home exhausted, wondering what we had gotten ourselves into. But the very next week, our customers were back and so were we. We were addicted to the connection happening there and didn't know at the time that we were part of a sustainable community being born, brought together by mutual trust and caring about humanely raised meat animals.

A few months after joining the Hollywood Farmers' Market, we learned that Greg the beef guy had started selling beef in Santa Monica. Later, he joined the Hollywood market too, so now there were two of us in the Southern California farmers' markets selling red meat. This was quite an accomplishment, if only because of the difficulty in finding small meat processors willing to process smaller quantities of meat, as well as the long drive every week. At the time, we both appreciated that most small ranchers preferred to sell at auction, rather than double as both producer and sales person. Perhaps because of this, our efforts seemed to make us red meat comrades rather than competitors, a relationship we continue to enjoy as other species meat producers join the markets.

CHAPTER 10

Buying Heritage Ranch
(2004)

Many are surprised to learn that our ranch is in northeastern California, a ten-hour drive from Los Angeles. The reasons for this are many and chief among them is the fact that rather than inherit land, we started from scratch. Affordability, adequate water, proven hay yields and surrounding land use/ zoning with direct access to potential customers were nearly insurmountable factors.

For decades we had seen industry financed based on the strength of an idea and a well thought-out business plan. We believed this practice would extend to an agricultural business. Unable to show ranching experience on loan applications, we listed our business experience. Trusting that an innovative, a high quality product and reasonable projection of profits would be enough, we put on our rose-colored glasses and forged ahead.

———————◆———————

As we began to have repeat customers, Ken and I renewed our focus to find ranchland. We agreed it was advisable to line up financing before we started looking, the way we had with home buying. That way when we found something we liked and could afford, we would already be pre-qualified.

Starting with our own bank, we sat down with the local manager. We described what we wanted to do and asked what programs they might have for a ranch or land loan. She said the bank might be interested and suggested that we work first through the Small Business Administration (SBA) and then submit an application.

"If the SBA sprinkles holy water on it," the manager said, "that's pretty much all we need."

We immediately contacted the SBA and arranged an appointment. Two days later, we met with a young man and went over the entire scenario with him. When we finished, he recommended we put together a business plan and described what numbers they would need to see over a specified period of time. Based on his suggestions, we crafted our business plan and arranged for several follow-up meetings to make sure we were on track with their requirements. If we could get the SBA's approval of our plan, the government would guarantee up to 80 percent of the loan amount, making it more attractive to any bank providing the loan.

Three weeks later the SBA representative said everything looked great, and gave us a list of banks to call. With that endorsement, our next step was to secure a pre-approved loan.

First, we made a return visit to our local bank. The person we had talked with now referred us to the department that handled agricultural loans. To our surprise, this department said they had no loan packages for the kind of business we were in.

We then contacted two more banks on the list and filled out their applications. Again we were turned down. Confused and concerned, we called the SBA office and left messages for our representative, who was on vacation. On the Monday he was due back, we called again and were told he no longer worked for them and that his position hadn't been filled yet. So much for the SBA. We would continue our search, but it was becoming increasingly apparent that getting a loan for agricultural land was not going to be the slam-dunk that we had been led to believe.

Meanwhile, our ongoing education of selling meat at weekend farmers' markets continued. We found that buying red meat at the markets was a bit of a stretch for customers who were accustomed to buying only fruit and produce. Bison meat was even more of a stretch. Most people knew nothing about the flavor of bison or how to cook it. Or they got distracted with the term grassfed, which they'd never seen before. Few people were aware at that time of the importance of feeding ruminant animals a natural diet of grass only. Each sale required a lot of educating and we suspected this fact would make the conservative banks even less receptive. Ignoring this obstacle, we continued our search for ranchland.

During this time we learned of a new grazing school from a customer and aspiring farmer. The school was being held for the first time near Sacramento and only cost $75. Ken enrolled and attended for the three days. He learned a lot about the business of grazing animals only on grass and managing them using low-stress management techniques. Though intended for cattle, the information could easily be applied to bison.

After the last day of the class, Ken drove further north to meet with Steve, a realtor who said he'd be happy to show Ken some land which might work for our bison. Steve's invitation was unusual. Housing realtors in Southern California had referred us to other agricultural realtors in the northern part of the state, but most of them lost interest once they learned we did not live in the immediate area. Invariably, we heard the same thing:

"First go look at what ever land you think you might be interested in," they said. "Then come see us."

This didn't work for us because as newbies, we knew nothing about the area farms or ranchland, much less what to ask about, or even what to look for. Well, okay, we had the basics. We knew we needed land with grass rather than rocks, and water rather than no water, but that was about it. Because we lived so far away, we also would have only a day or two at the most during each trip to look for land, and without knowing the area, we couldn't imagine where to begin looking on our own.

We were thankful that Steve was happy for our call and offered to show us property. Later we learned that he was just entering real estate after working for years as an engineer in the Bay Area. He left the area after a divorce and being laid off. Hoping that real estate would be his new career, he was willing to show us around.

When Ken returned from his visit with Steve he was enthusiastic about what he had seen and learned. He showed me photographs and described two potential properties he thought might work. Ten days later we both drove up to look at them.

For two days, Steve showed us around and even accompanied us to look at property offered through another office. After hundreds of miles of driving and plenty of walking, we agreed on the property we wanted. It was a decent size, had water, was a productive hay ranch, and was located at a higher altitude which meant more omega 3s in the grass. It was farther away than we hoped—a 10-hour drive from L.A.—but in a part of the state where the bison had been native in the 1500s.

We asked Steve to write up an offer for us. Though the SBA representative we had worked with was gone, he had at least indicated before he left that our loan package could be supported by the SBA. Eventually another SBA representative would take over our file and would be able to validate that the SBA criteria had been met.

Steve agreed, too, that the banks would love us. Our credit scores were excellent at 850 and 830. Having found the property, we enthusiastically returned to L.A. and resumed contacting the banks on our list. Confidently, we filled out application forms and returned them along with the required supporting papers. We would choose the bank and loan package that offered the best terms.

Nine banks later, there was still no loan. We hadn't known there were so many ways to say *No*. We weren't being declined because of poor credit, and it certainly wasn't because we didn't know about business plans. We had created plenty of budgets and plans in corporate America. We knew the numbers made sense and the potential was clearly demonstrated in the plan.

Art had cautioned us years ago that there would be those who would want to see us fail. "Don't expect help from anyone," Art had said.

We now wondered if this is what he had meant. As if to prove him right, the number-ten finance person agreed to meet with us. We drove to Sacramento and showed him our plan. He said, yes he knew of others who had tried the bison business and failed. He looked at us and said in an amused manner, "So what do they know that you don't know." It was a statement rather than a question and we'd had enough.

"You're asking the wrong question," I said. "The question is: 'What are we willing to do, that others weren't willing to do?'"

We could tell it was a new thought for him, but of little consequence. We left. We were tired, angry and discouraged.

Not long after that, while we were still trying to decide where to go next, we opened up our mailbox to find a "Notice to Perform" letter from the seller of the property. In other words, they had accepted our offer long ago, but we had yet to provide evidence of a loan.

There was still no replacement SBA representative, and no estimate as to when—or if—his position would be filled. Then the SBA told us that our file and all our paperwork had been misplaced. It would have to be resubmitted and the process would have to be restarted all over again.

We had exhausted the list of banks given to us by the SBA, as well as additional banks they referred us to. All denied our application. We were out of options and out of time.

After an agonizing discussion, Ken and I agreed to email Steve. We had gone forward with our offer in good faith, and in good faith the offer had been accepted. We had no choice but to tell him that in spite of our excellent credit and what we'd been told by the SBA, we had been unsuccessful in getting a loan. We would abandon our efforts to buy the property.

I was numb. It was devastating to have come so far, to have guarded and protected our credit rating so jealously while we built the herd, and to now be unable to secure an agricultural loan. For the first time, I felt completely beaten. We had nowhere to move our animals. Neither one of us had a job, and we would soon exhaust our funds which meant we would need to sell the herd. The herd had always provided our most tangible evidence of hope. As the herd had grown, so had our hopes. Once we sold them, I couldn't see how we would ever be able to start over.

Ken and I drafted the email. We both sat in front of the computer and agreed to the wording. Everything was in slow motion. I saw Ken press the Return key, watched the email leave the screen. Once the confirming *Sent!* message appeared, we stood up without a word and walked out of the office into the living room. Ken sat down across from me on the couch. Neither one of us spoke. His energy seemed solid, while I felt empty and broken.

"There's nothing more we can do," Ken said.

I whispered my agreement. Of course he was right. I knew it. I just needed a moment to accept defeat. From the beginning, we had been determined. We had kept each other going. We had fought long and hard. Now what? We sat in silence, not exactly sure what to say. I was having a hard time reconciling with this devastating loss of hope. How do you get hope back once you allow it to leave? Seeing the look on my face, he tried to reassure me.

"We're not giving up," he said.

I was grateful for his words, but couldn't see where we would go from there. We couldn't afford to keep the herd at Art's place; there were too many now. It had taken so long just to find affordable land. So many of our loan applications had been turned down, it seemed there were no banks left to approach. What was there left to do? In the meantime, the price of land was going up again.

I was feeling so overwhelmed that I wasn't aware until later that Ken wasn't sharing the same feelings. To him, the email only represented the loss, because of the seller's Notice to Perform, of that particular piece of property. He said he knew we would still somehow get it done.

Thinking back to that morning, I can still see him sitting there with his clear, strong energy and sense of purpose intact. This is a good example of why it's so important to have a partner who is completely committed to the same goal from the beginning. That way, when one partner falters and loses hope, the other one doesn't. And so it was with us.

A few hours after sending the email, we received a call from Steve. Not exactly surprising, since he had worked so hard to help us find banks that gave agricultural loans. He was no doubt disappointed as well and wanted to offer condolences.

Instead, he had another idea: private money. He knew of a broker who made private loans in situations such as ours. With our permission, he would contact her. We knew private money typically meant higher interest rates, but we agreed to get more information. At this point, we had nothing to lose.

Within a month, a potential deal for the property had been patched together. It required 20 percent cash down from us, 50 percent from the private investor, and a 20 percent seller carry. This left 10 percent uncovered and Steve surprised us by offering to invest his own money to complete the deal. The terms included an interest rate for all investors that was significantly higher than any bank rate and the entire loan would have to be refinanced within one year.

We had planned to put down five percent, which was typical for this type of bank loan and would have left us with some badly needed capital from our savings for non-negotiable improvements such as fencing, stock water tanks and irrigation systems for the pasture and hay fields. The 20 percent cash requirement would mean that our savings would be gone and we would need to take out a second mortgage on our condo for improvements.

The entire deal represented a tremendous risk. If we couldn't pay it back or refinance within 12 months, we would lose the ranch, our herd and our savings. On top of that, we would still owe the second mortgage on our Valencia condo.

For the next few days, we repeatedly reviewed the deal, projected income and expenses. No business model existed to confirm that we were on the right track. Everywhere we looked, it seemed we were pioneering something: red meat into southern California farmers' markets, and not just any red meat, bison meat. Along with that, the value added concept of 100 percent grassfed meat and using a K-Line pod irrigation system with bison which had never been done, nor had anyone even installed K-Lines in our area. And on top of that—long distance ranching. Not just a few hours away, but a full day's drive.

After sleepless nights and more agonizing, we agreed to take the biggest gamble of our lives. Land for the ranch was acquired.

May God protect grassfed bison ranchers and fools.

CHAPTER 11

Preparing Heritage Ranch
(2005)

Knowing there was no turning back, we sprang into action to ready the land for our bison. We planned for appropriate fencing, domestic well, stock tanks for water and a pasture irrigation system. Now that we actually had the property, we found we also had to deal with a lot more than we had bargained for in the way of trash, broken equipment and discarded junk. With three months to get the ranch ready, we rolled up our sleeves and began.

———◆———

Once the deal was agreed to and the paperwork was in motion, we called Art. He was glad to hear about our plans and helped define our roles in preparation of moving the herd. I was to call livestock haulers to get their rates and availability. Art would get the necessary health certificate from the State vet, required to transport live bison from South Dakota into California. Art suggested the move be done in two stages, which would give our bison the elbowroom needed for the long trip. The first group would arrive in June, the second in the fall. With the exception of one breeding bull, all bulls over two years old would be harvested.

After the move, we'd give the South Dakota herd time to settle in before adding the smaller California herd. We called Bob and let him know about our schedule. Describing the sequence of events, we provided a timeline when our bison would be off his place in the fall. For us, it meant a total of three trips in order to consolidate the herd.

Ken confirmed a deal with the fencing contractor and began calling irrigation companies and drilling contractors for estimates on the domestic well, stock water tanks and an irrigation system. All of these things had to happen in order and at a time when he could make the 10-hour trip to be on the ranch. His supervision there was especially important concerning property lines, irrigation mainlines and allowing for appropriate buffer strips. The new pump controls and pressure tank for the stock water had to be housed and arrangements made to bring electricity onto the ranch.

Whether we were there or not, daily operation of the ranch now fell on us. This included seeding, weeding, hay pasture irrigation, and cutting, baling and stacking two to three cuttings of hay. Anticipating our need for help, our realtor Steve arranged a meeting with Chris, a neighbor. As a long time hay and cattle rancher and former owner of the property, he would know the land best. He had also seen the property change hands several times.

Though somewhat dubious about us and what we were trying to accomplish long distance, Chris was receptive to possibly doing our haying. With our savings nearly gone, we asked if he was willing to do a partial barter by haying some of the land for his own use. Understandably, he preferred to be paid cash; it seems both of us were on tight budgets.

We then met another neighbor. Formerly working on oilrigs as a pipe fitter, Rick and his family had moved from the Bay area a few years before. They had built a house and he was growing commercial alfalfa hay while his wife did phone work for a Bay Area insurance company. Farming had always been a dream of Rick's. When we asked if he'd be willing do our haying and take part of the payment in barter, he agreed. In addition, we hired his teenage son and a friend to move the irrigation wheel lines twice a day. With help in place for daily operations, we could now concentrate on getting the ranch ready for the bison.

Back in L.A., we continued to sell in the farmers' markets. More than ever, every dime was critical. The irrigation bill was sometimes was over $3000/month and we only had so much money left. Once it was gone, well, we didn't want to even think about it.

Our schedule became unlike anything we'd ever known. We sold at the farmers' markets on Tuesdays and weekends. On market days, we were up at 3 a.m. and were enroute to the market by 5 a.m. with coolers of frozen meat. To increase sales, we split our efforts and began going to separate markets. We unloaded, set up our space, talked for five hours, reloaded the coolers into the car and drove back through traffic. Returning from the markets between 3 and 4 p.m., we offloaded, ate a quick meal and on Sunday nights made a night deposit to the bank. Then we packed clothes and food for the ranch trip and fell into bed around 9 p.m.

Monday mornings found us up at 4 a.m., car loaded and on the road headed to the ranch by 5:30 a.m. Mapping out which Costco stores sold gas, we routed our trip accordingly. We were especially glad for Costco's $1.50 hotdog-and-drink deal and always added extra ketchup, pickles and onions to fill ourselves up.

With no outbuildings on the ranch, we stayed at a small hotel in town that allowed pets. Checking in between 4 and 5pm, we ignored our travel vertigo and road fatigue as we planned out what we could accomplish in two days. Whether or not we then got a good night's sleep depended on the loudness of our motel neighbors. Six a.m. found us at the local restaurant for breakfast and stopping at Safeway for sandwiches on our way out of town as we headed to the ranch.

Depending on weather, exhaustion, or both, we called it quits by 6 or 7 p.m. Wednesday nights so we could pack and be ready to leave the next morning by 4:30 a.m. for the 10-hour return trip to Valencia.

Getting back at the condo late Thursdays left Fridays to do the wash and get ready for weekend farmers' markets. The next week was mostly recuperation and catch-up and by the following Friday, we were again getting ready for weekend markets so we could repeat the cycle: Every 11 days, we drove 600 miles to work two days at the ranch, then drove 600 miles back to pack and sell meat at the farmers' markets.

Though we didn't know how, we agreed this would be our schedule for two years while we built our business at one end and the ranch at the other. Then we'd sell the condo, build a house at the ranch and move there. In the meantime, there would be no holidays, no vacations, no down time. Based on the weather and livestock hauler's schedule, the first group of animals would arrive in June, the second in October before winter set in. Our herd, our ranch and our survival depended on us.

Back at the ranch, six-foot high game fencing soon proudly outlined the two lower 60-acres which we dubbed the south and middle pastures. We had wanted a minimum of three pastures for grazing, but we found the fencing too expensive so two pastures were all we could initially afford. We asked the fencing guy to put us on next year's schedule for the north pasture while we scrambled to make more sales to replenish our quickly disappearing bank balance.

Over the next two months, a domestic well was drilled which would provide stock water as well as domestic water. A cement foundation was laid and a 10-foot by 12-foot pump house was bolted onto it. Once it was determined where the stock water tanks should be, a trenching machine was rented to dig a 3-foot deep trench line that stretched 1600 feet across both pastures. Then concrete stock tanks for each pasture were built from dimensions we'd received from Art. To this, Ken added wood frames wide enough for bison heads and horns, but small enough to keep them out of the stock tanks.

The spring of 2005 was exciting, joyful and exhausting beyond anything we could have imagined and only a taste of what lie ahead. All we knew is that after seven years of owning our bison and growing the herd, we were getting our own place ready for them. Other than what we erected, there were no structures and just a few basic tools that we brought with us. In fact, the sum total of our farm equipment was the 4-cylinder Toyota pickup that I had inherited when my dad passed away.

While Ken worked with contractors for fencing, the well, the pump house, and the stock tanks, I declared war on a three-strand barbed wire fence. This stretched a good half mile through both pastures, overgrown sagebrush and small olive trees with piercing thorns. As staples were removed, the barbed wire sprang away from the posts. Even with new stiff work gloves to protect my hands, I still ended up with head-to-toe cuts and torn clothes, as wire unexpectedly fought back.

This war played out for six weeks. After each trip, there was less wire and more cuts, as well as varying colors and sizes of iron-on patches on my clothes. By the time the three strands of wire were gone from both pastures, a five-ton trash bin was completely filled with wire, posts and assorted junk, including empty oil cans, broken pipe, clothing, beer bottles, soda cans, fence posts and steel rods.

Somewhere between eighty and one hundred 40-foot sections of assorted irrigation pipes strewn about the place had to be removed from the pasture areas. Working as a team, we lifted them one at a time and carried them to the small pickup. The lighter ones were placed on top of the pickup cab and extended over the camper shell. The heavier ones we slid inside the truck bed with the tailgate down. After tying them all down and one of us walking along with them, slowly we relocated them all outside of the fenced pasture. Here, we untied them and one at a time, unloaded and neatly stacked each one.

Other than Steve, the motel people and waitresses at the restaurant, our neighbors gave us a wide berth. They too had seen the property change hands. We got to know Rick and his family a little, but other than that we were on our own.

June arrived and the livestock hauler's schedule was confirmed. Art advised that the roads in South Dakota looked good for the first move.

Ken's son Rob drove over from Phoenix to pack and sell at two of the weekend farmers' markets to help minimize our loss of income. The other markets we would have to miss.

Arriving late to the motel Monday night, the next morning we took our sleeping bags and an air mattress to the ranch. We'd sleep on the floor of the pumphouse when we got back to make sure the herd settled in okay. Wednesday before breakfast, we called Art to confirm our schedule.

"We'll leave here early tomorrow morning and get in there late Friday," I said. "We've been able to get the one pasture ready for them. The stock tank is in and running, the barbed wire is gone. We got everything out except the t-posts, which we'll do after they get here."

We had found that most of the steel t-posts supporting the barbed wire fence had refused to budge from the ground. I'd been able to remove a few using brute strength, but without proper equipment, we had simply run out of time and human energy.

"That's good," Art replied. "Because the calves sometimes get to jumping around and they can impale themselves on t-posts left in the ground."

Hearing this, I felt the pit of my stomach drop. He was saying that the pasture wasn't safe. I hung up the phone and told Ken. Concerned, we left the hotel for breakfast.

"Maybe Rick can help," I said. Ken agreed it was worth a try.

Rick had already told us that we wouldn't see him that day because he had other work he needed to get done. It was still early, maybe he hadn't left yet. When we arrived at the restaurant I took my cell phone into an adjoining empty dining room while Ken ordered for us.

The phone rang and I heard Rick's familiar voice instead of an answering machine. Quickly I explained what Art had told me.

"I know you said you were busy today, but we were wondering, is there any way that you can you help us?" I asked. It was the first time we had asked for help from any neighbor.

"Sure," he said. "Let me make a couple of calls and move things around. When will you be here?" he asked. As soon as I heard him agree, exhaustion and relief flooded in. Unable to stop the tears, I lifted the phone receiver up while I tried to regain control. When he asked again what time we'd be there, my voice betrayed me. To change the subject, I asked how he was doing.

"Better 'n you," he said matter-of-factly and we hung up. For a while, I just sat in the empty dining room and cried. Finally I blew my nose and rejoined Ken. As soon as I told him that Rick would help, I began crying again. Ken just looked back at me helplessly. Again I tried to stop and couldn't. The exhaustion, excitement, anxiety, relief, all blended together in uncontrollable waves of sobbing. All I could do is cry, look at the scrambled eggs in front of me, then cry some more.

Linda, our wonderful and caring waitress whom we'd gotten to know the past several months asked Ken what was wrong. Ken warmly thanked her, explaining I was *just tired*. Somehow I managed to eat and that helped. Then finally and gratefully, I ran out of tears.

Forty minutes later, we were at the ranch. I can't remember a more welcome sight than Rick and his tractor. We watched as he left his house a half-mile away. We heard the friendly chugging as he crossed the main road to our property and watched as he slowly turned down the fence line and made his way to where we stood. It crossed my mind that this is what the early settlers felt like when they saw the cavalry coming.

All morning, Ken and Rick worked together, removing one t-post at a time. Rick brought a hefty tow chain with him, about 30 feet long. While he positioned the huge tractor bucket over each t-post, Ken wrapped the chain around it so it gripped on the side teeth of the post, then hooked the other end of the chain to the edge of the bucket. The tractor engine roared as the bucket lifted skyward. Seconds later, a t-post, which had been cemented in the ground for decades, swung innocuously in the air above our heads. They sure didn't look so tough now I thought, with a new awareness of how having the right equipment makes all the difference.

By 1 p.m., over forty t-posts had been pulled and gathered into the tractor bucket, then placed outside of the pasture area. In four hours, Rick had done with his tractor, what would have taken us two days, that is, if our strength and stamina had held. Then as purposefully as he had arrived, Rick and his tractor chugged back the way they came. And we were left wondering how we could ever repay this kindness. The calves would be safe now. They would never know those who had helped to prepare their new home. But we knew.

That night we fell into bed exhausted and relieved. If we were to reach Salt Lake before dark, we had to leave early.

CHAPTER 12

Bringing Them Home!

As they are to most of the United States, bison were native to northern California up to the 1500s. In 2005, we joined a handful of others who were helping them return. While there are unforgettable moments throughout our entire journey, perhaps the most memorable was when we brought our South Dakota animals to our own land. After years of research, planning, risk, hard work and being able to see them only a few days each year, our dream was manifesting. It was a huge deal.

———— ·•· ————

"So where are you now?" asked Rob over the phone from the Sunday farmers' market. Though he hadn't been to the ranch yet, Rob seemed excited to be part of what we were doing and we were glad. Ken and I were 56 and 57 years old, so Rob's enthusiasm fueled our hope for his future involvement in the business we were building.

"We're still in South Dakota," Ken said. "We're going out to get them loaded this morning, then leave around 3 p.m. and drive straight through."

Ken smiled as he hung up the phone. "He's excited," he said.

"That's good," I smiled back. "Let's keep our fingers crossed."

It had been two long driving days and Art wouldn't be ready for us until Sunday morning. The timing of the loading was planned so the bison would have eaten and had water just before leaving. They would have neither for the duration of the trip.

On Saturday we arranged to visit the meat processor Art had used for our animals over the years. We wanted to see the set-up since most California meat processing plants were set up to handle only cattle. It would be in our best interest to learn more about processing, either in an effort to find those interested in processing bison, or to be able to establish our own small processing plant in future years. Ron, the owner, was great. He showed us around and answered all of our questions.

Finally Sunday morning arrived. We confirmed the time with Art, packed up our things and checked out of the hotel. We would be leaving from his ranch. It had been raining off and on the past few days and signs of spring were everywhere. And mud. Lots of mud.

Art opened the door with a big smile. "Well, I see you made it," he laughed shaking Ken's hand. I gave him a hug.

"Good weather for ducks," he joked.

It was small talk. We were there to learn and we sensed Art had been—understandably— reluctant to have us there. He was used to working alone. You have to watch yourself in handling bison. They can be unpredictable. And, as I remember hearing when I was growing up in Montana, greenhorns could, too. It was common knowledge that you should never trust a greenhorn to use their common sense once they got around animals.

Art knew we needed to learn. We assured him we would only do what he told us to do and we wouldn't get in his way, if this was what he wanted. But if we could help, we wanted to help and to learn. We wanted to take full advantage of the opportunity, but it was his place and his call.

Inside his familiar pickup truck, we turned onto the same deeply rutted road. It was the first time we were there in the spring and after a rain. The truck fishtailed a few times on the climb up the hill. Art smiled at me.

"Remember what I said about this road in the spring?" he chuckled.

"I sure do," was all I said. I wanted him to pay attention to the road. It sure was spring and here we were on the infamous lookie-loo-discourager road. What a mess.

"With the rain, we couldn't take a chance on bringing the semi in," he said. "The driver might be able to get in okay, but once it's loaded, he may not be able to get out. So instead, I brought in a few smaller trailers yesterday. What we'll do is get 'em loaded and bring 'em down to the ranch. Then we'll transfer them into the bigger truck. The driver will bring it in and just leave it for us down there. He wants to get some sleep before you leave so he's fresh and can make the drive with minimal stops. The animals won't have food or water, so it's best to keep up a steady pace and just get there first, sleep afterwards."

When we arrived at the corral system where the animals were, we saw what he meant. The corral's weathered wood was wet and dark and the ground was muddy and wet. There was no way a huge semi-truck would have worked. Instead, he had what looked like a large horse trailer backed up to a chute.

Art calls this area his water trap. When it's time to load animals, he uses this system. Waiting until the animals he wants are taking water, he closes the portable fencing behind them. Then, instead of being able to return to the pasture, they are herded into a narrow wooden alleyway, where one at a time, they are loaded into the back of the livestock trailer.

I looked around as Art and Ken talked. Art was describing the sequence of events to expect. He wanted to separate off the big bull first. This is common. Experienced handlers will always load bulls first in the front of a stock trailer and keep them separated from the others by a steel gate inside the truck. This is because they may be dangerous and more aggressive to nearby animals.

"They know something's up," said Art. "So I don't know how long it's going to take. They can read my mind, I swear," he chuckled. "We all need to stay calm and just act casual. I need to scramble my brain, so they can't read my thoughts."

With that last comment, he looked at us both. "You might try doing the same thing," he smiled.

As soon as I heard him say that, I forced myself to relax. I decided to think about anything else, other than getting them loaded into the trailer, or the fact that the bull would go first, and therefore was the initial target.

"Here comes an opportunity now," said Art in a quieter tone. "That bull looks like he's getting ready to go down for water, but he's hesitating. So Ken, you go over there and get behind that open gate. Be ready. I need to separate him from those cows he's with. Once I get down there, those cows will want to leave. Let 'em get through that gate and I'll sort him off. Once they get through, you close the gate quick so he can't get back out."

Yikes, I thought, relinquishing any residual threads of feminism.

Ken took his position behind the open gate near the opening to the water trap.

"Kathy, you just stand over there."

I went the direction of a nearby hill and began climbing to get completely out of the way. I mused that I had certainly come a long way from my earlier days of rejecting anything that remotely resembled gender discrimination. What mattered right now is that the animals be loaded without injury or incident. If Art preferred me out of the way, it didn't matter. Sometimes one extra person is just one too many.

Halfway up the hill, I stopped and surveyed those below. Art wanted to make sure I wasn't visible to the animals in the water trap, so I sat down on a nearby rock.

As the bison drank from the stock tank, I saw Art begin slowly walking head down, in an exaggerated casual manner, toward a rope lying on the ground. The other end was tied to the gate. If he could get there in time, he would pull the rope and close the gate that way, keeping himself separated. Then open it back up again to sort off the cows from the bull. The bull had wandered down with three cows to drink. They eyed Art suspiciously, then dropped their heads to drink.

In a flash, the scene changed.

One of the cows, seeing Art slowly walking toward them, decided it was time to leave. She began going up the hill. Another cow followed, then the third cow and the bull close behind. Art timed his move, grabbed the rope and pulled. As the four bison got closer to the unsecured gate, he yelled and waved his arms. They stopped and returned to the water area. Instead of drinking this time, they milled around, watching him.

Art let himself in on the other side of the gate and waved to Ken.

"Okay, I'm going to go down and separate the cows off that bull," he said. "Stay back so they don't shy away and let 'em get through that gate. As soon as they get through, you close that gate quick. I'll do my best to keep that bull down there, but he's going to want to go with them."

Ken positioned himself behind the gate which Art opened. Slowly Art began to walk down toward the bison. Using his body as a barrier, he soon flushed the three cows from the bull's side. As the cows ran through the gate to freedom, Ken moved quickly to close the long gate. I saw a brown blur through the nearby wood fence slats, heard the sound of hooves in mud and heard Art yelling in an attempt to drive the bull back.

It worked. The bull turned and went back toward the water.

"Ken, get to the back of the trailer and be ready to close that gate. I'm going to move him toward the alleyway.

I saw Ken run along the outside of the wooden alleyway, which curved around into a wooden chute that was connected to the back of the open trailer.

"Okay," he yelled.

Once again, I heard hooves on mud. I couldn't see a thing, but heard Art yelling "Hah, hah!" to flush the bull from behind the water tank.

It was enough pressure on the bull, who headed back up the hill.

Finding the gate closed and Art coming toward him, he veered off to the left into the wooden alleyway.

The sounds changed then, as the bull's hooves went from the dirt ground to the floor of the wooden loading chute. He went up the ramp and I saw the whole trailer shake as the bull entered. I heard a loud metal clang as Ken closed the trailer gate.

Art reopened the corral water trap gate and joined Ken.

"Well, that's one," he laughed, face red with adrenalin. "The rest we'll bring down with the other trailer. It should be a little easier now."

Art climbed into the truck hitched to the trailer and pulled the trailer with the bull out of the way. Then he took the truck and hitched it to a second, larger empty trailer parked nearby.

About this same time, we heard a separate truck engine. It was Art's daughter-in-law being dropped off by her husband.

Art got out and made the introductions.

"Jackie said she thought you might need some help," she said, waving goodbye to her husband.

"That would be right," said Art, trying not to be impolite. He was doing a balancing act between wanting to be a good host to us and not wanting to be sabotaged by our lack of experience.

"Ken's been helping. We just got the bull loaded," Art said.

"Well, that's good," she said, sounding surprised. As she eyed the remaining herd yet to be loaded, I proceeded back to my rock station. Climbing the hill, a tree stump on top of the hill caught my eye. It was dark from the rain too, I noted. In fact, almost black.

I studied it. Funny, I hadn't noticed a tree stump there before. All the trees here were mostly scrub oak. There weren't any trees around here with that thick of a base. Even if there were, I couldn't imagine Art wanting to cut it down.

Suddenly, I made out the thick, grey tips of bison horns emerging from each side of the stump.

Oh my gosh, it's 803! I blinked hard to make sure. Sure enough, it was 803, our big, beautiful breeding bull that we reluctantly agreed not to move. He must have the rest of the herd behind him somewhere up on that hill. It was the top of his massive black head that I thought was a tree stump. His head was just high enough over the crest of the hill for him to see down to where we were. Perfectly still, he was nearly invisible. He was watching and learning. The realization took my breath away. It was impressive.

Looking back down the hill, the herd had bunched up near the hay bunker at the wider end of the corral system. Art had positioned himself to work a smaller group back down the hill to the stock water. The alley way and chute located off the water trap could comfortably accommodate four or five animals single file so that's how he would sort and load them.

Mindful of the two unexpected calves born the day before, he walked slowly toward them. The herd moved predictably toward the far end of the wide corral, down the hill, through the gate to the water trap. As he ran to sort one group off, the herd crowded and bumped against some wooden fence slats.

Suddenly, we saw a tiny calf wiggle through an opening in the slats and escape into the wide grassy pasture, running off toward distant trees. Everything stopped while we watched the calf and reconsidered the new situation. Instinctively, I immediately followed the calf, thinking I could pressure it back to its mom. Shortly, Art's daughter-in-law joined me, saying Art wanted me back. As I rejoined them at the corral, Art explained.

"Yah, in a case like this, the calf will just go back to the spot where it was born, because that's all it knows. It must have been born in those trees over there somewhere. It'll come back. This is where dinner is," he said, referring to the cow.

With the little calf gone Art decided it was a good time for lunch break.

"It'll come back to where its mom is," he said. "And it'll probably happen faster if we're not here, so I'll just leave the gate open over here and we'll go have lunch."

Drawing a sigh of relief, I joined Art and Ken in the truck cab, while Art's daughter-in-law hopped in the back. It was an emotional trip even before having the calf escape and seeing 803 above the ridge line. I was glad for a break.

Back at Art's place, Ken and I transferred into our car. Then we followed Art's truck as it headed down the road toward the highway.

"Gosh, look at that adrenalin," Ken said.

Ahead of us on the dirt road, Art's truck was about a mile in front of us, leaving dusty trail behind. Seconds before, we had been about a car length behind him. While remaining outwardly calm, sorting bison on foot requires a clear head, quick reflexes and plenty of energy. Art disappeared into a cloud of dust powered by left over adrenalin from the morning's activities.

Over lunch at a local tavern, we had a chance to unwind and regroup.

Art was among friends and neighbors here. We inhaled our bison burgers as he laughed and kidded with passers-by. Soon it was time to leave, so we returned to the ranch, climbed into the truck and drove back out to the water trap.

As we crossed the creek and rounded the final curve in the road, I saw that Art had been right. The little calf had returned and stood outside the fence near its mom on the other side. Art stopped the truck and ran over and closed the gate with the calf safely inside.

The next few hours flew by. Before I knew it, the rest of the herd was loaded into the trailer. Now all that was left was the final transfer into the stock semi-truck.

I had a hard time picturing how the transfer would work. But once we got back to Art's ranch, it became clear. The semi-truck was there, parked in place and waiting for us. A portable chute led from the back of the truck to the ground. Over the top of the chute, a tractor front-end loader bucket had been strategically moved into place creating an overhead barrier. Bison tend to look for any opening and they are so agile that if motivated they can clear a six-foot fence. If they can see daylight above them, they may try to jump up and out of the chute. When no sky is visible overhead, this helps to keep them moving forward.

Again Art positioned Ken alongside the chute, near the ramp to the back of the semi-truck. As soon as an animal went through the chute and into the back of the semi-truck, Ken was to quickly lower the gate so it couldn't get back out.

From 100 feet away, I saw Art place a stick with a white plastic bag tied at the end through a front opening of the smaller trailer. The rustle and appearance of the plastic makes the bison shy away and is a humane tool for use in a confined situation like this. At the same time he was waving the stick, Art beat his other hand on the outside of the trailer and yelled a few times. Within seconds, I heard the clanging of bison hooves on metal as the bull left the trailer going down the metal ramp. Following the bull's large hump above the portable connected fence, I again heard hooves on metal as the animal went up the ramp and into the semi-truck. Ken immediately dropped the gate in place. Art joined him and soon had the bull partitioned safely off towards the front of the truck.

Next came the cows and two calves. They, too, were loaded without incident. When I saw the last bison go in and the gate drop in place, I realized how tense and anxious I had been. When the back of the semi door closed, I felt weak-kneed. They were in. No injuries, no one was hurt. Experience made all the difference and we had learned a lot.

Around Art and Jackie's familiar kitchen table, Jackie served coffee and gave us some cookies for the trip. When the truck driver joined us 20 minutes later, it was hard to say goodbye. Again, I told Art that we wished he could make the trip with us and see them offloaded at the other end. It was such a special time and he had been with us from the beginning. Now we were moving them as we had always planned to do. Their care would soon be completely on us. Art wouldn't be looking after them as he had for the past eight years.

Art reminded us that there were still ongoing items we had to attend to and that he'd give us a call once he'd taken the other bull to the processor. We were to let him know what progress we'd made in finding a home for 803 as a breeding bull. And then of course, the rest of the mature animals would be loaded and trucked in the fall. My attention returned to 803 and I told my story of him watching us from the hill, barely visible.

"I won't try to talk you out of moving him," he said. "Just let me know what you decide and I'll be here to help."

I was grateful. There had been so many kindnesses from him, this was just one more. Art knew we wanted to give 803 a longer life elsewhere if possible and let him pass on his genes, too. Following Art's counsel, we agreed not to try to bring him to California. When we were at the water trap, he showed us the 100 yards of fencing he had to replace because of 803.

"If I'd had a gun with me, I can't guarantee what would've happened," Art said. "But of course he's your bull. But if he was mine, that would've been the last fence of mine he ever took out," he said in earnest. "He's smart and that makes him dangerous. I'm really glad he's not going with you folks."

We knew he was right. Hearing this again, I wondered if it was reasonable to want someone else to take him. Or even ask Art to help get him trapped and loaded.

"Well, it's almost 3 o'clock, we'd better get going," I heard Ken say.

He and Art shook hands. I gave him a big hug. I felt like I had known Art all my life and I would miss him.

Ken and I agreed to take turns driving as we followed the truck back to our ranch. About an hour into the drive, it hit me. This is what we'd been working toward since we started our first research 14 years earlier. We'd succeeded despite all the job relocations due to company mergers, takeovers, layoffs, and questionable treatment. In spite of multiple denied loan applications for ranch land. Now our bison were on that truck. We were taking them to our own ranch. It was really happening. It wasn't a dream any more. We were really doing it.

Entering Wyoming just before dusk, Ken got out the camera and took pictures of the stock truck ahead of us while we still had light.

I think I must have cried most of the way back and Ken choked up once or twice as well. We stopped a few times and got out to stretch our legs with the driver. Together we'd peek through the peepholes of the truck. Most of the bison were lying down and the calves were doing fine. Driving at night was cooler for them. Still there was no time to waste. The animals would be without water or food until we could get them unloaded.

Ken and I took turns driving. Neither one of us really slept, but at least we could close our eyes for a while. In touch with the driver by cell phone, around 1 a.m. he let us know he was going to pull over and sleep for about 20 minutes. We drove a little further, then we, too, pulled over so we didn't get too far ahead. He called us again when he was back on the road and we rejoined him once we saw the stock truck go by.

Around 4 p.m. Monday afternoon, we pulled up to the front gate of our ranch. The truck was now behind us, so I got out and opened the gate. Ken pulled through and the semi-truck followed. I quickly closed and locked the gate while Ken helped the semi-truck back up to the south pasture gate, nesting up to the new unloading chute Ken had so proudly built.

We were all tired and the driver had another pick-up the next morning, so he was anxious to get them unloaded and take off. But as eager as we all were to unload them, the bison wouldn't budge.

The driver called Art who told him to leave them there with the door open and sometimes they'll come off by themselves during the night. That sounded fine to us. The semi would stay right where it was and we would start early the next morning.

We said our goodnights. The driver had a bed in his cab and Ken and I went to the pump house, happy with our decision to sleep there instead of going into town. All we had to do is fill up the air mattress. Once that was done, we put our sleeping bags down and promptly went to sleep. At 1 a.m. we woke up. All of the air had left the mattress and we were lying on the cold, hard floor. Swearing and grumbling about how cheaply things are made, Ken found the tire pump and pumped the mattress full of air again. After confirming the truck outline in the pasture, we said good night again. The mattress allowed us another three hours of sleep before the air leaked out a second time. Exhausted, we made friends with the floor and fell back asleep.

Early in the morning I woke up to the sound of the semi-truck's heavy engine. I figured the driver had gotten cold and started the engine for some heat. Then I heard gears shift. Where in the world was he going?

Looking out the window, I saw the truck leave our front gate. I couldn't see the bison in the pasture and thought it was strange that he was leaving without a word. I grabbed the keys, got into the car and raced down the dirt road after him. Catching up with him, we both pulled over and I ran to the driver's side as he rolled down his window.

He cheerfully said that earlier that morning, he had moved the truck closer to the stock tank. The animals had unloaded themselves, so he was done. He said I probably didn't see them because they had headed toward the far side of the pasture. He guessed they were probably checking out the fences and he had to get going.

I thanked him and drove back to the pump house. Ken was dressed and just putting away the sleeping bags and the miserable air mattress.

"So?" he asked.

"He said they all unloaded this morning, but I sure can't see them."

"We'll use the binoculars," Ken said, reaching for the black case. I followed him out into the cold spring morning.

"There they are," he said. "They're on the far side near Millers' checking out the fence. It looks like they're moving along the fence line."

"That's what Art said they'd do," I commented as he handed me the binoculars.

With my own eyes, I saw that they were really there. Though disappointed that I had missed the actual moment they stepped onto our ground, they were a beautiful sight to see. The grass was so high they were belly-deep in it. The calves couldn't be seen at all.

For the next few days, we went about our chores as if they had always been there. We watched approvingly as they drank from the stock tank for the first time and grazed in the orchard grass-alfalfa mix pasture that was free of debris and t-posts.

Wednesday came and it was clear that the herd was settling in to their new home. With a neighbor to keep an eye on things, we reluctantly began our drive back to the condo.

Now, more than ever, we had to build our customer base by teaching others about this wonderful meat. And our bison would have to do what we had, for eight years, planned that they would do. Now they would have to pay their own way.

1. Shortage of Small Load Trucking Companies

Back in L.A. we touched base with Art. The first group was settling in fine and Art advised the processor had an opening that week. This meant there was still about a month to find a way to get the meat to us in California.

"Have you decided what you want to do with 803?" he asked.

"You've convinced us that he's too much bull for us to bring here," I said. "But we want to see if we can find another home for him. He's such a good bull, we hate to waste his genetics if someone else can take him."

Art hesitated before answering.

"Well, you still have time," he said. "After you bring the rest of the herd down in the fall, there's still time after that."

"If we did find someone, Art, how difficult would it be to load him?"

"Well, I still believe that the best way for him to leave the ranch is with a bullet," Art said. "That's the best way. But if you can find a place for him, I'll help get him loaded."

Art had his experience seeing 803 gore a two-year old bull that later died. After that, 803 tore out 100 yards of his fence. For him to offer to help get him loaded was beyond generous. I renewed my resolve to find 803 a home.

But first, we needed to line up a refrigerated truck. This time, instead of needing to transport two pallets from South Dakota to Pennsylvania, it would be a half pallet into California. Years before it had been like finding hens teeth to find someone to deliver a small quantity of meat to Pennsylvania. The only California producer we knew who imported his meat back into the state said his Colorado processor made all the arrangements and they were for full truckloads.

I began searching online for refrigerated trucking firms in South Dakota and then started calling. Repeatedly I heard the same thing: our shipment was too small. Occasionally, they would have extra room in a truck, I was told, but they never knew when. Even then, there would be an extra pickup charge and we would be charged the full pallet rate of 2000 pounds. Bottom line: instead of the usual rate of 15–20 cents per pound for shipping, we would be paying more like $1.50 per pound.

Determined, I kept calling. Over and over, it was the same: the shipment was too small. I began asking for referrals to others who trucked smaller quantities. No one knew of anyone who could help us.

Finally someone said he said he might know someone who could help. He had a friend worked for a large trucking company that came to Los Angeles on a regular basis; maybe he'd bring it down for us.

"He won't want any paperwork," the man said. "He'll do it as a favor to me, but you guys can work out the details."

"How much would he want?" I asked.

"I don't know, what ever is fair. You work it out. *If* he'll do it," he added. I wrote down the truck driver's phone number, then immediately called and left a message.

The next day, I received a call from the driver. I explained our situation and asked him if he could somehow help us out. He hesitated. It wasn't until I mentioned the other man's name that he seemed to relax. Finally, he agreed to bring the half-pallet of meat with another load he was hauling. But there were conditions.

I would have to bring cash when I picked up our load and meet him early in the morning in the desert outside of L.A. There would be no manifest and no way to contact him. He would call us. We swallowed hard and agreed. We felt we had no other choice; no other truck was willing to bring the meat to us and it was too far away for us to pick up. Even if we could, we had no way to keep the meat cold. Later we realized that if the truck disappeared with our meat, it would be our tough luck.

We lined up the pick-up date and time between the processor and trucker. It was beginning to sound like an illegal drug deal unfolding on TV. The pick-up day was narrowed down to a week, then a few days. One night the phone rang. A man identified himself as the truck driver. He was outside of Cody, Wyoming and had the meat with him. We wrote down instructions on where to meet him in the desert outside of L.A. He said he'd be there around 4:30 a.m. and described the color of his truck and the words on the cab doors.

At 3:30 a.m. the next morning, I started the SUV. As the engine idled, I activated the GPS thinking about Ken, who was sleeping peacefully in our warm bed. It was a workday and though he couldn't go with me, I was sorry to have been so good at not waking him. Now all I had was *me* to reassure myself that everything would be fine. The sick feeling in the bottom of my stomach though wasn't going away.

I wonder if he'll be at work when I get back.

I entered the intersection destination into the GPS.

If I got back. Of course I'll get back.

I double-checked to make sure my cell phone was on and fully charged.

I hope there's cell phone coverage.

Perfect. Now I think of it. I'll just have to make a note of any restaurants or gas stations along the way, just in case.

On hearing the GPS's cheerful ding, I turned on the headlights and backed out of the parking spot. Phoebe (Ken's name for our GPS) showed the destination as 48 miles away. Pulling out onto the street, I couldn't help thinking about stories of people who mysteriously disappear in the desert. I checked again to make sure that my cell phone was on and that I had my pepper spray.

As I pulled onto the freeway, I reassured myself that at least the GPS would be more accurate than an Internet map I had used back East. Two weeks after 9/11, I had driven across Pennsylvania to attend a Natural Food Expo while Ken was at work. Reaching Baltimore at dusk, I found myself in a rough neighborhood instead of at the convention center. From the directions provided by a group of eager kids hanging out at a 7-Eleven store, I reached the real hotel address about 30 minutes later. Remembering those helpful bright-eyed kids made me smile, though at the time it was nothing to smile about.

Now here I was again, but with a slightly different twist. This time I was driving to a less populated area, somewhere I'd never been before, and I was meeting someone I didn't know, alone, in the dark, with cash in $20 bills.

When I wasn't debating with myself as to whether or not this now made me some kind of criminal, I was thinking about Steven Spielberg's movie *Duel,* his directorial debut. It was about the psychotic driver of a semi-truck who plays a deadly cat and mouse game with the hero, played by Dennis Weaver. The truck driver's face is never seen, which made it all even spookier.

I must be crazy to be doing this.

No, my practical self corrected. *I'm just a desperate person trying to get our small bison business going with limited funds. I'll be fine.*

An hour later, I arrived at a dark intersection in the desert. Phoebe confirmed the rendezvous point. Two huge semi-trucks were idling off to the side with their parking lights on.

Their windows were dark and there was no sign of life in either one.

Great. Duel's sequel.

I parked near one of the trucks. Pocketing my cell phone, I got out of the car and with pepper spray in hand, tentatively approached the cab of the larger truck. I looked up. No one was there. I looked at the other truck about 100 feet away, but it didn't seem to be the right color. My cell phone rang.

"You're backed up to the wrong trailer."

Relieved to hear a human voice, I laughed nervously. The driver flipped his lights so I could see he was in the other truck.

"Oh, there you are. Okay, let me just move the car."

"Bring it around to the back," was all he said.

I drove the Honda over and backed up to the end of the 50-foot long trailer. The driver jumped down from his cab and came over. As we shook hands, I saw that he was almost as nervous as I was. Later I learned that large trucking companies know that their drivers sometimes pick up extra freight, so they often practice something called "sealing the truck." I'm not sure how it's done, but it's a way to insure that they can tell if a load has been altered somehow during the trip. The companies don't care if the trailers are only partially filled or not; they don't want to share or be slowed down. No doubt there are Interstate Commerce Commission (ICC) regulations factored in too.

The whole experience gave me a completely new appreciation for truck drivers. In this case, the man was a very nice, salt-of-the-earth kind of guy, just trying to feed his family. As he opened the back of the truck, I saw our boxes of meat there and gave him the cash. Five minutes later, we went our separate ways.

Safely back home again, I had just finished putting the meat into our chest freezer as Ken was leaving for work. His matter-of-fact kiss goodbye confirmed that he was oblivious to the fact that I had just risked life and limb for Lindner Bison.

Oh, well. Time to feed Sam.

2. PREDATOR CONTROL

Not long after they had settled in, we received our first example of our bison's ability to defend themselves against predators. In fact, our long-distance ranching start may have been impossible with most any other species. Dating back to the ice age, bison's wild instincts remain fully and gratefully intact.

Though our bison were now here, we knew little about them. Because we couldn't yet live there with them, we were handicapped in helping to create a positive perception and sense of accountability or caretaking, which our daily presence could provide as new neighbors. In short, our neighbors got to see them daily and therefore learn about them far more quickly than we did.

The first realization of this was a casual comment made by Rick that he daily looks out at the bison and as usual, they were just running around. At first, I was alarmed that this meant there was a predator in the area. We later learned that they love to run and unlike most domestic livestock, Art had said they are generally more gregarious. Our years of industry research said nothing about this aspect. We began to wonder if, because we had kept the family units intact and have a hands off approach to managing them, it encouraged the normal herd behavior of running. In our case, the combination of a lack of funds and experience in building handling corrals had worked in both our favors. It is more respectful of their instincts and their nature.

Compared to domestic livestock, bison know how to survive. They can take care of business without any help from us. We saw one example of this soon after they arrived. After casually mentioning that we wanted to raise heritage turkeys at our ranch, one day we received a surprise delivery from a neighbor who lives over the ridge. He had put his young turkey poults in with his chickens and soon found that the turkeys were getting significantly beat up by the chickens. He welcomed a chance to get rid of them and dropped off three sad looking heritage turkeys the day before we were to leave. Almost immediately two disappeared. A third one lasted about a month, but only because Nancy, Chris's wife had taken pity on it and began feeding it.

Sadly, though, this young turkey also disappeared, though no one could say what happened. Walking the pasture one evening, I happened upon the turkey carcass. It was completely intact, except for the head. I called to Ken who joined me, agreeing it certainly seemed strange that any predator would take only the head and leave the entire body to waste. We didn't know of any predators in our area that were so well fed that they would hunt just for sport of it the way some well-fed domestic cats do.

We began looking around the immediate area for the head, thinking it might have been a strike from a territorial hawk that then dropped the head nearby. Instead, about 10 feet away, Ken found a canine skull, but without a carcass attached. The skull had been picked clean, so we couldn't identify it beyond that. It was, however, evidence of two very strange animal deaths not far from each other—one without a head and the other without a body.

"Good heavens, what's going on here?" I said out loud. Suddenly Ken called to me from 20 feet away.

"Here's what happened," he said and I immediately joined him.

"It was a coyote. See, here and here."

He was pointing at what looked like pieces of fur. At least it looked like fur, but I failed to see the connection.

"It had to be the bison," he said. "Remember what Art said? He said that if they catch a predator, they not only kill it, but they spread the remains to warn off any other predators in the area. The turkey must have been the target. As turkeys do, it probably laid down and froze, and the coyote just came up and neatly chomped off its head. This must have gotten the attention of the bison, who decided the coyote was a little too close for comfort, so they decided to make an example of him before he could remove or finish his meal." He began walking again.

"Look, here and here," he followed the trail of evidence. "Here's the tail!" he exclaimed holding up his prize.

"Wow," I said.

With new respect, I looked over at our bison peacefully grazing 100 feet away. Any sadness that we had been unable to protect the turkey was replaced by a sense of comfort and pride that the bison provided their own best protection.

CHAPTER 13

Integration of the California and South Dakota Herds

"Years ago my mother used to say to me, she'd say, 'In this world, Elwood, you must be'— she always called me Elwood—'In this world, Elwood, you must be oh so smart or oh so pleasant.' Well, for years I was smart. I recommend pleasant. You may quote me."
—Elwood P. Dowd, James Stewart in "Harvey" (1950)—

———◆———

Shortly before our South Dakota trip, we had heard from Bob, the bison rancher taking care of our small California herd. He had sold his ranch and the new owners had agreed to assume our AOP contract. Similar to his background, theirs too was in Southern California land development and construction. They had no experience raising bison, but they told Bob they liked the idea and had purchased the ranch with the entire herd.

We were sorry to see our relationship with Bob come to an end so soon, but also looked forward to meeting the new owners. As newcomers themselves, perhaps we might find that we have a lot in common and be able to work together to bring this wonderful meat to others in California. It seems there were so few bison producers in the state, it felt good to know more people were interested in raising them.

Three weeks later, we received a letter in the mail from the new owners. We were familiar with the legal protocol when businesses change hands, so we were expecting this confirmation that they were now the owners and that our AOP contract had transferred to them. Their letter did that and more.

Effective immediately, the letter announced that the monthly AOP fee had *quadrupled*. Without explanation of any kind, immediate payment was demanded or they would take possession of our animals.

We were incredulous. Months earlier we had described our situation to Bob and the reason for careful timing when moving the herd from his place. The middle pasture, where we would first place the California herd, still needed work and because we couldn't be at the ranch for more than two days at a time, we had to do things in stages. Most of the debris had been removed, but there was a quarter-mile-long section of an irrigation wheel line that had to be disassembled and hand-carried one piece at a time into the adjoining hay pasture. If we put the herd in the same pasture as the wheel lines, the bison would quickly destroy them with their natural rubbing and scratching.

And there was another reason for the careful timing. As we had learned from Art, putting new animals into adjoining pastures gives them a chance to get used to each other. This humane practice gives both herds an adjustment period before asking them to integrate and determine dominance. This is especially important given bison's strong pecking order.

Our first step was to call Bob to find out what he could tell us about the new owners' situation and approach. He said he knew nothing. We then called the new owners. Perhaps they were unfamiliar with industry standards for AOP rates or our unusual situation. We soon discovered that neither mattered to them. Their response was that they had expenses to cover and couldn't be expected to feed the animals for free.

Our discussion with the new owners was devoid of even a hint of a reasonable compromise or an interest in a future relationship as fellow bison producers. We withdrew money from our savings to pay the exorbitant sum they had demanded, then made arrangements to have the California herd moved to our ranch. It meant that both herds would be asked to immediately share the same pasture.

As soon as the relocation date was confirmed we rearranged our travel schedule. What was to have been a long-anticipated joyful event became one filled with anxiety and stress. The only silver lining was that we would no longer be paying absentee owner fees and both herds would be together—another milestone after years of effort and risk. The not-so-good news was that we didn't know if the sudden integration of the two herds would result in wounded or dead animals as they established their pecking order.

Two days before the California herd was to be picked up, we received an unexpected phone call from the new owners stating new terms. They would only release the herd after our final payment had been deposited safely into their bank account. A personal check would not be honored; a cashier's check was now required.

Because of the last-minute arrival of this information, again we had to scurry to make additional arrangements. We rushed to our bank, drew a cashier's check and had it sent overnight via FedEx Priority. It was the only way we could meet their demands and still stay on schedule to be there to receive them. In our 12 years in and around the bison industry, we had never heard of these kinds of ultimatums. Such requests could be justified, we thought, only if there was a history of late paying, or not paying, certainly never the case with us. Finally we considered that these demands had nothing to do with our honor and integrity while speaking volumes about theirs. Clearly it was wise to distance ourselves.

We finished up the weekend farmers' markets and left early Monday morning to go to the ranch. The next morning we met the truck driver at the main gate. While he pulled through the gate, I anxiously checked the herd's reaction in the back corner of the adjacent pasture. Nothing. Most were laying down ruminating and others were standing nearby. They all seemed either unaware or unconcerned about the truck that had just arrived.

Slowly the driver positioned the trailer for offloading. He then got out and lowered the ramp through the connecting pasture gate. First the bull came off. After walking down the ramp and taking a few steps into the lush grass, the bull turned and waited. The cows came next and as soon as they joined him, the small herd began moving away from us toward the opposite side of the pasture. The belly-deep grasses and alfalfa made it an effort just move through it.

After letting the driver back out the front gate, Ken rejoined me. The small herd had reached the farthest side of the pasture and was now following the fence line toward the back. Surprisingly, the South Dakota herd was still oblivious to the newcomers. Like parents anxious for new family members to meet and treat each other kindly, we held our breath. Rounding the last corner of the back fence line, the new herd was now headed directly toward the South Dakota herd.

A gentle downwind breeze must have taken the scent of the South Dakota herd toward the California herd because without warning, the small herd suddenly began running at top speed toward the larger herd.

Good grief. This is going to be some surprise, I thought, fighting a growing sense of panic.

Helplessly we could only watch and pray that we weren't about to see a train wreck. Led by the two-and-a-half-year-old bull, the smaller herd quickly crossed the pasture. When they had arrived within 50 feet of the South Dakota herd, the scene dramatically shifted. The entire herd quickly rose to its feet, the standing members whirling around and uniting together to face the intruders.

Deftly, the South Dakota cows encircled the California cows, peeling them off from the bull. Everything came to a standstill.

The dominant South Dakota bull swiftly moved forward and now stood within 10 feet of the California bull. He lowered his massive head and pawed the ground in a challenge. The challenge was not returned. In deference, the California bull simply looked back at the challenger and the herd dynamics shifted again. Within seconds that seemed like hours, the entire herd moved together into the center of the pasture and began grazing as if they had known each other for years.

We continued to monitor them throughout the day and were relieved to see no overt signs of posturing. Now sharing a lighter mood, Ken reflected later that he had been puzzled by the initial behavior of the South Dakota herd. They were perhaps in the lushest pasture they'd ever seen, yet they seemed to be in a funk. Weeks after exploring their new home, they seemed to prefer to remain in the back corner, taking more time to acclimate than he expected. Talking about it, we decided that unlike Art's ranch, here they were exposed to more frequent and nearby human activity and this may have been what took a little longer getting used to.

In contrast, the California animals, having had daily exposure to humans also arrived to the thickest, most lush pasture they had probably ever known. Sensing no danger from the South Dakota herd, they had rushed toward them as if they had just gone for a ride around the block.

In fact, Ken and I have told our separate versions of this story several times because we each saw the communication exchange between the two herds differently.

My version goes like this:

Mommy, daddy, mommy, daddy, you'll never guess what happened. We just went for a ride, and . . . . oooooopps! You're not my mommy. You're not my daddy.

That's right and we're in charge. We'll just take those cows, thank you very much. Any problems with that? All righty then, let's go eat.

Ken, who I tease about being able to relate nearly any situation with food, offers his version:

Hey you guys! Isn't this just the best pasture you've ever seen in your entire lives?! What are you doing moping around?! Come on, let's go eat! This is great!

Both versions seem to fit pretty well. The two herds integrated so quickly and so well that we were flabbergasted as well as relieved. There is no question that with the arrival of the California animals, the South Dakota herd perked up and seemed to adjust better to their new home.

Aside from the stressful manner in which it all happened, the positive outcome from the integration of the two herds gave us a sense that we were being protected as well as being led. We gave thanks for the positive omen it represented for us, for Heritage Ranch and for the return of bison to California.

CHAPTER 14

Miracle Hay Wagon

Sometimes an event occurs which defies explanation. When it happens, you know that somehow you've been guided and looked after by something greater than your best efforts alone could have ever provided.

———◆———

The first year at the ranch we leased the irrigation wheel lines from the previous owners in order to pump water to grow hay. To save money, we watered 12 hours per day rather than 24 hours as many hay farmers did. Even then, our monthly irrigation bill could be as high as $3000. A neighbor did our haying for us, part of which we sold to offset expenses. The rest we saved for our bison.

Fifty tons of an alfalfa/orchard grass hay mix had been included in the purchase price of the ranch. This would be needed to feed the animals the first winter. The only problem was that we had no way to move the hay, so we had to allow the bison free access to the haystacks. This practice drew a cautionary tale from a neighbor about how deer can be killed by a 100-pound bale of hay falling on it and breaking its neck. Later Ken assured me this was unlikely with our bison, since they packed most of their power in their shorter and stronger necks and shoulders. While I knew he was right, I also knew that I would rest easier when the stacks were gone.

A second cautionary tale about the hay bales came from Art who told us to be sure to remove all hay twine that we found on the ground. This had nothing to do with neatness. If ingested, the twine can get twisted inside their intestines and kill them. Or it could become twisted around a leg, cutting off blood flow and resulting in a lame animal.

Following that conversation, my single mission during each trip to the ranch was to maniacally retrieve all bale twine found on the ground. With three strings per bale, there was plenty. As the bison moved around, the strings were imbedded into the muddy ground. I would pull them up and stuff them into large garbage bags. Just when I thought I had found every possible string, more would surface in the feeding area.

After capturing all visible twine, as a pre-emptive measure I began to cut twine from remaining bales before we left. The next trip, there would be more twine on the ground and the effort started again. It didn't matter if I was tired or if it was snowing, raining or blowing. After two days, I had three or four giant sized garbage bags full of twine. There seemed to be no end to the twine recovery effort.

As winter progressed and the original hay supply dwindled, we began noticing hoof prints in the snow leading to the electric fence that protected the newly baled and stacked hay. Finally the old hay was almost gone and it would soon be time to feed from the new stacks.

One Monday night after a particularly long day, we arrived at the ranch during an unexpected snowstorm. Though dark and cold, we knew from our previous trip that the other hay was almost gone so we needed to check on the bison before going to the hotel.

After driving in the storm for hours, Ken was especially tired. Now we were navigating slippery wet roads struggling to get to the ranch gate so we could put out feed if necessary. As we pulled up to the gate, our headlights revealed bison waiting for us. Their presence at the gate told us the other stack was gone and they were hungry. Ken stopped the truck and fought his way through the wind into the pump house to turn off the electric fence. While I opened the gate and shooed them away, he drove through and over to the haystack, parking so the headlights were on the hay.

The cold wind and driving snow at our backs, we stepped through the electric fence strings and made our way across the sloppy ground to the stack. I had wanted to use the tailgate of the truck to feed, but Ken was afraid we'd get stuck if we tried. Somehow we had to get the bales out by hand.

Coming from Southern California, we had not factored in storm conditions. With our savings and a second mortgage used for land, improvements and herd relocations, there was nothing left to buy equipment for getting the hay to the animals. We had discussed hiring someone with their own equipment, but since no one in the area had experience with bison, we didn't want to do this without being able to train them first—assuming we could afford to pay what they asked. In order to train them, though, we had to first train ourselves.

Tonight would be the first night. Through the blowing snow, Ken and I looked up at the towering 12-foot-high haystacks. One end was shorter, so we started there.

"How do we do this?" I yelled into the wind.

"Just grab and pull," he yelled back.

I watched him as he reached up, worked his fingers underneath one of the three hay bale strings. He yanked a few times and got out of the way just as a huge bale fell to the ground.

He's got to be kidding. How am I going to pull down a 100-pound bale? Somehow through the driving snow, he saw—or sensed—my hesitation.

"Never mind," he yelled. "I'll pull them down and we'll both drag them out."

The next yank brought down two bales together.

"That's good," I yelled, noticing the herd had gathered on the other side of the electric fence. "They're hungry. Let's pull these out and get them started."

Ken got on one side of a nearby bale.

"Just grab that side of the bale string and I'll grab the other," he yelled.

Pulling and dragging the 100-pound bale, we kept our faces down as best we could, away from the sting of the blowing snow. Reaching the electric fence, we climbed through it, and pulled the bale under it, then resumed dragging it further away from the fence. The ground was soft from the snow, and the bale began gathering mud as we dragged it.

About 50 feet from the fence, we stopped. While Ken got out his knife to cut the hay twine, I realized that the herd, which had been milling around, was now moving in closer and jockeying for position to get at the lone bale. One of the cows was just a few feet from Ken.

"Come on! We've got to get out of here!" I yelled as he turned to see what I was talking about. We'd seen bison milling around before. The pecking order plays out repeatedly over food, water and sex. We could become inadvertently hurt simply by one animal trying to avoid a herd mate's horns. We ran back to the other side of the electric fence.

"This won't work," I yelled over the roar of the wind. "We need to go into town and get some kind of wagon before the stores close."

"Tonight?!" he yelled back. He was so tired from the full day's drive that he couldn't believe what he was hearing.

"They're hungry!" I yelled.

"Yah, well I'm hungry too!" he yelled. "Let's pull out a few more and see."

By the time we had pulled two more bales out and cut the twine, he agreed to go into town. The ground wasn't frozen, so the falling snow made it muddy. It was quickly becoming impossible to drag the heavy bales across the wet surface.

Arriving in town before the hardware store closed, we found the only thing we could see might work: a garden wagon. Maybe we could put two or three bales on at a time, and pull them out rather than drag them. We paid $99, loaded the wagon into the pickup and drove back to the ranch.

Concerned the truck wouldn't make it in or out using our dirt access road, we left the truck on the heavily graveled main road. Unloading the garden cart from the back, we began the third-mile trek across the hay pasture taking turns pulling the wagon. I was grateful for the cloak of night so our neighbors couldn't see our amateurish efforts. Unlike them, we had no agricultural equipment. Now we were on foot in a snowstorm with our little green wagon bouncing and rattling along behind us.

Finally we reached the electric fence with the haystacks inside. Again we opened the pump house and turned off the fence. This time we had no truck headlights, so in the dark we pulled down two bales of hay and placed them in the wagon.

"Great!" I yelled. "This will go faster!"

"You push and I'll pull!" he yelled back.

With Ken pulling and me pushing, we made our way out past the electric fence to the waiting bison. At first they backed away, then smelling the hay, they returned and began milling around.

"Hurry up, cut the strings!" I yelled as the bison began crowding in closer.

"I am! I am!" he yelled back. The two bales were on the ground and we scrambled out of the way as the hungry bison pressed in.

Back we went with the garden wagon. Soaked now to the skin, we figured we still needed about three or four more loads.

This time, we loaded three bales onto the cart to make our effort more efficient. Two were fitted across the cart, and the third one we lifted and straddled on top. Again, with Ken pulling the cart, and me pushing, we headed back the same direction and to the right of where the animals were.

Reaching the other side of the electric fence, in the dark I felt a slight shift in the hay cargo. Suddenly the cart wouldn't budge.

"What happened?" I yelled. I heard Ken swear.

"Worthless piece of junk," he yelled. "The damn wheel just broke!"

In the howling wind and snow, I couldn't see a thing. I only knew that a corner of the cart was in the soft, wet ground. The next day I saw that the front wheel hadn't been able to handle the weight and had neatly folded onto itself.

After considerable swearing, we resumed dragging the three bales into the pasture and cut the twine.

"We need to get to the hotel while we still can!" yelled Ken and I had to agree. We didn't know when it would begin freezing and if we couldn't get the truck out, we had no place to stay.

Exhausted and wet, Ken turned the electric fence back on and we made our way back across the hay ground to the truck. At least they had enough to get them through the night. Ken would try to repair the garden cart in the morning and we would feed more then.

Arriving at the ranch the next day, we were relieved to see that there was still enough hay from the old stacks to keep them going a few more weeks. According to our calculations, they would do fine for 11 more days and then that would be it. Somehow, someway, before we came back, we had to find a more efficient way to get the hay out to them.

When we returned to Southern California late Thursday, I began immediately searching the Internet for some kind of hay wagon. What I found made my heart sink. The cheapest used ones were *thousands* of dollars. Most required a tractor or diesel truck to pull them because of the weight. All we had was my dad's four-cylinder Toyota pickup. I turned the search to used flatbed trucks and trailers; I had seen these used to feed hay. They, too, were thousands of dollars.

Exhaustion turned to despair as I fell into bed that night. Our bison were hundreds of miles away. It was cold. We needed to find a way to feed them and we knew no one with equipment who could help. Even if we did know someone, we couldn't take a chance on their being on the property without us there. As little experience as we had, someone else would have even less. Art had always said if you don't want them to go anywhere, just give them everything they need: food, water, breeding. At the time, it sounded so easy.

The next day, after getting ready for the weekend markets, I resumed my Internet search. We couldn't go back without a way to feed them.

We couldn't. There *had* to be something somewhere online. Hours later, nothing had emerged.

The following week, I checked every day online. We read newspapers and magazines in Kern County where there was more farming activity. We called a few used truck dealerships near San Bernardino for flatbed trucks, but they were all too expensive.

Before we knew it, it was Thursday and we were getting ready for the market. After the weekend, we'd be driving back to the ranch. We couldn't go back without a way to feed them.

There had to be something somewhere that we could use, there had to be. But, where? *Where?*

Thursday afternoon, again I decided to try eBay. When the search page came up, I typed in the words *hay wagon*. Scanning the expensive listings and pictures, suddenly a description and price nearly jumped off the screen. I couldn't believe what I was seeing. Someone had just moved from Idaho to Southern California. Now in Irvine, about 80 miles south of Valencia, they were selling an old hay wagon that they had used to move their household belongings. It was described as being built like a brick outhouse, with tail lights and old, worn tires. The minimum price was $400 with free delivery within 50 miles.

I showed it to Ken who confirmed it was the right size and weight and that the Toyota could handle it. Excited, I rushed back to see when the auction ended. My heart sank. It ended at 10:30 a.m. that Saturday. We both would be at farmers' markets selling our meat. There was no way we could bid on the item just before the auction ended.

Fighting a sense of panic, Ken and I talked. We couldn't let it go. It was too much of a coincidence that we would find an affordable hay wagon in Southern California and of all places, in an upscale community like Irvine. We also noted that it would be available a day before we had to leave for the ranch. But staying home from the market wasn't an option; we needed the money. If we could only find a way to submit a same day bid.

In the end, we called Anita, Ken's friend and former co-worker in Georgia. Usually out of the country on business, miraculously she picked up the phone and cheerfully agreed to bid for us, saying she was up for the challenge. I got on the phone and, swearing her to secrecy, shared the bidding strategy I had learned years before in order to win the item for the lowest possible price. By the time we hung up, all three of us were excited.

Saturday morning, in between customers, I kept tabs on the time.

The auction ended at 10:30 a.m. At 11 a.m. I got a call from Anita who was still wound up from bidding. She had won the hay wagon auction for $400, the original asking price. She had also been in touch with the seller who agreed to deliver the hay wagon to Ken in a few hours before he left the Torrance Farmers' Market!

I immediately called the seller. He was as eager to get it to us as we were to get it and relieved that he didn't have to drive far. Then I called Ken and gave him the man's phone number so they could make the final arrangements. After the market, I packed up and waited back at the condo to hear from Ken. Mid-afternoon he called. He and the seller had just finished hitching the wagon up to the pickup and he was already back on the freeway.

"That's great," I said. "How does it look?"

"Well, it's a hay wagon," he said. "You'll see. I should be home about four."

When Ken arrived at the condo, I saw what he meant. Weathered wood was bouncing loosely on top of the rusty, but solid custom-welded steel frame. The tires were bald and one of the taillights didn't work. It was the most beautiful thing I'd ever seen. Parked along the curb in front of the condo, our new treasure looked out of place, but even then Ken had to reassure me that no one would want to steal it. He was right; after our Sunday markets, to my relief the wagon was still there. That night Ken hitched it again to the truck and rewired the lights. The next morning we proudly made the 10-hour trip to the ranch, trailer in tow, bouncing noisily all the way.

That night, 16 hay bales were immediately loaded onto our miracle eBay hay wagon. The truck in four-wheel drive, we slowly made our way out into the pasture, unsure if the truck would be able to handle the combined weight of the wagon and the hay—almost a ton. It did. Within 20 minutes, in the snow and blowing wind, we had offloaded the hay, spacing it out so the dominant as well as less dominant animals could eat. While our hungry bison enjoyed their dinner, we unhitched the trailer next to the haystack, turned the electric fence back on and left for the hotel. It was the first good night's sleep I had in weeks.

When we returned from the ranch, we sent a gift to Anita with our profound thanks. The next year, Ken replaced the rotting wood deck on the wagon, and the tire that kept going flat every other week. To this day, our $400 eBay hay wagon serves as a constant reminder that miracles come in all shapes and sizes.

III

STANDING INTO
THE STORM
(2006 – Present)

Just as Great-Grandma Carlston had placed her faith in banks, so had we placed our trust in the economy and the housing market. She believed her money was safe once deposited, just as we believed our investment was secure as long as we paid our mortgage. She discovered her money had vanished with the bankers, just as we found real estate values plummeted through the questionable investment and banking practices that caused the housing market collapse in 2007.

Just as she had experienced the effects of the Great Depression, which spanned decades, we entered the Great Recession of unknown duration. We continued to claim her spirit, her tenaciousness, her strength. As we heard of others going out of business, losing their jobs and their homes, we held firm and resolute.

A Montana 10-year drought had preceded the national Great Depression and crumbling of the national economy. While Great-Grandma had no options beyond the Chicago stockyards and auction barns, we did. A new and caring connection had been created with farmers' markets customers. Five times each week, rain or shine, we met in bustling open-air markets held in parking lots or on city streets. This connection added even further to the growing love and respect Ken and I had for each other, our bison and the ranch. All became community.

Rather than rely on the traditional commercial markets that had denied us entry, we sold our meat one customer at a time. Our bison depended on our survival and we depended on theirs. Beside us, supporting us, were customers and friends made over the last several years.

And just as our bison taught us to stand into the storm to survive when others perish, so too would we stand into this, our storm. And we, too, would survive.

CHAPTER 15

The Valley of 2006 and the Resiliency of Passion

Courage does not always roar. Sometimes, it is the quiet voice at the end of the day saying 'I will try again tomorrow.'
—MARYANNE RADANBACHER—

———— ⬩ ————

After the holidays, there was usually a dip in sales, but this January was better. People were not only buying our meat, they were telling their friends. When they learned how far the ranch was, their look of disbelief gave way to thanks and we reminded ourselves that the commute was only for two years. Before then we'd sell the condo, build and relocate to the ranch so we could continue with improvements and add other species such as turkeys, pigs and chickens. By then, we'd hire someone in Los Angeles to sell the meat. Until then, we had no choice but to put added fencing and pasture improvements for rotational grazing on hold, as well as on site management for an operation such as ours.

1. MAURICE AND 803

I had watched 803 watching us as we loaded the first group of animals. Acting on Art's advice, we kept him and over the years watched as he grew from calf, to gangly adolescent, to a magnificent 8-year old bull easily weighing over a ton. As a breeding bull, Art said he just couldn't fault him. But as greenhorn producers, he was too dangerous and we didn't need any more challenges in getting the herd settled in California.

For months I ran an ad to find a new home for 803 as a breeding bull. We had one response to our ad. When the rancher described his set-up, it just didn't sound like the right fit, so we regretfully declined. There were no other responses and now we were out of time. Art arranged for the processor to come out to his place for a field harvest. This method is the most humane way to end an animal's life because they die in familiar surroundings, avoiding the stress of being transported to a processing facility.

The harvest day finally arrived. It was a Friday and I was at the farmers' market in Venice. Mid-morning I got the call from Art.

"It's done," he said.

"It is? Did it go okay?" I asked, not knowing what to say.

"Yup."

I wanted to ask more details, but knew that Art cared too and I didn't want to burden him. All I could do is repeat what I had said earlier about having mixed feelings.

Politely, Art cut me off. "Well, I gotta go," he said.

"Okay."

We hung up. Suddenly I found myself overcome with a sense of grief and loss. How had this happened? He was a magnificent bull; it wasn't fair. If I'd been able to find another home for him, he would have lived a longer life, just as his ancestors might have lived a longer life on the Plains before European settlers arrived. Unbeknownst to me, Maurice, the raw milk vendor two booths over, noticed the shift in my energy. He came over immediately as I put the cell phone down.

"What's wrong?" he asked.

"We had to put our breeding bull down," I said, and began crying. "We couldn't bring him."

Maurice put his arms around me and said, "Oh, Kathy, I'm so sorry."

A handsome, gentle man in his forties, Maurice had been raised on a dairy farm. He had left the farm some years earlier and now sold for another dairy farmer at the market. I didn't know him well, but in casual exchanges we had found him witty, intelligent, as well as shy and gentle. Later I learned that when he wasn't selling in the farmers' markets he taught yoga. Mutual customers referred to him as gifted.

"When does it get easier, Maurice?" I asked.

He hesitated a moment.

"I'm not sure it's supposed to," he said.

That's all he said. We both had customers waiting now so after assuring him I was okay, we went back to work. Though I wanted to talk with him more, somehow the moment never came. Instead, his statement became yet another loving example of how it's not Life's moments that define us, but how we use the moments. Crying didn't feel good and the moment didn't feel good. But having a caring commitment to meat animals was important. That was the message gifted in the moment. It was the message I shared with Ken and one we internalized, nurtured and protected until we could more fully understand what it meant. Then we invoked it for ourselves and shared it with others.

We had found no other alternatives for 803. Exhausting our options, it was important that his death be entrusted to a competent individual who would insure it was humane. It was important that I, his owner, cared. Though 803 and Art had their moments, Art respected 803. And as Art would explain later, he saw his role at the end of 803's life as a matter of personal pride and accountability. He felt the same with all of his animals.

In later years, as Ken and I moved forward with our own field harvests, a new connection occurred between us and the animals. When people tell us, "I don't know how you do it," or "I just couldn't do it," we know what they mean. Yet we also know that choosing to insulate ourselves from the discomfort or pain of the life and death cycle of meat animals may well speed them into the inhumane hands of non-caring individuals. This lesson is reinforced whenever we see the alarming videos of animals being slaughtered inside industrial/commercial meat production plants. The corporate CEOs and board members for these companies work and live hundreds of miles away, far removed from the moment of death. To them, the animal may be only a thing, a non-entity. Their value may be only as a commodity, a unit of volume, a number on a profit and loss sheet.

Today when a well-meaning person asks, "How can you do it?" I have a new appreciation for the role we only recently have begun to understand and adopt as ours.

"If you see what I see, know what I know, and care as I care, how can I not do it? Think about it. Educate yourself. Then come back and see if you have a different question to ask."

We have come to realize that the reconnect that occurs when we participate in the humane harvesting of our bison, as painful as it may be, is important. It somehow has provided a missing link to our own life cycle. Instead of just enjoying them when they're calves, admiring them as adults, being mildly annoyed when they outsmart us by opening a gate, we stand by them, as Art does, on their last day.

In many ways, it doesn't get easier. We've decided, as Maurice said, that perhaps it shouldn't get easier. In this way, we bless and thank them for their lives. In this way, we honor their gifts by educating others so that nothing is wasted.

2. Securing the Ranch

We were thrilled when Ken's only son Rob, after selling at the farmer's markets and helping at the ranch, said he was interested in permanently joining Lindner Bison. We encouraged him to talk with his fiancé, whom we'd met briefly. The next morning he repeated her response: "*It's like a dream come true,*" she told him over the phone. Immediately and happily we invited her to come visit the ranch and looked forward to getting to know her.

As time passed and when renewed invitations yielded vague results about when she would visit, we told ourselves that she was busy with the next year's wedding preparations and we understood. Still, we held off putting the condo up for sale until she could visit and we could all discuss the situation further. It could be that they may want to rent the condo while they sold in the farmers' markets. If it worked out that way, at least they would have a far easier time entering ranching than we did.

As it turned out, the first year anniversary of our ranch ownership shared the same month as Rob's wedding. In March, our existing ranch deal had to be refinanced or we would lose it all.

Ken is a relentless and fastidious pro-active planner. He handles our money and does it well, lining things up far ahead of any due dates, leaving nothing to chance. In the case of the ranch, he had gotten the original loan broker to agree ahead of time that she would be available to refinance the following year. However, when Ken began working on the refinancing process during the fall of 2005, she was unavailable. Her phone had been disconnected and we could not find a new number for her until weeks later. This time we reached her. Again she assured us she was available for the refinancing effort. She was in the middle of a move, she said, so her phone might not work for a while. If we couldn't reach her, she'd call us back in a few days. We never heard from her again.

February arrived without word from her, so Ken called the bank she had assured us would be receptive to a refinance loan. They had declined our original request for a loan and now, a year later, they turned us down again—despite our high credit ratings, the improvements we had made, and proven income from the property. Once again, despite our proactive planning and assurances from professionals, we found ourselves on our own, starting from scratch to look for refinancing.

A week later an ad in an agricultural newspaper caught my eye.
We finance agricultural lands. Call - - - -

It was in Oregon. Not knowing where else to turn, we called and
for the next several weeks, the financing process labored along through
agricultural brokers. Finally in early March, the brokers introduced us to
a bank in South Dakota called Dakota Mac. One week before the note
was due, we signed for a 30-year loan. The seller's and private investor's
portion of the original loan was paid off and the realtor's portion was
extended for two years. The ranch was still ours.

3. First Death Loss

Shortly after the new loan was in place, we received a call from Rick
that one of our bison cows had been found dead. It was an unexpected
blow. We made arrangements for him and another man to come in and
remove the carcass as quickly as possible so it wouldn't attract predators.
It was the first loss on our ranch and though Ken had estimated a two-
percent mortality rate from natural causes, I agonized because we weren't
there to handle the situation firsthand. Talking by phone, we learned that
Rick could see a few scrapes on the cow, but no open wounds.

Our drive to the ranch was shrouded in sadness and concern. We
asked Rick not to bury her until we could have a look, so on arrival we
immediately went to where the carcass had been moved. We saw that
she was pregnant. Art had cautioned us that the cows in particular may
be rough on each other. Maybe she had lost an argument about pecking
order; we could only speculate. I resisted the temptation to have an
autopsy done; it was something else we couldn't afford. Instead, we said
a blessing and asked for strength and guidance. She was buried within an
hour after we arrived.

Early the next day, as Ken and I were checking weeds along the
main road, one of the men who had helped Rick with the carcass drove
up. We were glad for a chance to thank him and learn about what he had
observed.

Five minutes later, a man we didn't know pulled up in his truck and
stopped. While Ken continued talking, I approached the second truck.

"I'm one of your neighbors," he said. Before I could reply, he
continued, "I noticed you pulled a dead cow out of your pasture a few
days ago."

"Yes," I said, dubiously, wondering what he wanted to say.

"Well, if you want, I'm available to help," the man said.

Instantly my heart melted. We needed help so badly and knew so few people we could ask. To have a neighbor offer to help was the first sign of friendship we'd received.

"I want you to know," he continued evenly, "I wouldn't do it for you. But I'd do it for them. I'd do it for the animals."

It felt like I'd just hit a brick wall at warp speed. For some reason, without meeting or knowing us, this neighbor had decided he had little regard for us and he wanted to make sure I knew it. My loneliness, fear, exhaustion and sense of loss collided. I burst into tears and could only sob in a voice I didn't recognize, "We're doing the best we can. We're doing the best we can."

The shocked look on the man's face brought me up short. He clearly hadn't expected this reaction. Immediately his energy changed and he started trying to comfort me. He soon left and I rejoined Ken, who thought I had been crying about the bison cow. Later I told him about the encounter.

"You just taught him that we care, honey," Ken said. "He wasn't expecting that. We're gone all the time; he may have thought we didn't care. No one knows what we go through to be able to do this. I can hardly believe it myself sometimes."

Not long after this, the man became the first of a small caring group of neighbors living nearby that we began to get to know. As we slowly learned more about each other, we found we shared common values. At the center of it all was our protective love for the land and the bison.

4. Pioneering K-Lines with Bison

Unless we wanted to see the aluminum irrigation wheel lines on the ranch become bison tinker toys, Art advised, we needed to find another way to irrigate their pastures. Unfortunately, this time he had no suggestions for what might work. Searching online, we found few options. Even if we could afford an expensive pivot irrigation system, it, too, would be subject to the infamous bison rubbing and scratching.

There was a new irrigation system being used in New Zealand. Invented in 1998 by John Kirk, a new pod system called K-Line Irrigation System was being used there for grassfed cattle. The system consists of bowl-shaped plastic pods that are open on top with individual sprinklers inside. The pods are connected by heavy hoses, which are fastened to a hydrant at one end. A cap and metal loop at the other end make it possible to be hooked to an ATV.

The idea behind the system was that the pods could then be pulled to the opposite side of each hydrant. By routinely moving the pods back and forth in this manner, pastures could be irrigated with grazing livestock present. While the K-Line system was enjoying new and limited distribution in the U.S., no one had heard of it being used with bison, and there were no known users in California that we could call for testimonials.

With no other feasible options in sight, we ordered the K-Line system on a lease to own plan.

For days, the bison watched as we trenched, installed mainline pipe and placed hydrants across both pastures. Finally, it was time for the last phase of the installation: pulling thirteen 650-foot, 1500 pound K-Lines into position and connecting them to the hydrants. One at a time, we hooked them to the back of the pickup and slowly pulled them into place. By noon we had finished the middle pasture and broke for lunch.

Now it was time to pull them into the south pasture where they had been grazing. Ken hooked the first pod line to the back of the pickup and we slowly drove over to the gate. Thirty feet away inside the gate, three cows and two calves were at the stock tank. After they finished and left to rejoin the herd, I got out of the truck and swung open the gate, stepping into the pasture.

Slowly Ken began pulling the first line. My job was to monitor the pods to make sure none of them caught on anything. The line was so long, Ken couldn't see the other end of it, so we had purchased walkie-talkies to coordinate our efforts. Once the last line cleared the gate, I would close the gate again, but keep watching and call him if the end of it caught on anything as he began his turn to pull each one into place.

One by one, the black pods dutifully followed each other at 50-foot intervals through the gate, neatly clearing the posts on each side. I watched as the pickup passed the stock tank and headed toward the opposite side of the pasture where the herd was grazing.

From out of nowhere, a mature cow suddenly appeared, her tail in the air. At first I thought she was going to the stock tank for a drink and had become annoyed at seeing the slow moving pods. Quickly I realized that was not the problem. She was on full alert. She looked at me and then back to the stock tank. I followed her gaze. There on the far side of the stock tank, separated from its mom by the moving pod line, was her calf, which had obviously dawdled. We hadn't been able to see it from our vantage point before going in.

Not knowing what to do, I watched the cow, which was loudly

grunting to her calf. The calf responded with baby-sized grunts and stayed motionless beside the tank. The moving pod line was about 10 feet from the calf.

The effect of my adrenalin began to slow the event down into micro seconds as I considered my options. If I called Ken and he stopped the truck, I wouldn't be able to close the gate should the cow elect to come through it. If either animal got tangled up in the moving pod line, they or the equipment may be hurt, or both. If I did nothing and the animals stayed put, the pod line would soon be completely inside and I could close the gate. I drew a deep breath and told myself to stay calm.

For what seemed like an eternity, the cow studied the threatening pod line. I watched as her gaze traced the line to its passage through the open gate and then to me, the one holding the gate open for the snake-like intruder. What came next was unexpected.

At the instant the cow made the connection between me and the pods separating her from her calf, I saw what can only be described as a silver stream of energy bolt directly from her chest to me. Though I felt nothing, alarmed, I instinctively turned away, wondering if she getting ready to charge. Keeping my back to her, I began to slowly close the gate, stopping just short so as not to interfere with the pods.

I looked back over my shoulder to see what effect this had. Tail still in the air, she was looking back to her calf. She dropped her nose to the ground and snorted. Taking a few steps toward the moving pods, she suddenly charged toward them and, with a flick of her tail, jumped over the moving pods. She turned immediately to again face the interloper, calf by her side, tail still in the air.

At the gate, an eternity passed. Finally, the entire line was in and I quickly closed the gate, returning safely outside. As the last pod slid by the pair, both trotted forward into the pasture with the cow grunting loudly and repeatedly. She stopped one last time, looked toward the last pod moving away, flicked her tail and they both ran toward the herd. A quarter mile away, Ken finished hooking up the first line and rejoined me at the gate.

Not long after, we began to hear from neighbors how our bison cows would charge the fence if they thought horseback riders were getting too close to their calves. While we've never seen this with our animals, the presence of the bison apparently caused the horses to whirl in place, nearly unseating their riders. Horse and rider quickly learned to take a different route. Because of my experience, we now consider the horses may have experienced a message similar to what I received. When it comes to protecting their calves, bison cows mean business. And when it comes to K-Lines and bison, we're happy to report that while they occasionally flip the heavy pods upside down, they co-exist just fine.

5. Lemon ATV

To pull the K-Lines, that spring we purchased a new ATV from an off brand shop in LA. After it was delivered to the ranch and before we could unload it from the pallet where it was stored behind locked gates and high fences, the battery was stolen. Replacing the battery, we found the ATV engine would overheat after 15 minutes without anything connected to it. The salesman refused to take it back or exchange it.

Frantic to get water on our pastures, it was repeatedly taken to a repair shop two hours away. After several failed repair attempts, they finally discovered dirt had been placed inside two engine compartments and had been there for some time. For months, we unsuccessfully sought resolution from the seller for either a working vehicle or refund of thousands of dollars.

By fall, we had no choice but to buy another vehicle, this time a Polaris Ranger. However the damage to our pastures had been done. Without the ATV to move the K-Line irrigation system, both pastures had continued to dry up in what we later learned was the first year of a four-year drought.

Bittersweet resolution occurred a full year later only by filing a complaint with the California Department of Motor vehicles. Meeting with an arbitrator, we received a full refund plus repair costs. They declined our invitation to take the vehicle back.

6. Kat

As our last cutting of hay was baled and stacked in September, competing priorities threatened to overwhelm our two ranch days. We need to winterize the wheel lines, tarp and tie the hay, and arrange harvesting to coincide with the processor's schedule and ours. The work was equitable enough. Ken was in charge of equipment and all technical aspects of operations, maintenance and repairs, while I gravitated to the animals, their feeding, care and overall safety. But because the pastures had not been irrigated during the summer, we were forced to begin supplementing early with our hay. And because we had no one working for us at the ranch, we had to put out enough hay for the bison to last them 11 days until we could get back.

Agreeing that we needed outside help, I called a neighbor and got the phone number of a nearby ranch manager who sometimes had extra helpers available.

"What do you need?" Raoul asked over the phone.

"We just need someone to help me load and feed hay to our bison," I said. "We can't pay much, but we could sure use some help for a few days."

"Does it have to be a man?" he asked.

His accent was so thick, I wasn't sure I understood him correctly, so he repeated it.

"Well, no, I guess not. As long as she's strong. Is she strong?" I asked.

"Yes, I think so." he said. "I think she's strong."

"Okay," I said, then asked again. "Are you sure? She needs to be able to help me lift 100-pound bales. If she's strong, then that's fine."

"How soon do you need help?" he asked.

"Today," I said. "I need to feed this afternoon."

"Well, I can bring her over after lunch when we get done here. You can meet her and see what you think."

It was 11 a.m. This meant I had plenty of time to tackle the thistle so it didn't seed into the hay pasture. Around 1:30 p.m., a white pickup pulled onto the hay ground and slowly made it's way along the fence line. A Hispanic male with a big smile emerged and walked over. He was about 5 feet, 7 inches and I guessed him to be in his forties.

"You Kathy?" he asked.

"Hi, Raoul," I said as we shook hands. "Glad you found us okay. We're sure glad for the help."

He gestured to someone in the pickup. A petite blond Caucasian woman emerged. Also in her forties, and no taller than 5 feet, 3 inches, I tried picturing her on the other end of a 100–pound bale of hay. It was a stretch, as were her choice of work clothes. Sporting a summer tan, she wore short jean cutoffs, a sleeveless tank top and tennis shoes without socks. Silently she stood, arms crossed and looking out at the bison.

"This is Kat," he said. "She's my lady. She's not working right now, so this is fine."

Kat and I shook hands. She didn't look particularly happy to be there.

"We're glad to have the help," I said. "So, are you ready?"

Kat and Raoul looked at each other in stunned silence. Apparently it wasn't clear that I needed help today. Raoul recovered first.

"Well, I can come back and get you later," he offered to Kat.

"Sure," she said shrugging off her surprise and looking at the ground.

"I'm not sure those are the best clothes," I said, "but I have an extra pair of jeans if you want to change."

"No, this is fine," she said and Raoul excused himself and drove away.

"Where do we start?" Kat asked.

"Right back here," I said. We walked back into the pasture and toward the hay stack and the hay wagon hooked up to the pickup.

"I don't know if you've done this before," I said as we walked, "but we're glad for the help. The bales are heavy, probably about a hundred pounds, but between the two of us, we'll do fine."

"Do you have any hay hooks?" Kat asked when we reached the stacks.

"Hay hooks?" I echoed. I'd never heard of hay hooks. "No, we just grab them here by the string and load them that way."

"The guys at the ranch use hay hooks," she said. "But this is fine."

"If we load them end to end, this way," I said, "we can fit 18 on the wagon. That's what Ken and I do. We need to put out about six more loads today and more tomorrow.

Together we climbed up on the hay stack and had just begun to pull down the first bale, when sounds of a truck engine reached us. I heard a loud "Hello!" and heard Ken yell for me that Lenny and Jolyn were there.

Jolyn, a handsome blond divorcé in her late 40s, owns the adjoining 1600 acres to the north and east of our property. She leases it out for grazing and has a massage business in town. Lenny and Debbie are her close friends and neighbors, living next door to Jo and any number and size of mostly affable dogs. We rarely see Debbie who teaches at the local community college and makes lovely pottery which she sells. Lenny trains race horses, his first love, and also works at the local tractor store. Our individual schedules rarely matched up, so it was a real treat to have them stop by.

"Sorry, Kat. These are neighbors that we never get to see, so I need to excuse myself for a few minutes. Wait for me though—don't try to do any of this yourself. I'll be right back."

Kat agreed. When I joined the trio at the bunkhouse, they were comparing the weight of the last bull we had harvested with the weight of Jo's deer that she had just shot. I've always admired strong, self-sufficient women. A woman shooting and dressing out her own deer was impressive and I told her so. She shrugged off the compliment saying it was for meat rather than sport. Ken and I agreed that was how we had been taught, too, though neither one of us had ever shot our own deer, let alone dress it.

"So, did you get some help?" Lenny asked, changing the subject.

"Yes, thank goodness. At least we hope so. Raoul just dropped off a little gal named Kat. We're just getting started so we'll see."

"Haven't heard of her," said Lenny.

"Me either," said Jo.

The lively conversation quickly turned to the amount of work we were trying to do in a short time and where Jo got her buck and how she hoisted it into a tree to dress it out and age it. It was a friendly visit and I was glad for the opportunity to get to know them a little.

"Kathy, I'm ready!" I heard Kat yell from the back.

"Oh my gosh, I forgot," I said, realizing we'd been visiting a good 10 or 15 minutes.

"Coming!" I yelled and started to excuse myself.

"Don't forget who's boss," Lenny said eyeing me evenly.

I looked at him not knowing what to say.

"Huh? Who's boss?" asked Jo, being the perfect straight person.

"Oh, right," I finally said. "It's okay. She's been waiting—I told her I'd be right back."

Lenny kept looking at me and I knew he meant well. He had no way of knowing I was so glad to have the help that establishing lines of authority was the furthest thing from my mind. Saying my goodbyes, I hurried to get back.

"Sorry, Kat," I said rounding the haystack. "We never get to see them so it was . . ."

I was stopped mid-sentence by what I saw. There was Kat casually sitting on top of a hay bale, elbows propped on tanned knees. She had an impish grin on her face. The entire hay wagon had been loaded and was now full with eighteen 100-pound bales of hay piled exactly as I had wanted.

"Good heavens! How in the world did you do that?" I exclaimed. I literally couldn't believe my eyes. It took both Ken and me to lift each bale and about half an hour to load the wagon. She had done it in 15 minutes without help.

"Oh, they weren't that heavy," she said, pleased she had made an impression.

And she had. We fed several loads that afternoon. When she returned the next day to help with the remaining loads, Ken and I offered her a part-time job if she was interested. She was. It turned out Kat had been working at the Dollar Tree store in town. They liked her work and she enjoyed it, but her boss, who was younger, wouldn't give her a raise. Instead he brought in new employees for her to train. Then she learned that the people she was training were making more money than she was, though she has been there over a year. She'd asked again for a raise and when the boss declined, she quit.

Since we didn't know her, we gave her the ground rules of being on the ranch.

"This is a no smoking, drinking or drugs environment," I said, "as well as no radios or cell phones. This is the animals' home. We believe it's a privilege to have them here. This is how we show them respect and we ask that you do, too. Plus, it's safer to have no distractions while here. When we're in the same pasture and they're nearby, we're never more than about three feet from the vehicle. They are wild. They're not aggressive and wouldn't intentionally hurt us, but there's always posturing going on, so it's important to remember that." There was more I wanted her to know, but it could wait until we came back.

"They're beautiful," she said, looking out at them.

"We think so, too," I said. "Just remember they're not cattle. They're wild."

Kat was with us for five years. Aside from her being a hard worker who seemed to enjoy being with us and the bison, we came to appreciate her spunkiness and reliability. Despite some initial skepticism, she won the hearts, minds and support of neighbors and those we did business with, based largely on the strength of her personality.

An incessant talker, we rarely had to wonder what was on Kat's mind. Pulling up to the bunkhouse after our long drives, she would often start talking from 100 feet away, her voice carrying over all kinds of weather and equipment. As she helped us unload the truck, we knew in five minutes what we needed to know about the weather, the animals, deliveries, neighbors, hay schedules, any harvests and, of course, assorted rumors.

Inside the bunkhouse, Kat always had a bowl of cold, fresh well water waiting for Sam and often the prize of a hawk tail feather or horn cap she had found while out moving the K-Lines. Though new to this kind of work and the organic philosophy of the ranch, most of the time she proved herself up to any task that arose. A special bonus for Ken was that she was as fastidious as he was about putting tools back where she found them.

Perhaps because we were all new to ranching, we came to depend on each other the way people do when they are thrust together into unfamiliar situations and have to rely on each other to achieve a goal. With each passing year, our fondness for Kat and bond of trust grew stronger. After five years, Kat remarried and suddenly quit. We like to believe that up until that time, in coming to know the bison, we came to know each other's hearts.

7. Placing Heritage Ranch in Trust

For two years, Ken and I had mapped out how best to leave L.A. so we could better manage the growing demands of the ranch. But first we needed to find and train people who would sell for us at the markets. It was important that the meat continue to be available to our customers and that the business side be maintained and grown. Our first choice was Ken's son Rob, who had expressed sincere interest in joining Lindner Bison, and whose fiancé, now wife, had said it would be like a dream come true. Rob had visited the ranch and helped out often at markets, proving himself a quick study as well as likable. Since his wedding earlier that year though, it was becoming increasingly clear that he and his wife's priorities had changed. After several visits, extensive emails, lots of questions and conversations, we sadly and reluctantly concluded it wasn't a good fit. It was a difficult decision to reach.

By now, the demands of the business required all of our energy and more. Securing the ranch wouldn't happen with compromised priorities and focus. We also saw how our efforts had grown into a protectiveness of the herd, land and resources. Survival of what we had started depended on somehow maintaining the same strength, determination and purpose after we were gone—which, at this rate, I occasionally mused when tired, might be sooner rather than later.

Long before then though, it must be protected and planned for. Several inquiries were made to non-profit land trusts in California. The few who responded expressed no interest. We then sent out a loving but formal query letter to both sides of our families to see if anyone—nieces, nephews, cousins or second-cousins—was interested in eventually owning Heritage Ranch and raising bison. We made sure that Rob and his new wife were included in this second invitation, just in case their priorities had changed again. The only response received was from a young nephew who before we could visit, elected to follow in the proud footsteps of his grandfather and enlist in the military.

With no family members interested in ranching, we activated our last option. Papers were drawn up, signed and filed placing Heritage Ranch into a trust. Our dear friend Dan agreed to be the executor with us as the trustees.

Then we identified another element that might fit into our plan. We had learned that there was a critical shortage of farmers. Retiring farmers were outnumbering new farmers by a ratio of 60:1. Our experience had shown us that there was no reasonable or practical financial support available for those who wanted to transition into bison ranching. So we established a new goal for the ranch, as a teaching and working ranch. This was to especially encourage individuals, who, like us, had little money, yet were honest, reliable, ethical hard workers eager to learn about the humane and sustainable ranching of bison and other species, including selling the meat in farmers' markets. In short, the model would encourage beginners who wanted to learn but lacked the funds or support. When the time came, they could apply to become the new trustees of the Heritage Ranch, paying forward what they learned and keeping the ranch sustainable and alive.

8. THE MESSAGE

Fall arrived, and with it our first scheduled field harvest. For some small ranchers, the timing of the harvest is often dictated by nature. For bison, like many 100 percent grassfed meat animals allowed to follow Nature's cycles, fall is when the animals' weight is the highest weight because it is just before grasses go dormant. During the summer, they're gaining weight and bulking up for the colder winter months. Then in response to the shorter days, the bison's metabolisms begin to slow down. As a result, during the winter they eat less and by spring, they may have lost up to 15 percent of their body weight. As the days become long again, their appetites return for the first flush of green grass which makes the richest milk for calves about to be born. Old timers tell us this is how Nature encourages robust bison calves and fewer calving problems than are often seen in domestic livestock.

For small ranchers, there may be other reasons for fall harvesting of meat animals. Some may not want a certain animal to breed, so they will cull animals with inferior genetics from the herd before the beginning of the August-September rut. Or there may not be enough money to feed through the winter. When all is said and done, the caring producer considers the health of the herd and health of the land. Rather than becoming attached to individuals within the group, the wise producers— like Art—seek instead to love the herd as a whole. It's my experience that few people understand and appreciate the cycle of Life more fully or completely than conscientious small farmers and ranchers.

Ken and I were not looking forward to our first field harvest. We had only witnessed one harvest and were uncomfortable with the idea of having to kill an animal. Fishing, which Ken loved, seemed different somehow. Other than my having hunted with my dad—at least right up to the day I saw the Disney movie *Bambi*—neither one of us were hunters.

By now we had visited several small meat processing plants to learn as much as we could about this part of the business. We had also learned from several bison producers along the way. The ranchers we were drawn to, those who seemed to care the most, seemed to also be the ones who insisted that they be with their animals at the end.

"It's a matter of personal pride," Art explained one day. "I raise them up from calves, I feed them, take care of them, worry about them. It's my responsibility to see they have a good life. So it's a matter of personal pride that I see them through to the end. I don't pass this off to anyone else. It's part of what I do. They deserve nothing less than my best."

We are fortunate to have access to two small meat processors willing and able to process bison. One prefers the animals be brought to him. The other prefers to come to the ranch and do a field harvest. Both use humane practices.

Our first harvest needed to occur before the start of the rut so we could take off one particular bull before he bred. Finally we agreed upon a date with the processor and our trip to the ranch was lined up. We tried to ready ourselves as best we could.

"We need a blessing," I said one afternoon. Ken nodded. "Let's try to think of one and I'll see what I can find out. Maybe somebody will tell us what they do."

Over the years, we had read stories about gratitude, prayers and offerings made by Native Americans and we knew we wanted to make it a regular practice for ourselves. In fact, we had always given thanks long distance when we knew Art was taking our animals in to the processor. But few producers we knew talked openly about any specific blessing for the animals they were harvesting, and we couldn't think of anyone we knew well enough to ask for details. We knew only that it was an important extension of our caring, an acknowledgement of gifts received.

Years earlier I read about a Native American man named Larry who seemed to be doing a great grassfed bison meat business in Oregon. At the time, I was searching for small meat processors in northern California who could process bison. Over the phone, Larry explained that he used a processing plant on his reservation and that it was only available to tribal members. Still he had a great personality and a love for the animals and by the time we hung up, I felt I'd met another kindred spirit.

Buoyed by the conversation, I went back online and found several articles describing Larry and the community support for his growing business. One article described tours he gave at the ranch; another outlined the humane practices he used as well as the deep caring he felt for his buffalo. In another article, to my surprise, he confessed to the reporter that there had once come a time when he had conflicted feelings and wanted to quit the meat business. He knew too that many people were now depending on him for his meat, and this made it an even more difficult decision.

"So finally one day, I went to the lodge of my elders," he told the reporter. "I told them 'I can't do this anymore. I'm the man with the gun. I love them. It hurts too much.' Then I waited for an answer. After awhile, an old woman spoke. 'Who better than one who loves them?' she asked. So I'm still here."

With the weekend markets behind us, Monday morning we were on our way to the ranch. Instead of lively chatter and a review of things we needed to do during our short two-day stay, this trip we said little. We knew what had to be done and we were gentle with each other.

Arriving late that night, we unpacked and went to bed, still without a blessing for the bull. The next afternoon while Ken was working on equipment, I decided to drive out to spend time with the herd.

"Maybe I can figure out a blessing," I told Ken as I kissed him goodbye.

Emotionally, I was struggling. By his silence, I knew Ken was, too. If I spent time with them, perhaps I could find the answer to another question that had emerged. *How do I reconcile killing that which I love? There can be no joy in it. So then, how?*

Even if no answer came to this new question, at the very least maybe by being with them, I could come up with a special blessing. Arriving at the south gate, a few yearlings looked over from the middle of the pasture.

I opened the gate, pulled the truck in just far enough to clear the gate, then hopped back out, closed the gate, and quickly returned to the truck. Two hundred feet later, I stopped and turned off the engine. One by one the bison were beginning to wander over now, curious.

Before they reached the truck, I got out and climbed up on the roof of the cab, ignoring the metal groaning under my weight. There on my perch, I sat cross-legged and just watched. For the next hour, the entire herd slowly gathered around the truck. Some lay down nearby, ruminating. It was comforting and poignant at the same time.

I looked over at the little bull. He didn't know this was his last day and I was envious of his ability to know only the moment. The sadness was mine. Things would change after tomorrow and my relationship with them would be different as I knew it must.

They aren't pets, I reminded myself. *This harvest is the first of many which are necessary for the health of the herd. As their caretaker, it's my duty and responsibility to learn how to do this. Otherwise they will starve and how is that better? It isn't. Natural predators aren't kind to their prey either.* I shuddered remembering ranch stories, news articles and scenes from wilderness documentaries.

After awhile the sun began setting and I realized that I'd been gone too long. There was still no blessing for the bull and I thought how appropriate that the cooler air outside matched the cold feeling I had inside. A sense of defeat and resignation began to wash over me as I slowly eased down off the cab of the truck. Back inside, I turned the key in the ignition. The bison closest to me rose to their feet. More animals stood up and they all began slowly moving off as I drove toward the closed gate. I stopped and opened the gate, then pulling the truck through again, I turned off the engine and closed and locked the gate.

For a moment, I just stood watching them, tears welling up. *How could it be that tomorrow we would be killing another living thing. Something that we loved. How was it that at this moment in time, our lives had come to this? How could I, caring this much, not even be able to come up with any kind of a blessing?* Answerless, I sought comfort by considering a delay, a temporary reprieve. Now that we were co-presidents of our own business, we had the freedom to change our decisions.

The thought was like a candle flame in the wind, flickering and then gone. *What's the use? It would only postpone the inevitable and that would only make it harder.* With a deepening sense of despair and sudden burst of anger, I looked up to the pale sky in defiant surrender. I felt my head slump wearily back into my shoulders.

I don't know how to do this! I railed silently. *I don't know how to do this!*

Unexpectedly another dimension seemed to open and I heard Native Americans chanting. A powerful energy filled the immediate area.

"We will take him," a man's voice said.

Looking slightly to my left toward the gully, against the sky I saw the face of an older Native American wearing a chief's headdress. He looked at me and again said, "We will take him." Behind him some distance away, younger warriors were dancing and chanting.

Of course! My involuntary response was immediate as hope began to replace the despair. I was being shown that preparation was already underway to receive the bison's spirit. They were expecting him. They knew what to do. The bull would be okay. There was a shared sense of understanding, acceptance and gratitude.

My mind raced then with mostly *Why* questions and as quickly as they formed, answers came. There was so much information given, it was as if words, impressions and energy all had been downloaded within seconds.

"It is the way of the buffalo," was the last message received.

Peace followed then, and with it came a new sense of humility. Greater elements were at work here. I was just a tiny speck in this energy shift and flow.

Driving back to share this experience with Ken, my confidence faltered. *How would I tell him? What would I tell him?* Rather than worry about his reaction, I instead remembered our wedding vows. We had promised each other that we would always be willing to be teachable. We didn't promise that we would be teachable, but that we would be *willing* to be teachable. This had to be one of those times.

Ken looked over and smiled as I drove up. Walking to him, I wrapped my arms around him.

"It's going to be okay, honey," I said. Before he could ask, with a shaky voice I described what had just happened. Though I've relayed a few similar experiences over the years and as supportive as he has always been, I wasn't sure if this may be just a little over the top for him. Searching his face for reassurance that he didn't now think he was married to a crazy woman, I soon had my answer.

"That's great," he said softly. It made me wish even more that he'd been able to hear and see what I'd experienced, so he could receive the same sense of comfort. Others who had gone before knew well what we were struggling to learn, that tomorrow's humane harvest was one small element of our relationship within a life cycle of multiple species, beings and energies. Without completely understanding or even accepting it, a door was opening.

That night as I watched Sam eat his dinner of ground bison, carrots and rice, a sense of purpose and calm returned. Given our history, it is a miracle that bison are with us today. If it weren't for the gift of their meat and sustenance, they would soon disappear as they almost once did. Two things that night were especially clear to me: (1) no one is proud of the great slaughtering of the bison in the 1800s, and (2) it was Ken's and my desire to turn away from industry—the commercial production and sale of goods—that led us to rediscover bison. Or perhaps it was the bison that led us here to the ranch, far away from corporate offices and cubicles. However it happened, here we were, wanting to help restore and bring them home where they once numbered into the millions. Perhaps this afternoon's message was an offer of reassurance and strength for the task ahead.

Well, I thought, suddenly tired, *perhaps the strength part will come in the morning.*

That night in bed, I said another prayer and Ken told me later he did too. Asking for continued strength, I thanked the bison for its gifts. And I thanked the Native American spirits for their presence at our ranch.

9. The Harvest

Early the next morning, the meat processor arrived right on time. The animals were in the south pasture eating the fresh hay put out that morning. I was hoping it would distract them and they wouldn't notice the processor's arrival.

My own heart jumped at seeing the strange truck and trailer make its way up to the ranch. The butterflies in my stomach settled down as I drove over and unlocked the gate. Dale, our processor, who would cut up the meat when it was ready, introduced me to his helper, Joe. Joe was a big, easy going man with a warm smile and firm handshake. I liked him immediately.

"So this is your place," Joe said, looking around. "It's beautiful."

"Thanks," I said. "It's nice to meet you. Ken's on his way, he had to pick up something." We looked across the pasture and saw Ken now driving towards us.

I wanted to visit with them more, but after they pulled in and I closed the gate, they continued over to meet Ken before I had a chance to share my "plan" with them. I had it all carefully figured out: which gate Dale and Joe would enter and exit, where the animals would be, what they would be doing, where Ken and I would be. But before it even had a chance to get off the ground, my great plan was obsolete.

First, the animals didn't cooperate at all. Rather than be where I thought they should be, they instead lined up along the fence and just watched us. Second, Dale and Joe began talking to Ken, asking him to point out the bull we wanted harvested. Though Joe looked over and tried to include me in the conversation, sensing that Dale was more comfortable with Ken, I let it go. Putting feminism aside, the more important issue was making sure the shooter had what he needed to do a good job. I was glad to hear Ken describe what we had learned from an experienced bison producer who preferred field harvests.

"Pretty much, you just draw an imaginary X across the forehead. From the base of the left horn to the right eye and vice versa," he said.

"Yeah, that's pretty much it," Dale said, "between the eyes and up a little."

We stood for another moment in the silence, studying the herd studying us.

"So this is the one?" he asked nodding to the bull standing thirty feet away.

"Yes," Ken said. "We don't want him breeding. He just isn't right. We had a non-specific AOP agreement with a California rancher who decided which bull we got. He'll be the first, and then, as you can see, we have several other bulls. But he's first and we need the meat."

I knew Ken had butterflies too. As much as we had dreaded today and this part of the learning curve, it was a necessary part of our business. We certainly couldn't raise the bison or pay for the land if we had no meat to sell. At least I had gone hunting with my dad. Ken had never been hunting in his life. Fishing yes, hunting no.

"Gosh, I can't believe how calm they all are," Dale said.

"It makes a difference when they're all kept together, rather than separating off the animal to be harvested," Ken explained.

"Isn't this something, Joe?" Dale continued, "I'm not sure I've ever seen this before."

Joe agreed, studying the herd.

Dale's previous experience with bison was at various ranches where the animals to be harvested were separated from the herd. This caused stress and strain for both animals and humans. After a moment, Dale decided he could line up the shot from our side of the fence.

I got back in the pickup and drove to the back gate. My job was to protect the carcass. According to Art, when doing a field harvest, some herd members may see it as an opportunity to move up in the pecking order.

"Some may occasionally want to come in and finish off a dead bison," Art had said. "You don't want any bruising of good meat. So I'm right there. Always support your processor."

With these words, I decided the best way to keep myself and the meat safe would be to drive up along side the carcass and basically claim it with the length of the pickup on one side. Art's place was somewhat hilly, so he never described this approach. I hoped it would work.

Dale skillfully drew the rifle up to his shoulder and took careful aim. From inside the truck, I drew a deep breath, fighting back the urge to cry. I had given my thanks, said my prayers and knew the bull would be well taken care of.

In seconds, which seemed like an eternity, I became incredulous of the moment. Here I was, in my late 50s sitting inside a truck on our property waiting for a bison to be shot. How did this happen? I drew another deep breath.

Tears have no place here, I counseled. *They may even be counterproductive to a humane harvest if I allow them or cause a distraction. It wouldn't be fair to the processor or the bison.*

Suddenly Dale's shot rang out and I saw the bull immediately crumple to the ground. Adrenaline racing, I started the engine and shifted into first gear. As I drove toward the carcass, about two hundred feet away, simultaneous things were occurring.

The herd, startled by the shot, ran the opposite direction away from us while Dale put his rifle down and ran toward the carcass on foot. We arrived at nearly the same time. While I pulled along side the carcass, Dale unsnapped his knife from a leather holster and pulled it out. Quickly he leaned forward and skillfully cut the jugular vein at the neck to begin the bleed process. Replacing the knife in his holster, he stood up and eyeing the herd, began walking back to where Joe was standing with a second rifle. Joe was also watching the herd. Ken was at the gate next to the Ranger. After Dale and Joe brought in the truck and trailer, Ken drove in and closed the gate behind him. He pulled along side me near the carcass.

The herd, which had started at the sound of the gun, ran the opposite direction. But within seconds, they seemed to stop, turn and slowly begin drifting back to where we were, noses to the ground for scent, trying to figure out what had happened. As Dale backed the trailer into place, they kept their distance on the other side of my truck.

I watched as a more relaxed Dale emerged from his truck and unwound a cable from the back hoist as he had done countless times elsewhere. Leaning over, he hooked the hind legs to his hoist. Then, powering up the electric winch, lifted the carcass as high as his truck hoist would allow.

As the truck and trailer slowly left the pasture, Ken and I drove behind on either side of the carcass. When we looked back, we saw that most of the herd had moved to the kill site where the blood was. Art had said that blood can sometimes make them squirrely and some may even lick it up. This is exactly what we saw.

Joining them back at the shed, Dale and Joe had already begun gutting the animal. Hanging there, it seemed even more enormous. I was grateful to shift my attention to the technical aspects and good-natured chatter, and leave my own feelings for later.

In some ways I felt more protective of Ken's feelings. Growing up in Montana, I was raised during a time when I was taught that men are tough and it's only the women who are emotional. In some ways, despite progress made by the women's movement, this stereotypical mindset is still alive and well today.

As an adult though, I knew it wasn't true. We all have feelings about things we care about and love. In Ken's case, he had always loved music. Just before leaving San Diego, he regretfully had to decline an invitation to join the La Jolla Symphony after playing with them for a special performance of Berlioz's *Requiem*. His love now extended to include bison. Intelligent, articulate and practical, as well as a creative, sensitive and deeply caring man, and I wanted to make sure he was okay.

Knowing we would talk later, we instead watched as Dale skillfully cut the entire length of the carcass, while Joe began work on the head. It would be the first time we'd been able to be there for the entire process and we welcomed the chance to learn more.

Joe asked if we wanted to leave the head part of the hide attached to the rest of the hide. Remembering how these are sometimes used in Native American ceremonies, I said yes. Just in case.

Dale asked for our hose, which I pulled over from the back side of the pump house and placed nearby. As we watched, there was a sudden release of internal organs in a heap, connected with and cushioned by the huge rumen. Dale asked what we wanted to save.

"As much as possible," Ken said.

"Right," Dale replied. "Most people want the liver, tongue, kidneys, do you want the kidneys?"

"Absolutely," Ken said.

"What about the testicles," Dale asked looking at Ken.

"Yup," he said. "We want it all. Just as much as possible."

"Bones, kidney fat," I added.

"You want the bones too? And the fat?" Dale asked.

"You bet," I said.

"We offer four different kinds of bones," said Ken. "Marrow, neck bones, soup/dog knuckle bones and meaty soup bones. People love them."

Dale seemed surprised at us wanting to keep the bones.

"They make an incredible soup stock," I said, and was glad to hear Joe enthusiastically agree. He began describing how they too used everything on cattle or sheep that they had, including the intestines for sausage casings.

"So what do you use the fat for?" Dale asked.

"For cooking," Ken said.

"It makes the most wonderful biscuits," I said. "Use the fat instead of shortening. Pastry ends up so light and fluffy, it's amazing."

"And for soap too," Ken continued. "We want to use the carcass the way the Native Americans did. They had it right all along," he said. "We're just trying to do the same thing. Use everything."

"People really want this stuff?" Dale asked as he continued working.

"Boy, I'll say," I said.

"And more," Ken said. "People want everything. The brains, the glands. They want it all, and if we can, we want to provide it all. Sure is better than just throwing it away. And by using everything possible, we honor all the gifts of the animal."

Dale considered this and continued hand cutting the hide, separating it from the carcass, while Joe worked on the head.

"So where do you want the skull?" Joe asked. He had finished his skinning.

"Probably up there," Ken said pointing to the roof of the cargo container. "That way birds can pick it clean, but a predator can't drag it off."

"So what do people do with the brains?" Dale asked.

"Eat 'em," I said. "We have a few customers who swear that they are delicious. One believes it is especially good nutrition for her young son." I remembered clearly the face of a young European mother who for weeks was nearly pleading that we secure brains for her family, especially her ten-month-old baby. She was shocked to find such things unavailable in the United States.

"But we can't sell the brains," said Ken.

"Why's that?" asked Joe.

"Mad cow disease," I said. "USDA disallows anything connected with the spine to go into food."

"Yeah, even though there have been no mad cow cases reported for bison," added Ken. "To the USDA it doesn't matter."

"Once we can find someone to do brain tanning of the hides, we hope to start saving it so we can use it for that," I added.

"There's so much more we want to do," Ken said. "But it's just the two of us, so we're pretty limited."

As if on cue, the huge hide fell to the ground.

Joe and Ken lifted the heavy hide into the back of the ranger. Then Ken and I drove over to the make-shift frame we had rigged from the large frame used for the ATV delivery. Now propped against a bale of hay, it was at a good angle for drying the hide. Together we wrestled with the heavy hide, spreading it out wool side down. Once it was spread, Ken got the salt bag and poured some salt on his side, handing it to me. I did the same to my side and together we worked the salt into the hide with rubber gloves.

The salt helps draw out the moisture so any fleshy parts of the hide can dry. As it dries, the follicles around the hair tightens. If the hair doesn't tighten, it later falls out and must be used for leather rather than a winter robe wall hanging or showcase rug.

After about ten minutes we finished and rejoined Dale and Joe who were almost done. Dale had taken a power saw and split the carcass in half down the spine. Because of the height of his truck, it couldn't accommodate the full length of the carcass. It had to be split neatly again into quarters. As Joe held the lower part of one half to keep it from swinging, Dale counted down ribs and began sawing between where the New York steaks end and ribeye steaks begin. Finally, four quarters hung neatly on separate rails inside the stainless steel box truck. It no longer resembled a live animal.

I looked over at the herd some distance away. Most were ruminating in the middle of the pasture. The pre-harvest innocence was now gone, replaced by a new kind of knowing. How my relationship with them would evolve, I didn't know, but I knew I would learn to deal with my feelings. In fact, as we left to return to L.A., I had a different goal and challenge: somewhere through all of this, I would learn to reconcile a humane harvest with loving these animals as I did, loving the meat and wanting our fledgling business and small ranch to not just survive, but prosper and grow. It was a new moral imperative.

10. POTPOURRI

From fall through winter, there were a series of unexpected events coming so quickly that we barely had time to catch our breath before another one occurred.

First, we sold Ken's beloved Miata on eBay to help pay for hay ground irrigation pumping costs. We reminisced briefly about our first date at the sports car rally, but acknowledged that our lives had changed now and the car no longer had a place in it. And we needed the money.

A month later, Ken parted with an even more treasured item—a tenor trombone generously sold to him for a paltry sum by John Coffey decades earlier in Boston. Ken had wonderful memories of studying with Coffey, the legendary bass trombonist for the Boston Symphony. Often during the middle of a lesson, musician greats would stop by to say hi and shoot the breeze. The only way Ken was able to part with the trombone was to remind himself that an excellent instrument is meant to be played. He sold it on eBay to a young woman trombonist who played for the Los Angeles Philharmonic. He also created a written history of the horn's ownership so that she would better understand what she had. The additional emotional impact for Ken was that the sale represented a continued decoupling he saw occurring between him and performing. Like a reliable and trustworthy friend, playing trombone had been a pivotal and important part of his life from childhood. He thought it would always be there. Though he still had a few instruments left, with the sale of the Coffee trombone he became less sure that he'd ever have the time or opportunity to play again.

Next we made two hay purchases, both of which were misrepresented to us, one in bale weight, the other in content. Our remedy for the first was to simply not do business with that person again. For the second, since our bison wouldn't eat the hay because of the extensive amount of foxtail in it, we asked for and received reimbursement. But we now had the added task of burning what we had already put out. Hopefully this would help keep the foxtail from going to seed in the pasture.

Around the same time as the hay purchases, one visit in early winter, we arrived at the ranch to find that the irrigation main line alongside the road had been run over by a heavy pickup truck. It was smashed flat in two places where the truck had entered and exited our property. The line would require extensive repair before spring.

11. KEN'S DAD PASSES

A few weeks later in mid-December, we got a call from Ken's mom. She and dad were in their Florida driveway that morning when Dad, age 87, lost his balance and fell. When he fell, he hit his head on a nearby cement stair. She was calling us from the hospital where her husband of 60 years lay unconscious. Ken's siblings, Jim and Jill, were enroute from Pennsylvania and New Hampshire.

When Ken got off the phone, we discussed whether or not he should fly to Florida too. He seemed to take the news in a measured fashion, the way his military father would. Ever practical, he reasoned that if his dad was unconscious, it wouldn't make any difference if he were there or not. Mom had her other two kids there, so she'd have plenty of support.

"We're going to do the farmers' markets this weekend," he said. "We can't afford to miss them and mom will know more by Monday. Of all people, Dad would understand. He's supported us from the beginning. They came with us to South Dakota, remember?"

I remembered. And I ached that Ken couldn't be on a plane immediately. For me, it was reminiscent of my experience a few years before. Over Christmas, my 92-year-old father had difficulty breathing and agreed to go into the hospital so they could keep an eye on him. Because of our small business and limited funds, I decided against flying to Montana to see him. Daddy passed away January first.

That Sunday, while Ken was at the Long Beach farmers' market, Ken got the call that Dad had passed away that morning. As much as he dearly loved his father, he finished the market as usual. None of his customers ever knew. That night he left for Florida and returned the following week, a few days before Christmas.

When he got back, we decided to spend New Year's Eve at the ranch. Even if we could only be there for a few days, being there and with our bison would provide the best hope for healing and to gather our strength for the beginning of a New Year.

Years before at Christmas time in Alpharetta when fear tried to crowd out hope, I had grabbed a paper plate, wrote the words "FAITH" and threaded it onto the top of our Christmas tree. Similarly one night during our stay at the ranch, despair began to threaten. I grabbed a pen and closest thing to paper I could find – again, a paper plate. On it I forcefully printed in large capital letters: *WE AND LINDNER BISON WILL PREVAIL!* It was placed in a visible, prominent position inside the small bunkhouse.

Though the moment has long since passed, every once in a while I come across that paper plate in the bunkhouse. Today it's a marker and milestone of how far we've come. A reminder of the resiliency of passion.

CHAPTER 16

Rainbow Lodge
(early 2007)

Many presents or material things given eventually wear out and need replacing. But the memory surrounding the moment may linger forever. Within the energy of the moment is the true gift.

———◆———

The beginning of 2007 found us feeling the cumulative effects of the past two years. As we left the ranch this particular January morning, I was anxious and irritable. Attributing it to low blood sugar and fatigue, eating a decent breakfast seemed a reasonable remedy. Decent meant not settling for commercial chain restaurants or drive-ins, though from experience we knew that there seemed to be painfully few options in and around large cities. This awareness only made me more irritable, as we passed marquee after marquee of fast food restaurants. I hated being boxed into a massive commercial food world when I *knew* other choices existed. If only we knew where to look!

Twenty minutes outside Reno we spotted a sign along I-80. The sign said *Rainbow Lodge*. Donner Pass lay ahead and we knew there wouldn't be another restaurant for well over an hour. Ken impulsively made the decision to pull off the freeway and head to the unseen destination hidden by pine trees. Five minutes later, we pulled up to the front of the lodge, the tires made a crunching sound on icy snow as we turned off the main road.

The three-story lodge looked old. It was made of dark wood logs, built on a stone foundation. Huge rocks adorned all areas of the property and continued in smaller sizes along the steep sides of the river below.

Above us, about a quarter-mile away, was the freeway, but the wind in the pines and the sound of the river in the background conspired well to conceal the freeway sounds. It was easy to be drawn to the peacefulness of the place.

The heavy wooden door creaked as we opened it and walked in from the cold. Inside, a few feet from the front desk were a comfortable pair of couches and a table full of magazines. To the right, a hallway opened up into another large room with over-stuffed chairs and couches and a fire flickering warmly in the fireplace. Several wooden end tables and coffee tables were strategically placed about the room to hold lamps and reading materials.

To the left of the front desk was the dining room. A petite, clean-cut, young blond woman with a polished, shiny face emerged. Looking every bit the college student, she demurely welcomed us, apologizing that we were the first customers of the morning. The cook was not quite ready, she said, but would be soon. We were escorted to a small window table with two chairs on either side. She excused herself then, promising to return with coffee, which, too, was almost ready.

We studied our surroundings. The table was small, draped with a crisp white tablecloth. In the center of the table was a tasteful bouquet of fresh wild flowers and a small candle, which she lit as we sat down. A foot away, old, rippled pane windows reached nearly floor to ceiling, draped with a heavy, smooth cotton forest-green paisley print, tied back at each side. The curtains barely touched a rich burgundy colored, similarly patterned carpet. Contrasting our warm indoor surroundings to the snow-covered yard full of pine trees, benches, and boulders, I had the feeling that we were snugly and safely tucked inside and outside at the same time.

Everything was still and quiet in the hush of morning yet to begin.

Overhead, huge wooden beams extended the entire length of the room. It was easy to envision oversized garlands of pine boughs draped and lit at Christmas time, their aroma filling the room.

Twenty feet away, our waitress had paused near the opening of the dining room's huge stone fireplace. Collecting an elongated lighter, she leaned down, lit the crumpled newspaper already placed beneath the wood and disappeared through a small nearby door. As the crackle of kindling wood reached us, light classical music softly filled the chilled air of the dining room.

At that moment, a collision of sensory worlds occurred. I realized that it was the first time since we had begun our ranching journey in earnest that we had been in surroundings like this. Previous decades had found us as guests at some of the finest levels of elegance and richness, warmth and welcome. We had reveled in concerts of the best symphonies, stayed in five-star hotels, and dined in exquisite restaurants and private homes. We were no strangers to pomp and circumstance, protocol, formal events, art, history and Broadway plays.

We had just spent two days at the ranch, wrestling with winter weather and dealing with new aches and pains from heavy hay bales. Exhausted from the events of 2006, we still had a 10 hour drive ahead.

The contrast between our new world and that of the lodge was jolting. Quite by accident, it was the first civilized and cultured moment we had shared in years. It felt like an angelic balm was being applied to my soul.

As the music softly surrounded us, over the flame of a small table candle, we looked at each other in new awareness and recognition. And there, in the empty dining room at 6:30 in the morning, we hung our heads and silently wept at the sheer beauty and peace of the place.

If the young woman noticed our loss of composure, she navigated the waters with finesse and grace so as not to intrude or embarrass us. She was gentle and kind. She brought fresh-squeezed orange juice for Ken, and for me, the most incredible cup of coffee I'd had in years. Refilling my cup several times, she explained that the coffee was a special blend of beans brewed with spring water from a well near the lodge.

The breakfast matched the ambiance. It was presented with an understated elegance and a creative blend of flavors and colors. I chose eggs and hash browns. Ken had fresh salmon. In between bites, I valiantly fought back the tears which continued to well up. We had traveled so far from this world and for the first time I was forced to see the stark contrast our lives had taken and truly acknowledge my exhaustion.

Our new world was full of unforgiving barbed wire, unrelenting wind and dust, long, hot days, snakes, coyotes and cougars. Even the beautiful deer that had enjoyed free run of the place before the bison, hissed at our presence. While we did everything in our power to protect our herd, we had lost a bison cow that spring. We had left friends and families who were speechless at what we were trying to do, while our neighbors, having seen the place change hands several times, gave us a wide berth.

Back in Los Angeles, the market was still unproven for our meat. No Southern California farmers' markets had ever carried 100 percent grassfed red meat of any kind, let alone bison meat. Market managers accommodated us with dubious feelings. Most were welcoming, but others remained skeptical, believing the meat was a fad, a novelty item. As such, it made their market unique, at least for as long as we lasted.

We had endured countless rejections from bankers and investors eager to see every detail of our business plan. We had placed ourselves under enormous pressure in order to honor loan terms that could have resulted in the loss of our cash investment of $68,000, our animals and the ranch. A second mortgage had been placed on the condo in exchange for game fencing and a lease-purchase agreement had been made in order to buy K-Line irrigation pods, a system unproven for use with bison.

We worked hard to create relationships with our customers, who represented real hope for our business. If we couldn't successfully develop relationships with customers, there would be no sales and no ranch. Without a way to pay the bills, the survival of the herd would be in jeopardy. And how could we adequately protect the animals from 600 miles away? There was no guarantee that our whole grand scheme would work. We knew only that we had to somehow keep going and not give up.

So, on that early January morning at Rainbow Lodge, the enormity of our vision and the difficulties it presented collided with a world we had known, trusted and then abandoned to create one that would be more fulfilling. Here was evidence of the beautiful parts of our previous world. They hadn't gone anywhere, we had. We had gladly walked away, as others had equally gladly taken our place. Was it the right choice, the right decision? Even through the exhaustion I knew it was. But neither one of us knew it would be or could be so difficult of a world to create let alone enter. We knew it shouldn't be this hard, but it was.

Restored somewhat by the peaceful strength of Rainbow Lodge, that morning we dawdled as long as we could, reluctant to leave. Finally it was time to go. Back on the freeway, we vowed to always make time for classical music at the ranch. Just because our ranching, traveling and farmers' markets schedules didn't match the live concert schedules in L.A., that was no reason to go without that which fed our hearts and souls.

For the next several trips, we stopped for breakfast at Rainbow Lodge and always, the same young woman waited on us. Then as hope grew again in our new world, Rainbow Lodge began to slowly fall away. The gentle young waitress became engaged, then married and finally quit her job to go back to school. Somehow Rainbow Lodge wasn't the same after she left. Or perhaps the lodge had served its purpose, providing a respite and a bridge, renewing our spirits while we gathered strength to continue.

As winter gave way to spring, we shared a renewed sense of optimism. The two years of our long commute were up. It was time. We would sell the condo to finance a house on the ranch. Finally, we'd be able to make needed pasture improvements, and better use and manage the land and animals by being there on a daily basis. We could add other species such as heritage turkeys, too.

In March 2007, after checking with a few realtors, we were ready. Prices had steadily climbed since we first bought the condo in 2002 and we listed it for sale. With any luck, we'd be moved by Christmas and reunited with all of the things we had put in storage. The long distance ranching would be over. And we'd finally be home with our bison.

CHAPTER 17

Running in Place

Life is what happens while you're busy making other plans.
—JOHN LENNON—

———◆———

March, 2007 found us busier than ever and excited to be moving toward living with our bison at the ranch. When we weren't there, on the road, or selling in farmers' markets, we were busy readying our two bedroom condo to be shown and sold. We cleaned out the garage and sorted and sold items in our storage unit.

In May, we flew to the Pacific Northwest to make a non-refundable deposit on a three bedroom modular house. Though not our first choice, a modular home would make the move easier and less stressful. More importantly, it would divert less energy from our business and travel schedules.

Determined to stay connected with our farmers' market customers, we began training someone to manage the markets in our absence. With the new house scheduled for delivery in September, our goal was to be moved and on the ranch by the end of the year. Then we would reduce our travel to Southern California, going every month or two instead of weekly.

It didn't happen.

By August we had changed realtors three times. In an urban area where several showings a week was the norm, over a nine-month period our condo had only three showings and one low offer from someone wanting an unusually short escrow. In November we pulled the condo off the market. The poor housing market was now being called a recession and no one knew how long it would last. We watched as local and state housing prices continued to plummet and words like "corruption" and "greed" were being used to describe deals made by Wall Street and financial institutions. Banks were demanding bale out money from the federal government, which was provided without terms or stipulations of any kind. Reports and videos emerged that some of the money was used for executive bonuses in the millions, as well as lavish corporate parties. Taxpayers shared a new sense of disbelief and outrage. How could this happen? ? As reports continued to surface, we became emotionally shell-shocked. We pulled back, settled in, waited and watched.

Finally we realized our move to the ranch had to be put on hold. The modular home people were sympathetic when we cancelled our order, but unwilling to refund our cash deposit. Business was down and they were affected too. Reluctantly, we contacted our trainee, explaining we were unable to offer him the position we had promised. He graciously understood and quickly located another job.

At the farmers' markets, customers' buying habits changed. Some bought less, others bought more affordable cuts. Weekly we received reports from customers that they, a friend or family member had suddenly lost their jobs and were unable to find work. Those who owned their own business had fewer customers. Others closed their business. Some announced they were moving out of state, while others reported they had moved in with friends or family. Many began collecting unemployment or filed for early retirement benefits. Still others moved to more affordable housing and were grateful to find one or two part time jobs.

Then we began to hear about an increase in bankruptcies. Some people were walking away from their homes. One report came in of an Ohio man who bulldozed a home he had built. Failing to persuade the bank to restructure his loan despite his excellent credit and many years of business, he systematically flattened the building rather than let the bank take it.

We watched a TV news report from Santa Barbara, the upscale community where we had once lived, about people who had lost their homes and were now living in their cars. In response, the city had designated a temporary parking lot, which they patrolled, for displaced residents.

Each week at the markets, stories were exchanged and we shared our customers' worries and concerns. Like us, most were shaken by the news reports. Many were fearful and angry.

The Southern California area was among the first to feel the effects of what later became known as the Great Recession. Having experienced recessions before, Ken and I were confident the economy would recover. Yet, the more we learned about Wall Street, the banks, insurance companies and the commercial real estate industry, the more we realized recovery may take longer. This one was different.

As we followed the TV news, each week customers asked us if we were doing okay and we asked the same of them. Those who had been able to keep their jobs seemed more overworked than ever. Canceling vacations or time off, they were concerned about job security and their future. Our sales leveled off, then went down, but we were still able to pay our bills.

As the nature and cause of the recession became known, more than ever we were glad to be working for ourselves. We hunkered down and concentrated on keeping the ranch going and selling our meat.

1. The Gift

Christmas found us still in Valencia and still continuing our commute. After talking about the weeds that had to be cleared and burned before spring, we reluctantly decided we could get more done over the holidays by Ken going to the ranch and me staying behind. It was necessary, but not a decision that we welcomed. After being together for 16 years, it would mark the first time we would be apart during the holidays as well as driving the freeways on a major holiday, something we tried to avoid.

There was no other way. He drove all day Monday and went to bed early that night. By the end of the next day, December 30th, he had constructed a rough tumbleweed plow out of old pieces of plywood and mounted it on the front of the Ranger. If it worked, it had the potential to provide a huge labor and monetary relief to our meager resources; the plow would clear the tumbleweeds and this represented a critical first step to planting.

Finally Ken was ready to take it out for a test run. As he was working the fence line where the tumbleweed was piled the highest, he soon found he had an audience. The bison, always curious about everything we do, gathered around and watched. As he pushed tumbleweed away from one section, they crowded in to check out what had been changed in their home. This went on for several hours as he pushed the tumbleweeds into piles for burning.

Toward dusk, flaws in the plow design became apparent. With only one day left before he had to return to Southern California, it started to break apart, forcing him to stop.

Wednesday, December 31st we kept in touch by cell phone as he finished working on the plow. Emotionally, we were struggling. He was alone and tired. Our part time ranch helper had a doctor's appointment that day and was unavailable to help. By mid-afternoon it was time for the redesigned plow to be taken out for a test run. As Ken began work, he saw that the new design held.

Before, the animals had remained nearby as he plowed the tumbleweed away from the fence into pile. Curiosity satisfied, they kept their distance, which allowed him to work more quickly. Soon 14 large piles of tumbleweed were in place. It was enough. The sun would be gone in a few hours and he knew he would have to leave early the next morning. Working his way down the fence line, Ken burned pile after pile of tumbleweed. It was early evening before he reached the last pile. As he lit it and watch it slowly start to burn, something caught the corner of his eye. He turned.

A small group of about 20 of the younger animals had started to run and jump in their stiff-legged fashion – we call it *The Dance*. They ran around in a large circle just in front of where he was working. Uplifted, he stopped work and watched as they continued, running up to each other, inviting the next one who would then join in and follow. Ken mused it was because they too were happy to see the tumbleweeds disappear.

But this dance was different. Rather than last the usual two to three minutes, by that time, the group dance had grown as more animals joined in the fun. Bison are gregarious by nature and when they feel good, they seem to look for any excuse to run. On achieving momentum, they do a stiff-legged boing, boing, boing. It is a joyful thing and a privilege to behold. Ken soon found himself busy both watching them and tending to the tumbleweed fire.

Unexpectedly, the entire herd, numbering over 100 animals, began joining the circle of youngsters. While Ken watched in wonder, the entire herd took off at a dead run in the lower pasture, forming a circle of about quarter-mile wide. His wonder quickly changed to concern. After completing a 360-degree circle, the circle was opening and he realized they were now headed directly toward him in the upper pasture at a dead run. Not one member of the herd was standing. All were running directly toward him, including our normally more reserved 16-year old cows.

Ken moved to the other side of the ATV and waited. At the last second, when they were about 50 feet away, the herd suddenly veered off, running back toward the lower pasture again. They ran another full circle away and back, alternating running and boinging as they went. Incredibly, they repeated this three times! Each time they ran straight toward him, each time they veered off at the last second. This continued for about five minutes, the longest dance either of us had ever seen.

The last time they went around, some of the younger animals, who had been at it from the beginning, passed by him with their tongues hanging out, panting like crazy and unwilling to stop. Finally, thirst prevailed and they all headed to the stock tank for water. Almost as quickly as it had started, it was over.

As Ken watched them take turns drinking, he realized he had received perhaps the highest compliment and honor a bison rancher can receive—an invitation to run with the herd. He blessed them and thanked them as he drove back to the bunkhouse. After packing his things to leave in the morning, he called me and described his unexpected New Year's Eve gift.

We decided it was going to be a good year.

CHAPTER 18

Margaret
(2009)

With each passing year, our bison continue to amaze us in countless ways. Constantly they teach us. The story that follows is about one of our original four cows, Margaret. At this point Margaret and her sisters were 16 years old. They provide the matriarchal glue that holds the herd together, creating structure and norm. Within this society and with us, Margaret has proven to be exceptional.

———◆———

1. July

The time had finally arrived. The processor called with an unexpected opening and said he could come out next week. We had been waiting for calving season to be over to see if any of the cows came up dry.

One did. It was Margaret.

Margaret was one of the first four cows we originally bought. We named the four of them after family and friends: Margaret for my great-grandmother; Mary for my maid-of-honor and dear friend of 35 years; Betty for Ken's much beloved mother; and Mary Ann for our wonderful, loving and joyfully wacky sister-in-law. Since bison can live 20–30 years, we expected to have them for many years and it was our way of acknowledging and including family and friends in our new business. As you might imagine, our first four hold special meaning for us, and as matriarchs, they keep the rest of the herd in line. Their success, and the overall success of the herd, is our report card.

For years, Margaret had been easy to spot because she had somehow developed a bulging right eye. It was red and somewhat angry-looking, so much so that at times I wondered if she might lose it. We don't give antibiotics because Art had cautioned that bison may become blind if given antibiotics and the herd will sense this weakness and drive them off or kill them.

"They're tough," he counseled. "Just leave them alone and most of the time they recover just fine."

Within a few years after we brought Margaret to our ranch, I realized that her eye had completely healed. Her horns hadn't changed much, though, and they still made her distinct from the others. One was crooked, short and sharp, the other one, extremely long and regal.

Margaret is perhaps the more docile of the bunch, if a wild bison can ever be docile. Often the first to calve, many of her calves became our breeding bulls. They always seemed larger than the other bull calves and had great conformation.

When Dale said he could come out the next week, with conflicted feelings, I encouraged Ken to stall. "They're getting into the rut, Dale, so we're not sure about the timing. When do you need to know? "

"Oh a few days are fine", he said.

Back in the car, as Ken drove, I immediately called Art. It was early enough to catch him before he left the house for chores. Though glad to reach him, I was disappointed when he said that the rut wouldn't make much difference if we wanted Dale to come out.

"You just always want to keep an eye on the bulls," he said.

"Our bulls aren't aggressive," Ken said as he was driving, so I repeated that back to Art.

"Does the processor go out on his own?" he asked.

"Yes," I said, "only because of our driving back and forth doesn't always work with his schedule."

"How does he know which one to take?" he asked.

"He's been out to our place a lot, so he knows our animals. And Ken always is teaching him how to tell them apart. And Kat knows too. We're usually only able to be there two days every 11 days, so we can't always get his schedule to match ours."

"Well, you've got a little different situation there," he said, "and you got over your jitters."

I replied "It's not our favorite part, but we know it's important. And our customers think so too. It makes a difference to them that we care enough to be there. We just can't always be there."

Art continued, "I've got just enough Indian in me that I just go out and make a little offering before I do it."

This was new information coming from someone we admired and respected.

"Art, I've never heard you say that before! We were too embarrassed to tell you that we say a blessing before each harvest. We had no idea you did that too."

"Well, it's not something I broadcast," he said. "And it's not a matter of easing my conscience either. That's not what it's about. It's just a stamp at the end to send them on their way. They've done their part. I need to do mine. And I take great personal pride in doing it. I suppose over the years, I've personally shot 1000 to 1500 buffalo. The only times it was hard, is when they did some damage and I had to take 'em off. It was hard, because it was usually something I could have prevented. Either in a corral system or something. It was something I could have done or not done."

He continued. "Having the processor come out is the absolute best thing in the whole world that you can do. There's just no better way, that's all there is to it."

I was getting choked up, knowing what he said was true and thinking of Margaret. It may be more difficult for us, but it is by far, the easiest for them.

"The best way for them to leave the ranch is in a truck with their feet hanging out of the back," he said. "That's the best way."

Finally it was time to hang up. Once again, it was good to connect with Art who reaffirmed his earlier teachings. His advice was welcome, sound and consistently sided on the humane care of the animal and being wholly present and accountable for that care.

Ken looked at me when I hung up. We'd be getting into a spotty cell area soon.

"We need the meat," he said gently.

"I know," I said, hesitating before I agreed. We did need the meat and selling the meat is how we paid for the ranch and the irrigation system that grew the grass for the herd. And I also knew that emotional attachments just didn't work for herd health. I would have to aspire harder to accept the wisdom of Art's words.

Ken immediately called Dale and Kat to line up the harvest. He hung up.

"We knew this time would come," he said. "We'll say a special blessing for Margaret."

I reached over and squeezed his hand. If he suspected tears, he kindly kept his eyes on the road and didn't let on.

Native Americans believe that at the time of harvest, when you're pure of heart, the bison will step forward and offer themselves as a gift. If we believe this, as we do more with each passing year, then it is not surprising that of the four, Margaret would be the first.

In the natural cycle of life, we knew it was inevitable. The harvest of Margaret marks the passage of time and signals the maturing of Lindner Bison and how far we have come in our journey.

A special blessing and offering would be made. Her harvest would contribute to the health of the herd, as well as honor Margaret, her gifts and her bison-ness. I hoped too, that in some way, it would honor the humanness of the humans who loved her longest and best.

The following week, for the first time in four years, instead of being at the weekend farmers' markets, Ken and I packed our bags and flew to Pittsburgh. The occasion was a joyful one. Our beautiful niece Beth was marrying the man of her dreams, Asaf. Since she's Catholic and he's Jewish, they chose a beautiful non-denominational chapel at the University of Pittsburgh campus where they met.

Beth's younger siblings Christy and Mike picked us up at the airport and at the hotel, we reunited with Ken's brother Jim and his wife, Mary Ann. Both were involved in last minute, blurry-eyed details, a rite of passage for parents of the bride.

The next day we joined mom and a menagerie of wedding helpers in her room. The excitement, chaos and joy were in full swing. Wedding favors were laid out on the bed in alphabetical order for seating at the dinner reception. Camera flash bulbs were going off as competing priorities collided in arranging for gifts, table seating, and favors. Unable to hear over the din, across the room I saw Ken reach in his pocket for his cell phone and put it up to his ear. Instinctively I went to him. He had a finger plugged in one ear and kept saying "What?" then began moving toward the door of the adjoining room. "Just a minute, Kat, let me go somewhere that's quieter."

I followed him to the next room where Mike was watching TV, so instead we moved into the bathroom and closed the door.

"Okay Kat, I can hear you now. So what happened?"

"We just couldn't get a clean shot," she said. "We went out there and that two-year old bull kept getting in the way," Kat said exasperated and apologetic. "Dale just finally said we had to give up. We must've been out there for over an hour. Every time he got lined up on a clean shot, that two-year old bull would just wander over and stand in front of her. And I know you want to hang onto him, right?"

"Right," said Ken. "Well, that's fine. Don't worry about it. It can wait, obviously."

"Yeah, well, we really tried," Kat said.

"Oh, I know you did, that's okay," he assured her. "That's the way it is sometimes. Tell Dale not to worry about it, though I'm sorry to take so much of his time."

"Oh he's okay, he just wanted to make sure you knew that we tried," she said.

"Okay, that's fine," Ken said again. "Tell him thanks for trying. We'll talk to you later."

Ken hung up the phone and turned to me.

"They couldn't get a clean shot," he said, half smiling. "So they gave up. Kat said that two-year old bull just kept getting in between them. They tried two or three times and each time they got the shot all lined up, she said that bull would just walk and stand right in front of her."

"My gosh," I said, remembering what Dave, a Native American, had told us. "It was offering itself."

"Well, I don't know about that," he said, "but I do know that Margaret is still with us." He stopped and just looked at me. It was the first time anything like that had happened. We both stood there for a moment, then I was in his arms.

"That's great," I said.

"Yes," he said, "it's just fine."

"Maybe we should keep her," I said.

As he does when I propose a less than practical solution, Ken said, "We'll see."

For several days, I savored the call and hoped that Dale wasn't too disappointed. Then Ken reminded me what Dale had told us when we first met him. He said that if a shot ever didn't feel right, he would always rather wait and just come back another time. He said some people don't like it and some even get mad at him, but that's the way he worked. Though it was the first time we'd ever heard this from a processor, we told him we would always prefer the exact same thing and assured him he had our full support. He had been true to his word.

2. AUGUST

I had worked too long in my crusade against thistle. We were nearly ready for our second cutting of hay and with only two days, if I was going to remove it before the hay was baled up, it had to be done regardless of the hot weather.

And it was hot. This year I finally became one of those older people who can't take the heat. In spite of staying hydrated and consuming bottles of Gatorade, by fall, I'd started having weird symptoms. Even if I stayed sheltered in our air-conditioned bunkhouse, it took days for me to recover from my weeding efforts.

Again, I had stayed out longer than intended. Rather than rest in the bunkhouse until it got cooler outside, I grabbed Sam, our 11-year-old Scottie, and went into town in our air-conditioned SUV to pick up hydraulic oil for the wheel lines and pump. When I got back, Ken and Kat were at the cargo container, engrossed in conversation, probably about the repair of something. Rather than join them, I went into the bunkhouse, turned on the air conditioner and just sat for a few minutes. If they needed me, they could see from the car that I was back.

Inside, I poured myself a glass of cold water and opened a bar of chocolate. There was more weeding to do, but I needed first to just sit here. It would be cooler soon.

The bunkhouse sits at the north end of our middle pasture. It is small and comfy. Ken insulated it and installed a used picture window donated by Lenny, which provides a great view of the mountains and of visiting bison coming for a drink at the stock water tank 100 feet away.

Right next to the bunkhouse, inside the fenced area, is a 3-sided shelter Ken built using shade cloth, wood posts and steel roofing. We keep equipment there out of the elements. In front of that is where the hay is stored. The entire area is enclosed by game fencing on one side and an electric fence on the other.

Off this area is a section of pasture without irrigation. When we put out hay, we usually put it in this area, where there is little grass to harm. We had put hay out all summer while we worked to restore pastures that had been hit hardest by three years of drought as well as our pump going out the previous year.

Savoring the chocolate in the quiet, I looked out at the herd. Strange. There was a cow off by herself, obviously finding something to eat. Her head was down—the same as the rest of the herd at the opposite end of the pasture. But it was odd she would find hay left over from what we put out yesterday and that the others preferred to stay at the other end. A cow off by herself is usually a signal to us that they are getting ready to calve. But calving normally occurs May through June and here it was almost

September. We were well into the rut, so I knew that couldn't be it.

Then I considered that she might just be less dominant and was keeping her distance. They do this from time to time, though usually they won't be this far from the main herd. I watched as she continued to eat and occasionally look down at the rest of the herd more than a thousand feet away.

Oh well. They'll work it out. I took another bite of chocolate and reveled in the wonders of this marvelous magnesium delivery device. A sip of our cold ranch water was next, and talking always to Sam, who was now telling me he was hungry.

A few minutes later, Sam had eaten and I sat back down in my chair to look out the window again at the cow. I saw a dark lump of something beside her that seemed to collapse to the ground. My heart raced as I grabbed the binoculars. Focusing, I found her. The cow was casually looking at the herd and eating. But wait, she wasn't eating. She was nudging a small, dark calf to its feet.

The pit of my stomach dropped. Two days before, we had lost a cow. Though I have come to accept these occasional losses, I can't help but wonder if it's something we're doing or not doing. We know bison are rough on each other. They establish and re-establish the pecking order on a regular basis. Art, has always cautioned it's best to follow Nature's Law. Part of that law is that the strong survive and, for the strength and health of the herd, the weak do not. Intellectually, we accept this; emotionally, it may sometimes take days to process. Now we had a calf that couldn't stand. *God, please tell me this is not a sick calf!*

The cow nudged the calf to its feet again. The calf stood there weak and trembling. Then the cow turned sideways and against the sky, I saw her outline and afterbirth. Oh my gosh! It's a newborn calf! We have a late calf in August. The cow hadn't been grazing. She had her head down licking the calf dry. I just couldn't see the calf through the brush.

Relieved and suddenly not tired any more, I quickly wrote the time down on our wall calendar and went out to tell Ken. Kat had left for the day and he was in the cargo container by himself, head down, intent on fastening something to something.

I walked into the container and over to where he was, wondering how to tell him.

"Hi honey. You know how you've been telling people we have 120 animals?"

"Yes," he said without looking up.

"Well, we don't. We have 121."

"So, we don't have 120," he said, not wanting to lose his concentration. It wasn't the best opening line I could've picked. Counting new calves is almost always a comedic adventure. Because the bison move around so much, it can take several days or weeks every spring to get an accurate count. Invariably the mature animals step in front of the smaller ones and we either lose count, under count or over count. Even the most experienced producers may never know how many they have until the calves are older and allowed to wander a little further away from mom.

"We just had another calf," I said.

He stopped and looked up. "You're kidding," he said.

"Just now, about 20 minutes ago."

"Where?"

"There," I said pointing toward a crack in the cargo door.

Ken carefully peaked around the door of the cargo container. She was only about 200 feet away and we didn't want to intrude or alarm her.

"It's that cow," he said. "I saw her there earlier."

"The calf is still wet."

"Let's go take a look."

We walked quickly to the bunkhouse and Ken sat down with the binoculars, while I laid down on the bottom bunk.

"Let me know, I said. "I haven't seen the calf nurse yet. I'm happy to have you give me a report."

Ken knows I tend to over-worry about our bison. I know they're extremely hardy and resilient, but as we both do, I feel accountable and responsible for them, as well as for the overall health of the entire herd. As tired as I was, I just couldn't stand the suspense of watching this late calf find the colostrum in its mother's milk that would provide the antibodies it needed to survive. I was glad Ken was there watching the first few moments of its life unfold.

"It's nursing."

"Thank God," I said.

"Yup. It's doing fine."

Relieved, I looked over at him smiling as he continued to look through the binoculars.

"The cow is Margaret," he said.

"You're kidding!" I said sitting up.

"Nope. It's Margaret."

I had written "C&C" on the calendar—for crooked and curved

horn—since the cow had no ear tag. But from my vantage point, the horns looked shorter than Margaret's.

"Are you sure?" I asked.

"Yup, it's Margaret," he said again, smiling broader. He put the binoculars down and looked over at me.

For a minute we just looked at each other in stunned silence. Again we sensed that greater forces were at work on our ranch, intervening, helping us. The moment took on a surreal tone to it as I struggled to assimilate feelings of joy, humility, gratitude, wonder and astonishment. Mostly though, it was a depth of grace and gratitude I hadn't known before.

Ken took another look through the binoculars.

"The calf just jumped around," he reported still smiling.

"Already?"

"Already, look."

I joined Ken at the window and watched the calf jump around, trying his new legs out.

"Well, so it ain't over until the fat lady sings," I mused cheerily to Ken who was always referring to Margaret's weight. And as soon as I said it, I could hear Great-grandma Carlston's voice in my head taking issue with my familiar tone and use of the word "fat."

"It ain't over until *I* say it's over," came the correction. Either way, it worked for me. Margaret was fine. Her calf was fine. We were fine. The herd was fine. It was another reconnect, another gift.

That evening, we found ourselves looking out at the herd inspecting its newest member. While Margaret maneuvered to protect it, Ken and I reveled in the quiet.

"Maybe we could do what Art did with 'Ol Curly Horn," I said quietly. "Maybe we could just keep her."

"Maybe," he replied. That's bison speak for *Yes*.

3. November

Most ranchers have what's called an attrition rate. That is, unavoidable death losses of livestock through predators, injury or other causes. Lindner Bison is no exception and our annual attrition rate seems to hover in the two percent range. The last death loss we had was a mature cow. She had always been on the puny side and was less dominant. Helplessly we watched as she got weaker knowing that she wouldn't make it through another winter.

Over the summer, I especially watched her calf with interest. Also on the small side, but with strong herding instincts, the calf seemed puzzled why her mom wouldn't even try to keep up with the herd. Instead the cow would slowly rejoin them and stay on the periphery. After nursing, I'd watch the calf flick its tail and want to join the other calves running nearby. Dashing about 10 feet ahead, it would stop, look back and dutifully rejoin its mom.

As the calf grew a few months older, we began see it with some of the other calves while it's mom was laying down resting. When the other calves returned to their mothers' sides, the little heifer calf stood alone, not knowing quite what to do. Eventually it would rejoin its ailing mom. It was sad for all of us.

We talked with Kat. Now that the calf was close to being weaned and eating grass, we were trying to get on Dale's schedule to come out rather than prolong the inevitable. Finally, we got a call from Kat saying that the skinny cow had died during the night. Her voice broke over the phone. As Ken had predicted, the cow just wasn't strong enough to survive after the second cold front of the season had come in.

The calf was somewhere with the herd, so we knew if it could get food, it would be okay. But in a situation where the mom has been less dominant, it's not unusual for this social standing to transfer to the calf. It was likely to remain on the lowest rung in the pecking order without a mature animal to look out for her. The more dominant animals always get first pick of the hay we put out and don't allow less dominant animals to come in until they are finished eating. When they are done, they often migrate to another section of the pasture, so the calf, without getting its fill, may follow the herd and not get the food it needs.

"We'll just keep an eye on her," Ken told Kat over the phone. "Nothing we can do."

Kat was already keeping an eye on her, we knew. A week later, we had our answer.

"Hey, you'll never guess what," Kat said over the phone. "That Margaret has adopted that orphan calf."

"You're kidding," I said, concealing my doubt. Margaret already had her own bull calf, so it was more likely that Kat had coincidentally happened to see the orphan eating near Margaret one day.

"Nope, she really has been adopted. She stays near Margaret and her calf." Kat paused a minute. "Boy, that Margaret . . . ," she said, her voice trailing off.

"I know," I said, hoping she was right. "She is something. I can hardly wait to see next time we're up."

A week later, we were back at the ranch and sure enough, it was exactly as Kat had described. The tiny calf was staying close to Margaret and Margaret's bull calf. Though the orphan was older than Margaret's calf, she was smaller.

"If she's a runt like her mom, we want to take her off before she breeds," said Ken.

Kat understood and I agreed. We sure didn't want more of the same, but for now it was nice to see her being accepted by her adoptive family. The next day I watched as the herd came for water. We had been working nearby, and as they often do, they hesitate and hold their noses in the air to identify scents, wary that we are nearby. I saw the orphan calf come forward and stand near the stock tank, quickly moving aside for other larger calves and cows as they approached.

Darn. It seems she was alone after all.

As the family groups took turns drinking and moved back toward the pasture, I noticed Margaret and her bull calf begin to slowly approach the tank. The orphan stood watching the other calves and moms walk away, unaware that Margaret had walked up to the tank and was standing there. Then the little calf turned to see who was there. When she saw Margaret, I swear I saw joy sparks fly. The calf immediately flicked its tail and raised it's bottom up in the air, springing two steps over to Margaret, immediately nuzzling along her side. I think she may have tried nursing a now dry Margaret, as Margaret pushed her away with an irritated W. C. Fields' air of "Get away, kid, you bother me." While the heifer calf readily obliged, neither one of them moved and instead drank side by side out of the stock tank. The orphan had indeed found a safe haven with Margaret.

Spellbound, I watched as they left the water tank. Margaret was slowly walking along with her bull calf and the orphan calf was between them. All three were walking together, side by side toward the main herd. A month later, we almost didn't recognize the orphan. She had gained so much weight, she was nearly the same size as the bull calf. By the following summer, she'd held her weight gain and had become a healthy yearling heifer.

This experience reconfirmed for us the importance of keeping bison in family groups and allowing the natural pecking order to be created. This is what provides a prosperous environment for the health of the herd. It's also interesting to note that no bison producer we've talked to has seen a bison cow adopt a calf when they have a calf of their own. Then again, we've known for some time that Margaret is extraordinary.

CHAPTER 19

Storm Standers

———◆•———

1. Bison as Teachers

With a college student available to do Wednesday markets for the summer, I was able to accompany Ken up to the ranch after a two-month absence.

There's something healing about having your own place, your own piece of land. After five years of owning the ranch, I was still straining for my first glimpse of the herd at the end of the trip and fighting to keep the butterflies down. Miraculously they were still there. It wasn't my imagination. We own this land and these incredible animals. They have good body condition and, each year, an abundance of calves.

After three years of drought and the pump going out late last fall before we could finish haying, the pastures were tired and showed it. We spent unbudgeted money for hay to make up for the shortfall and were grateful for the meat sales that allowed us to buy seed to begin restoring the pastures.

This year, for the first time, we'd fence off a third of the middle pasture. Kat will keep it wet with the K-Lines and the animals won't have access to it until next year. Even then, we'd only be able to let them in for a day, maybe two, and then shoo them back out. Each year, as we can afford it, we'll do the same thing until the pastures are restored. In fact, they will be in better shape than ever before since we'll have a good mix of cool and warm season grasses, rather than one or two monocrops being grown for hay.

With the new pump installed this spring, there had been a nice improvement in water pressure. But before we had even packed the car for this trip, we got a call that one of the K-Line mainlines had burst and the entire system had to be shut down. A pool and sinkhole had formed in the middle pasture where the animals were. It was another unexpected repair. Equally pressing was getting the animals and calves safely into the south pasture before their curiosity could get them into trouble. Fortunately they were eager for the move which Kat accomplished easily by the end of the day.

By the time we arrived late Monday, much of the water where the leak was had dried up and the pump people agreed to be there early the next morning. Luckily it had been overcast since Sunday, so we counted our blessings. The hay pasture, which shares the same irrigation system as the K-Lines, had just started to grow. Denying it water until the pipe could be replaced could jeopardize the entire hay crop.

Inside the bunkhouse, we made plans for our two days with Kat. As always, they were ambitious. We needed to mow, spike, and seed the designated third of the pasture area. Then we needed to fence it off. We wouldn't have time after seeding to do the fencing, so that would have to be done the next trip.

"So what's the weather been like?" Ken asked Kat.

"Pretty much like this," she said. "Overcast. Supposed to be overcast all this week, so we can be glad for that," she continued, gesturing toward the area of the broken pipe.

We agreed. There had been so much drought the past several years, it seemed strange to find it cloudy in June instead of hot. After Kat left, we asked the clouds for a good soaking. Well, actually, I asked for a torrential downpour until Ken corrected me.

"We don't need a downpour, honey. Just a good soaking will do."

The next day was cool and overcast as predicted. We ventured out. First, Kat and I put out a half-load of hay in the south pasture. Then, while the two of them did the mowing and spiking, I stayed in the bunkhouse and worked on the laptop I had brought along for the first time. My energy was low.

"You can't do anything anyway," Ken encouraged. "We only have the two vehicles, so working on the book is a better use of your time."

Grateful, I obliged. He was right. Pushing myself when I was tired was not the answer if it could be avoided, and this time it could. Inside was quiet, cool and peaceful. I was glad to be able to work on the laptop and almost dozed off a few times.

Between the comings and goings of the pump people, and Ken and Kat's work, the first day flew by. Miraculously, it rained that afternoon and into the night. Thanks to this answer to our prayer, the pastures wouldn't suffer from lack of water. The replacement pipe would be picked up the next day and the irrigation system should be operational before we left.

On the second day, more storm clouds gathered and shortly after lunch it began to rain again. Quickly we put the equipment under cover and dashed into the bunkhouse, excited by the sudden weather change. Billowing clouds over the mountains and a wind shift at the ranch gave us additional hope that this new storm wouldn't skip us, the way they often did.

And we weren't disappointed! In fact, instead of skipping us, from inside we watched as the rain turned into hail that bounced off the windows and quickly turned the ground white. Meanwhile, a quarter mile from us in the south pasture, we noticed the herd running the opposite direction of the storm, toward the back.

"It must be the hail," said Ken.

We watched spellbound, as they briefly milled around in the fenced corner, then turned to face into the storm. This was a phenomenon a Canadian customer, Anea, had asked us about. Something that we hadn't even heard about before she asked, and one that we were now witnessing. The entire herd had gathered near one another, standing into the storm, protected from the pelting hail by the massive fur and hair on their head, chest and hump. When the storm lessened and visibility returned, we could see this year's calves, any where from 2 days to 30 days old, laying on the ground inside a circle the herd had formed. The entire herd had surrounded them, protecting them from the weather. In a time of uncertainty, their instinct is to stand firm together, protect and defend.

Once again, we were grateful to be their caretakers. As native-heritage animals predating our arrival, bison well represent much of what we as Americans hold dear. Standing united and strong against all manner of dangers, defending the defenseless, standing into each storm no matter how threatening.

Today I better understand that this is what Ken and I have done for the privilege of starting a new life for which we were unschooled and untrained. Staying faithful to our course, we faced each obstacle we encountered, we didn't turn away and we didn't quit. We continued, not knowing when or even if we could succeed. Stubbornly, and sometimes in spite of evidence to the contrary, we clung to the notion that somehow we would prevail. If only because the path is a good path, filled with purpose and grace. At each fork in the road, we made choices. Months and years later, we see the bison were ever there, lighting the way and guiding us home. They remain our teachers.

2. Ken and Me

A woman recently asked, "Do you guys ever fight?"

Though united in love, shared values and purpose, as business co-partners, it's safe to say we're not always united in effort or approach. We refer to these moments as "getting out of sync." Also, we've learned that our differences are as much about our strengths as they are about our weaknesses. So there are storms and then there are storms. Many storms precede growth and this is what we found too.

As husband and wife, as well as business partners, our relationship may best be described this way: We absolutely married our best friend. The only way this has changed from the day we found each other is to expand and deepen in certainty. And you can bet we have each worked hard over the years for the privilege of being able to say that.

By the time we met, we had both experienced trust issues and reconciled most of them. But we were not immune to new or residual fears, which, we have learned, usually masquerade as avoidance or control and often start out as non-verbal. Overcoming these fears requires an effort by both of us to slow down, understand and communicate. And we do not allow trust-eroders such as deceit, lying or willed ignorance to take up permanent residence; each has the potential to become a game changer with serious repercussions and lasting negative effects. So we work hard to stay current on issues, especially during times of stress, uncertainty and doubt—and, like others, we have our fair share of them. As the saying goes, 'We're all basically a little dysfunctional, it's just a matter of degrees – some of us are more dysfunctional than others.'

Before we met, I had learned the principle of loving others with open arms. It is a way of loving that asks me to let go, step out on faith and be guided by a power greater than myself. If I unconditionally love someone, I must be willing to let them go. If they belong to me, if we're meant to be together, they will return. Together or not, the idea is that it works to the greatest good for everyone. At times, I haven't always agreed, but I've found that my acceptance often precedes the arrival of more wondrous gifts, such as Ken.

In our personal and business dealings with others, it's become a tossup as to who's more trusting and who's more skeptical, more guarded. We regularly seem to take turns, but Ken knows I have his back and he always has mine. As village elders, we believe we are better served by remaining reasonably and wisely skeptical rather than trusting. Our thought processes aren't as fast now, so this means slowing down and being patient as we work through and verbalize issues, questions and concerns. We are better at telling others that *we'll think about it and get back to them*. This has the added benefit of putting our relationship, our animals, ranch and our business first rather than at the mercy of someone else's emergencies or deadlines. Those who know us, respect and trust us as honorable people going about the business of humane bison meat production.

In our dealings with each other, we acknowledge and show respect for historic battleground areas. The first has to do with things thrown away –he's a tosser and I'm a saver. He tries to honor my not wanting to waste (time, money, compost gifts) and I try to honor his need for order (perhaps remnants of a military environment.) Our small kitchen can sometimes be an area of contention as we both rearrange things; he's tall and I'm shorter, so these arrangements don't always reflect a shared level of awareness or compromise. I'm less interested in food than he is, so we tend to eat better because of his willingness and ability to cook, though there would be fewer green nutrients without my insisting on and providing them. Like most people, we've had our share of extended family issues too. Most we've healed and the few that remain, we love with open arms.

Our roles are mostly interchangeable, but we each retain areas where we require reasonable dominion. For me, it's my computer and for him, his tools and of course, his music. There continue to be shared and emerging new areas of interest at the ranch. Here we discover and learn from the bison, the earth and other forms of life there, all providing us both with endless opportunities to expand and grow.

The sexism thing occasionally rears its head to see if I notice. I do of course, but the priorities and focus of my energy have expanded beyond self now to the achievement of shared goals with my best friend.

Emotionally, there are times when I feel minimized or that he hasn't heard me, and there are times when he feels minimized too. Being each other's best friend, we do what best friends do. We continue to talk and love each other. We admit fault, we forgive and we try again. Through our troubles and conflicts, we've established a deep trust in each other and the knowledge that neither of us will ever quit trying. Trust is the constant, the glue that holds everything together. It's this trust that propels us forward again.

Now in our early sixties, it's reassuring to discover what we have long suspected—that we're never really completely done learning. Because of our determination to break free and create a new life for ourselves, we have asked more of ourselves and each other than we could have ever imagined. And by listening to the whispers of our innermost hearts, we have surpassed even our own expectations. Acknowledging weaknesses and strengths, ignorance and wisdom, keeps us teachable.

Ken remarked once that when the whole is greater than the sum of its parts, then you know you've really got something. That's our love.

IV

WE'RE THE ONES WE'VE BEEN WAITING FOR

From this day forward, everything is changed.

—Joseph Haydn—

The first three parts of this book have been essentially a chronological memoir, describing events that guided us into grassfed bison ranching. It includes lessons learned that shaped our personal and business philosophies.

Part IV now shifts gears and focus to the eight years we spent selling in farmers' markets and building our ranch. We continued to learn from our customers, from other bison producers, various food organizations and food-wise media. This learning joined uniquely with our previous experiences. It raised our level of awareness to new heights and worked to synthesize many seemingly unrelated events into recognizable patterns and trends. We especially became aware of multiple disconnections between us, as consumers of food, and nearly all aspects of how that food was produced.

Here we share what we learned about these disconnects – for us, the animals and the earth – and what we did differently to begin crafting sustainable reconnects.

Finally, our Call to Action suggests how we each can encourage, nurture and protect new reconnects. We realize that not everyone can accomplish the actions recommended, so these are divided into sections for individual food customers, people who work in foodservice and bison producers. These suggestions are based on personal experience, research and what others have taught us. With limited time, funds and help, to date we've been unable to accomplish all of these ourselves, but our plans certainly include those that apply to our type of operation.

A Societal Call to Action addresses events and activity that may have the potential to negatively affect bison as a species.

No matter who we are or where we live, we know now that we either move forward or we stay the same. Positive action taken, no matter how small, may be significant. We encourage you to consider what you can reasonably do to help.

Even doing nothing is a choice. Silence gives permission.

Disconnect/Reconnect
—INTRODUCTION—

Ken and I had overcome incredible obstacles and now we were being asked to overcome yet another one: the recession. It was beyond our control. There was no way to know how it would affect our customers and our business. Resigned to staying put, we decided to bloom where we were planted.

---

disconnect *(verb)*
to dissolve the union or connection of; to disunite;
to separate; to sever

reconnect *(verb)*
to reunite, to link or be linked together again

As customers continued to express gratitude for what we were doing, the emotional impact of their words began to have a cumulative effect on us. Increasingly we found ourselves somewhat overwhelmed by the new customer connections and the many who thanked us for being there. We began to look more closely at why this was.

What we discovered is that we had been sharing a growing awareness of how deeply most of us had become disconnected from our food. Perhaps because we sold meat from our humanely raised animals, it resonated more deeply. It would be years later before we finally began to see that our physical presence at the farmers' markets meant more than weekly conversations and an exchange of money, meat and recipes. It meant an opportunity for us and our customers both to reconnect with the cycle of life.

Looking closer, I could see that I had somehow developed a kind of entitlement to good tasting, clean, safe food. As a child, I'd been taught that we lived in the best, the most powerful nation on earth. Other people were poor, indeed some were starving, but our family and friends were not and we should be grateful. We were. Good tasting, clean, safe food was one of the basic tenets of that reality.

That was then.

Now there were reports of meat and other food product recalls, some massive, numbering into the billions of units, whether tons, pounds, cartons or cases. There had been so many over the years that I had become desensitized to them. Busy surviving, over-saturated with 24-hour news, I shrouded myself in willed ignorance based on a belief that food recalls were inevitable. Because I believed I had no alternatives, I was better off not knowing or caring about them.

But as producers of grassfed bison, we ourselves now were accountable for food production. Motivated not to make the same mistakes as other food producers, we delved deeper into the issues surrounding the recalls. As we learned and better understood them, my willed ignorance and apathy gave way to awareness and later, annoyance. Through Ken's experience in the quality assurance, I had learned that most quality problems are not rocket science. They are indeed fixable at the source. The problem with the food recalls was that it seemed no one was going to the source to fix them. Instead, band-aids were being applied and symptoms treated while the root causes of the problems were being ignored. This represented just one disconnect element in how food was being produced.

It wasn't until we were face to face with customers that we became aware of a cultural shift. Many were moving away from commercially grown and prepared foods. I can't be sure either of us—the producers or the customers—realized the depth of that shift, until we met at farmers' markets.

Here, on a regular basis, Ken and I met and talked with strangers. After they tried our meat, they came back. The strangers became friends. Again, they bought our grassfed bison meat. Again, we received thanks and support for our efforts.

We were happy and encouraged. But something else was happening. Often I found myself puzzled, trying to understand why the whole experience was sometimes so touching as well as emotionally jarring. Before there could be this kind of impact, somewhere there had to have been a void, a disconnect. Now I was a producer of food. A reconnect was occurring and at times the gratitude and sense of welcome was palpable.

Once we embarked on our food reconnect path, we soon found ourselves at a sustainability fork in the road. But how would we choose?

Various stakeholders seemed to define the word differently and everyone claimed their version was correct. Confused, we tossed them all out and decided to create our own simple definition. Based on our experience, we've come to believe that sustainability is basically a three-legged stool. It includes all participants of our shared ecosystem - Us, the Animals and the Earth. If any of the three legs are compromised, missing, hijacked, anonymously cloned or genetically modified, a disconnect exists. A disconnect means that somewhere in the production of industrial food, it has become unsustainable. Put another way, when the life cycle is healthy, whole and complete, all three elements are living, inter-dependent and synergistically thriving. It is only then that true sustainability is realized.

The time has come and the smallest of beginnings is all that's needed. Awareness is the first step, so roll up your sleeves and join us on a wonderous path of reconnect and discovery. Of the countless gifts waiting, perhaps the one of the greatest is finding that we are – each and every one of us - worth the effort. So are the animals and the earth.

CHAPTER 20

Disconnect/Reconnect
—FOR US—

Over the last century, Americans have become increasingly disconnected from the people who produce the food they eat. But it didn't stop there. People have become disconnected not only from the people who produce their food, but from the animals that provided it, and the land that sustained them.

The more our awareness grew, the more we realized how deeply these disconnects ran throughout our lives. Indeed, our overwhelming desire to break free from our jobs in corporate America shared some of the same roots. We began to see repeating patterns as 'disconnects' from essential elements of our humanness. It was only when we began to identify and activate appropriate reconnects that things got better.

"For Us" is the first leg of our three-legged sustainability stool.

Disconnect #1: Profit margins override core values

Many decisions about which foods are available for people to eat are made on the basis of profit margins. Perhaps our most startling disconnect experience, which brought home to us the issue of profit margins, was the result of an incident that involved us as meat producers and the employees of a catering company and their customers.

At one of the farmers' markets where we sell, I met a chef. A bison meat enthusiast, he was thrilled to find us and soon began ordering burger for his catering jobs for film crews on location. Over several months, he regularly ordered boxes of our 100 percent grassfed bison. At his request, we provided fliers with nutritional information which he put out for his customers to read. After each event he would tell us how much people loved the bison and that we'd be hearing from him again.

A month later, he placed another order and we delivered it to the catering company. Weeks went by without seeing him at the market. Since he attended often and always seemed to enjoy reporting back about his events, not seeing or hearing from him was out of character. And we hadn't received another order either.

Finally one day he reappeared at the market. When I asked him how his last event went and how people liked the meat, he hesitated a moment. Then he replied. He said when he arrived on the set, he couldn't find the case of meat and asked people where it was. He was told it had been thrown out.

"What? They threw it out?" I exclaimed. "Why would they do that?"

"I know, " he said. "That's what I said."

I asked again, "But why would they throw it away?"

He half-heartedly laughed, as he reached for a plastic bag and opened it. "I don't know," he said shaking his head. Averting my gaze, he began selecting vegetables from the table next to our booth.

"Maybe they didn't know what it was," I offered, then I corrected myself. "But it had a label on the box."

"Oh they knew what it was, alright," he said. He smiled knowingly and nodded. "And I was plenty mad about it too."

"But why? Did you ask anyone?" I said.

"Yeah, I asked. No one knew anything," he said. He stopped and finally looked at me.

"I know," he said, acknowledging the look on my face. "It doesn't make any sense."

Suddenly sick to my stomach, my mind raced.

How could it have been an accident? How could anyone accidentally throw away 50 pounds of good meat? Someone who didn't know English? No, anyone could see that it was frozen meat. It couldn't be because their customers didn't like the meat. The chef repeatedly said everyone loved it and they had reordered several times. It felt similar to what happened at the Pennsylvania restaurant. But how and why would anyone throw away good meat? An animal had given its life for that meat! How could someone just throw it away?

I was grateful when the press of customers diverted me from this endless mental loop. For the rest of the morning I stood and talked with customers, answered questions, shared cooking tips, recipes, fliers. I became aware that I had begun seeking reassurance from them. I needed to know that our meat had value, that our efforts had value. I needed to know that they cared. That I hadn't imagined it.

The reassurance came. For six hours, customer after customer said how much they loved the meat, how glad they were that we were there, asking about the ranch, wanting to know about the animals, asking for their own reassurance that we wouldn't go anywhere, that we'd be back next week.

Were they just being polite, telling me what they thought I wanted to hear? No. This was real. Their gratitude was authentic. I hadn't imagined it. These people were telling me the truth.

Finally, the market was over. As I finished the paperwork, repacked the car and began the drive back, my mind involuntarily resumed its search of the unanswered question of *Why?*

A few hours later, I was especially glad when Ken rejoined me at condo. On the practical side, we were happy to know that we could pay our bills for another week. On the emotional side, we shared, as always, the high points of our markets and the customer feedback we'd received. He'd been asking for some time if I had ever heard back from the chef. When I told him what the chef had said, his reaction was identical to mine.

"What?" he exclaimed incredulously. "Why would anyone do that?"

With no answer forthcoming and exhausted from the weekend, we grew quiet. I had no answer. I could see that he, too, was struggling to make sense of it. We couldn't. We knew it couldn't be an accident. But *why?*

After talking about it at length and with no explanation offered, we surmised that, once again, the profit margin dictated. It may have been cheaper to throw away 50 pounds of precious 100 percent grassfed bison meat in the short term, than to miss an open-ended opportunity to capture a higher profit margin by selling inexpensive, commercially produced meat. If customers didn't have the opportunity to try grassfed bison, they couldn't ask for it. The commercial product would prevail and no one would be the wiser.

The next morning I found myself again revisiting the whole scenario of the thrown-away meat. By mid-afternoon, emotional aftershocks began to unexpectedly arrive and with them, a sense of sadness and defeat. It caught me quite by surprise. Despite the conclusion Ken and I had reached, there was still no sense of closure. Two unanswered questions remained. An animal had given its life for this meat—how could this not have value to someone? And if it had happened to us, how often was it happening elsewhere?

It was two days before I fully realized the implication and significance of the entire incident. It had exposed a wanton and flagrant disregard for life in pursuit of profit. Finally I had my answer. Now what?

Ken offered an explanation.

"Some people do not make the connection that meat actually comes from an animal, a living thing," he said. "There are those for whom meat is just a commodity, a non-entity."

The truth of these words later hit home with even more impact. To our disbelief and horror, we later learned about companies that ground up live baby chicks in machines as a cost-control measure.

We would learn, too, that in the world of high-volume commercial meat production, the terms meat cutting or meat processing weren't used any more. Cutting steaks, roasts and other items from a carcass was now referred to as *fabricating*. Just like widgets in a factory. For industry, commercial meat cutting is not about the skilled art of butchery, it's about efficiency, volume and profit. That's it.

I knew Ken was right. As all the pieces fell in place, I reached a new level of awareness and acceptance, then anger and outrage. The anger and outrage remain appropriate.

Reconnect #1: Core values first

The throw-away incident fueled the single, most important turning point for Lindner Bison. It further defined us and steeled our resolve: It would never happen again. Not to us. Not to our animals. After talking about it, Ken and I decided we would no longer pursue any kind of high volume, commercial account. We wanted no part of it. (Note: It would be several years before we learned that when the catering company owner heard why we were no longer taking orders from them, he said, "So, what's the problem? They were paid, weren't they?")

Reaching this decision, another door suddenly opened. It was now completely clear why we had not succeeded before with Bisurkey. It was so simple: Our core values didn't match with those in the world we had tried to enter! We would have forever been at odds on one level or another with that entire system. The solution was to sell our meat only to those who understood its value beyond the point of sale, beyond just having an incredible meal.

From the beginning, we had been educating by phone, emails and at farmers' markets. We had to do more, try harder. We now realized we had to teach about more than just flavor, nutritional information and cooking tips.

First and foremost, the heart of our educating would teach that *The meat from our bison is not a commodity. It is a gift.*

Second, there are ways to honor, respect and show gratitude for gifts and we would provide examples.

And third, we would give preference to those who could demonstrate an active understanding and appreciation for these core values.

We now realized that we had been pursuing and dealing with people who were completely disconnected from the fact that the source of meat was a living animal. To them, our humanely raised, 100 percent grassfed bison meat was just another product like hair gel or a toaster. It was a non-entity, an unimportant thing. It didn't matter. As a commodity, our meat had no value beyond a profit margin.

That day, Ken and I resolved we would work harder to create and strengthen a reconnect with customers, ourselves and our animals. If we ever did business with a chef or restaurant again, we would first need to be convinced that they understood the gift being offered to them, as well as be able to demonstrate a reasonable commitment to sustainability beyond recycling menus and cooking oils. Our bison and the meat they provide deserved to be respected as part of a sustainable and ethical life cycle. They deserved this respect and so did we. Anything less was unacceptable.

Realigned with our core values, we found ourselves on a reconnect path that complimented those values. One by one we discovered mis-alignments first in us and then in some of our customers. We weren't commodity meat producers. We no longer wanted to empire build or compete with those who fell into either category. Our new goals included educating ourselves, and encouraging and empowering individuals by sharing what we learned.

Disconnect #2: Commodity meat production

Most people buy their meat from supermarkets. When these stores receive meat, rather than dealing with hanging halves or whole carcasses, the meat arrives already cut into sections that no longer resemble an animal. Instead of a knowledgeable butcher behind the meat counter, there is a portion cutter and/or packager. This is far more cost effective for the store and saves them money by not having an actual butcher at each store.

To many people, "carcass yield," or the percentage of meat cuts available from a single meat animal, is an entirely new concept. As a result of the high- volume, high- speed, commodity feedlot model of meat production in place today, many of us are conditioned to having any quantity of prime cuts—usually steaks—that we want, pretty much whenever we want it. Rarely, if ever, do we have to deal with the fact that a single animal has only so many steaks or roasts to give. For most of us, the parts of an animal available in stores are preselected for us, based on corporate profits and overall. Within this model, few of us are given the opportunity to consider the less commonly known cuts or learn how much of any particular cut comes from a single carcass. For most of us, the parts of an animal available in stores are pre-selected for us, based on corporate profits and overall efficiency. Store customers are able only to buy from what is pre-selected for the prescribed cuts.

Reconnect #2: Small farmer meat production

Following our epiphany about the importance of realigning our activities with our core values, we sprang into action and created informational materials about who Lindner Bison was and what our values were. Soon our story, *Sustainable Appetite, Sustainable Passion,* was posted on our website. We created a separate handout called *What's in a Word?* that offered definitions of terms such as "grassfed," "free-range," and "pastured," as well as a broader definition of the word "sustainable." Both of these writings encouraged customers to adopt a sustainable appetite beyond just steaks in their home menu planning.

A year later, we created *The 15 percent Steak Rule,: Sustainable Menu Planning for Carnivores with a Conscience.* Listed here were the different cuts of meat that can be obtained from a carcass, along with typical yield percentages for each cut. For example, as the title implies, steaks are usually only 15 percent of the yield from an entire carcass. One customer at a time, we began educating people about carcass yield and the less common cuts such as tongue, tail, and all the choices in between, or "nose-to-tail." In this way, we began to further distinguish our meat from the standard supermarket or buying club commodity meats.

"When all parts of the animal are used, fewer harvests are necessary," wrote Ken. "We strive to waste nothing."

At the markets and on the phone, we taught on a new level. First, there is not an infinite amount of what ever cut people want, whenever they want it. Second, we have selections rarely offered in commercial stores. Some customers didn't know what to do with some of the less familiar cuts, so we created and handed out recipes. We encouraged and we taught. Response was gratifying as customers began to understand. Most regarded the nose-to-tail menu shift as a new adventure. They saw it as a missing link and a more sustainable connection with their meat producer. They were happy and willing to try new things.

A smaller percentage of customers remained inflexible in their choices and requests. Some even became angry. They weren't used to hearing about an allocation of cuts such as tenderloin, New York and ribeye steaks according to yield. Others became annoyed hearing we were out of single carcass items, such as tongue, heart or tail.

In explaining our allocation system, we asked our customers to sustainably and equitably share low-yield items with others, pointing out that when they do, they are honoring all the gifts of the animal. On first hearing of our steak allocation limit of two steaks from the same cut, one customer who wanted twelve ribeye steaks pulled out a thick wad of bills from his pocket and jokingly asked, "So even if I have all this money, it won't make any difference?"

Our short answer remains *Yes.*

But for these individuals, a new seed had to be planted. Respectfully, we offer this for consideration: For those who have an infinite amount of money and can afford what ever they want, perhaps just knowing that they can afford anything should be enough. Money thoughtfully spent, based on what's good for people, humane for the animals, friendly to the earth and sustainable for all three may be a better long-term investment. Try something different. The change may actually be enjoyable!

For the few who persist, we can and do respectfully reframe their request: "We won't kill an animal so someone can buy a particular cut, such as ribeye steaks. What you want is feedlot meat. There are many bison producers with far higher volume than we have. It may be feedlot commodity meat, but they will usually always be able to offer steaks because of their high volume feedlot model. Why don't you go to them?"

These comments are usually met with stunned silence. Some customers, struggling with the concept, quickly respond that they don't want commodity grainfed bison meat; they've tried it and prefer ours. Gratifying as it is to hear, we let our point sink in by saying nothing more. Only time will tell whether they are willing to connect the dots and look deeper into the issues of commodity versus gift, and sustainability versus instant gratification.

When Ken and I do our job well, carnivores with a conscience feel good about buying from us. They know and they care that not only do they benefit, but the animals and the earth benefit too.

Disconnect #3: Industrial meat processing methods

When we read about the 2010 recall of 66,000 lbs. of grainfed bison meat in Colorado, we couldn't help but be angry and saddened. Not only was this recall completely avoidable, but many bison had given their lives for meat that was ultimately declared unfit for human consumption. By applying commercial grainfed practices and processing methods to non-domestic bison, bison meat was now sharing the recall headlines usually reserved for other species.

Reconnect #3: Small meat processors and artisan butchers

The bison meat recall, coupled with the 2008 recall from Hallmark/Westland Meat Packing in Los Angeles—the largest meat recall in U.S. history—reinforced for us the wisdom of what we're doing and how we're doing it. It made us especially grateful for the small meat processors we use.

What we want for ourselves, we want for our small meat processors. We want them to stay in business and make a reasonable profit. We pray they never grow to the point where good quality standards are compromised. And that they don't allow themselves to be seduced by the promise of high volume and quick profit, causing them to regard the carcasses they cut as a "commodity" to "fabricate."

Small meat processors and artisan butchers are dear in our country. As reported by the New York Times and other newspapers, there's a nationwide shortage of small meat processors, creating a bottleneck for new small meat producers trying to get their meat to market. As the demand increases for humanely raised meat from small farms and ranches, we desperately need more small processors. Often they are able to provide three essential elements which the large commercial meat processors may be unwilling or unable to provide: (1) respectful and humane field harvest of animals, (2) the nearly lost art of skillful meat cutting, and (3) a reconnect with customers buying the meat.

The extent to which we all value, support and encourage these artisan men and women, reflects our own role in the authentic establishment of sustainable meat production and humane harvesting of meat animals.

Disconnect #4: Feedlots and the commodity market

Commodity trading date back to the 1500s, though they have recently changed. In 1971, the industry introduced futures trading which for the first time included financial products. And then in 1982, the first futures contract was launched which enabled stock index traders to protect their investments without having to actually buy or sell stocks. In 1991,

Goldman Sachs devised a Commodity Index, a mathematical formula for investing in 24 commodities, including cattle and hogs. According to Frederick Kaufman's brilliant and insightful April, 2011 article "How Goldman Sachs Created the Food Crisis," with the deregulation of futures markets in 1999, Kaufman writes "All of a sudden, bankers could take as large a position in grains as they liked, an opportunity that had, since the Great Depression, only been available to those who actually had something to do with the production of our food." Kaufman's article connects dots, reporting the 50-fold increase in commodities since the tech bubble burst in 2000. The 2008 global financial crisis resulted in a massive speculative bubble reflected by the commodities market going from $55 billion to $318 billion. "Food inflation has remained steady since," writes Kaufman.

With grain and corn as main ingredients of feedlots, and without having to understand the complex world of commodity derivatives and futures, our take-away is this: it is clear that investment bankers and their thinking may represent a significant disconnect element in how food may be sustainably grown and humanely produced.

Reconnect #4: Bison as a non-commodity.

In 2004, we received the news that bison had been newly listed as a commodity. Since the industry's collapse earlier, it seemed unlikely that volume warranted the new listing. We made note of it and continued with our grassfed bison operation. Today, it seems clear that much of that which many are moving away from includes feedlots and the meats produced there.

If listing bison as a commodity insures their destination into a feedlot and treatment as a thing receiving an unnatural diet that makes them sick, then our collective reconnect goal should be to delist them and remove them from any commodity index nationally and globally. They deserve better from us as a nation and as a global society.

Disconnect #5: Elitism and the small farmer

When I remarked to Ken about an uncharacteristically disrespectful attitude displayed by a brand new crop of customers at the farmers' market one day, he was puzzled by my surprise.

"I can completely understand it," he said. "Remember when we lived in Santa Barbara and went to the farmers' market? Don't you remember what we thought of the farmers there?"

It came back with a jolt.

"Not much," I remembered. "Oh, my gosh, we really didn't."

"Yes," he replied. "We felt sorry for them. Such poor schmucks, working so hard. They probably can't make it in the real world."

"Dry hands, red eyes, lined faces," I continued. "We thought the farmers' markets were quaint. Yet the food was all *so* amazing."

Ken was nodding.

"And we were the hotshots, making money working for corporations and living in Santa Barbara," I said. I was ashamed. Though I hadn't admitted it even to myself, my attitude had been one of superiority.

"Wow," I added quietly. "I had completely forgotten."

"I didn't," he said. "It turns out that we were the ones who were the poor schmucks."

"We were just ignorant," I protested. "We didn't know."

"A lot of people still don't know," he said.

"But even now, with the food movement, Jo Robinson, Joel Salatin, Michael Pollan and *Food, Inc.?*" I stopped. I wanted to say that things should be different by now, but he was shaking his head.

"We were wrapped up in our own lives. They are just trying to survive," he said. "They may have access to more information now than we did. That's about it."

"Santa Barbara was our first and last farmers' market until we moved back to California," I reminisced. I was trying to reconcile my disregard for the farmers who produced our food, citing how little experience we had actually had with farmers' markets.

"That had to be 14 years ago. Look at all that's happened in that time."

"We sure know differently now, don't we?" he asked with a knowing smile.

We did. We had been no different from those who were now finding the farmers' markets for the first time. Some may think we're quaint and hard working. We are hard working, for sure. Maybe even quaint.

What they may not yet know, which is something we hadn't initially understood either, is that food shopping at farmers' markets has become more than a nice morning out to visit quaint local farmers. It's an important vote with our food dollars to encourage and support the availability of sustainably and humanely raised food from small farms. It's a unique opportunity to reconnect. And it matters.

Reconnect #5: Know your food producer

Just as we take our production practices very seriously, most farmers' market customers take their food and meat buying seriously. Each week hundreds of thoughtful, new customers arrive seeking alternatives to commercially produced commodity meat offered in traditional supermarkets and chain stores. They want to get to know us, their producer, so we continue to educate and to answer questions about why our meat is different.

Before discovering farmers' markets, I had increasingly found that most meat, vegetables, fruit and produce that I ate didn't have much flavor. For me, if I have to add spices, sauces and toppings to make my food appealing or edible, something is wrong. I hadn't grown up with all the spices, flavorings and sauces that the food industry often labels as *gourmet*. They didn't make the food taste better to me, they just seemed to confuse my taste buds. Taste buds which were telling me there was little native flavor in the main ingredient, whether it was beef, poultry, pork, fish, or fruit, vegetables and other produce.

One of my first clues about flavorless meat had arrived decades earlier. I was in a supermarket shopping for a convenient can of precooked beef stew. When I read the ingredients listed on the label, I stopped when I saw sugar listed as an ingredient. I tried to picture myself sprinkling white table sugar on a bowl of stew the way I used to sprinkle it on breakfast cereal. Would I do that to meat? Um, no, I wouldn't even think of doing it. So why would I want to spend money to have someone do it for me? I trusted my instincts and returned the can to the shelf.

Today Ken and I make the time to get to know the producers that we buy from at the farmers' markets. We ask lots of questions, including ones about humane husbandry methods, the presence of antibiotics or drugs, and whether or not chemicals are used on fruit, produce and vegetables. Based on their answers, we buy or we don't buy. The point is, we know more, so we care more. We express that caring by taking the time to ask questions, knowing that the answers may mean inconvenience, menu adjustments, growing our own, or going without.

Disconnect #6: It's too hard!

Living in a town or city and working in an office often insulates people from manual labor. In fact, this was the whole appeal of the industrial age. People were more than willing to hand off the manual labor of farm life to the machine. City living was touted as more convenient and certainly less labor-intensive than farm living.

Today, other than carrying out the garbage, hauling in the groceries, or working in the yard, unless we pay for a fitness club or gym, most of us don't get much weight bearing or stamina building exercise. When we do, it's more about self rather than sustainable partnerships, humane animal husbandry and thoughtful agronomy.

Also, many must fit their fitness program in and around workdays and work hours. We benefit of course, but so does our employer. Most farmers on the other hand, stay in shape by performing routine physical tasks that vary with the season and the weather. When there is no option to tap into help from another department or hire extra help on the spot, the words "It's too hard," have no meaning.

Reconnect #6: Passion empowers

"We'd better put out some bales this afternoon," I said.

"OK," Kat said as she joined Ken in staking down the wheel lines for the winter.

It was late August. The last hay cutting would be baled the next week and in another month, the grasses would be dormant. I always look forward to feeding our bison and seem to find the energy to be up on that hay wagon tossing out our hay to them. This is when I talk to them, look them over good, check the herd dynamics and the size of the calves.

Kat and I found we made a good team, falling into a rhythm of loading the bales, pulling them into place, and offloading in a certain pattern. She had continued to grow into various aspects of her chores, seeing and understanding the reasons for why we fed a certain way. By the end of the previous feeding season, we had congratulated ourselves for making a round trip in about 20 minutes. It took 10 minutes for us to load a ton of hay, about another 10 minutes to feed and be back at the stack lined up for another load.

As we got ready to start, we agreed that our jobs were better than going to a gym. At a gym you have to pay to work out and the equipment is indoors. With us, we were outdoors, getting a great workout, and we're getting paid instead of paying someone else for our efforts.

We met at the haystack and assumed our familiar places. Starting at the top of the 12-foot-high block of hay, we were now using hay hooks. We hooked these into the bale, making it much easier to pull and direct it to where we wanted it to go. With gusto, we tackled the first four bales.

"Boy," said Kat, sitting down suddenly on the closest bale. "I'm more out of shape than I thought."

I looked over at her. Her cheeks were bright red and she was huffing and puffing, barely able to breath, much less talk. It was unusual to see her quiet. The first bales had been a strain for me, too, but I was too proud to admit it. Fifteen years her senior, Kat's spunk usually encouraged me. She was shorter than I was, but I had always been wiry and athletic. More than once I found myself thinking, "If she can do it, I can do it." It wouldn't surprise me if she was thinking the same thing about me. Either way, it worked and together we got things done.

Today, though, Kat looked concerned. Normally working at a faster pace, she seemed truly stunned at how much strength she had lost over the summer. I felt the same way. The bales seemed to weigh a ton. Just last winter we had been almost flipping them onto the hay wagon. After a five-minute break, we resumed. Thirty minutes later the wagon was loaded and we both had broken a good sweat.

Kat did a quick count of the bales so we could measure the bison's actual intake against our supply.

"Wait a minute," she said. "That's only 16 bales. Doesn't this hold 18?"

"Sure," I said and started counting. She was right. We had loaded only16 bales. The hay wagon was maxed out. While I was trying to wrap my brain around how the count could be so off, I heard Kat start laughing.

"They're bigger!" she exclaimed suddenly. "The bales are bigger!"

"How can that be?" I said.

"I don't know, but look, they're bigger! They must have used a larger bale setting!"

"I didn't know you could do that!" I said.

"I didn't either, but that's what they did!" she said. She fell back onto a haystack and we both collapsed into an uncontrollable fit of giggles.

"Thank God!" Kat laughed.

"Here we thought we had turned into girly-girl 90 lb. weaklings over the course of the summer," I said as she hurried to finish my sentence.

"In fact, we're probably lifting 125 lb. bales rather than the 100 lb. bales we're used to!" she exclaimed. Again we dissolved into laughter.

Now in some circles, this may seem hardly worth mentioning. But for two women aged 45 and 60, with no agricultural background, who feed bison and take pride in work often done by men, it struck us as positively hysterical.

As I proudly settled into the gentle bouncing of the hay bales, Kat slowly drove the full load out to our waiting bison. With reclaimed self-respect, the hay was unloaded and we completed two more round trips before calling it a day.

This is one of my all time favorite stories. I can never tell it without visualizing Kat sitting there on a hay bale, red faced, huffing and puffing with a stunned look of disbelief. I will forever treasure the shared moment of camaraderie and joy for our new life, made richer by the sound of laughter.

Disconnect #7: Corporate value system: the invisible customer

When working in the corporate world, we received a paycheck, vacation days, and benefits. We were taught to expect little else. At work we exhibited appropriate emotions and behaved a certain way in order to earn good performance reviews and a sense of job security. The customers who use the company's products, in most cases, we will never meet. They will never know what our individual efforts were on their behalf. We were encouraged to distance ourselves from customers and leave interactions to public relations or customer service departments. Our real job was to build value for owners and investors.

Reconnect #7: Community value system: customer and farmer meet

In small farming and ranching and especially for those of us who sell what we produce directly to customers, it's different. One market day, Ken became aware of a customer quietly and patiently standing off to the side of the booth while he waited on customers standing in line. Almost ten minutes later, the line was finally gone and the man stepped forward. He was in his late fifties, probably a retired professional.

Looking Ken straight in the eye, he held out his hand. As Ken held out his, he gave him a firm handshake.

"I just want to shake your hand," he said. "That was absolutely the best prime rib I have ever had in my entire life. I had a friend over and he said the same thing. Thank you. Thank you for what you're doing."

"That means a lot to us," Ken said to the man. "We appreciate your support and we're glad you're enjoying the meat."

Our customers may be surprised to learn that their comments can mean so much. They have no way of knowing the efforts made and challenges met in bringing this meat to them. To receive expressions of heartfelt gratitude means too that a significant reconnect has happened. On the surface, it means we care about our positive impact on each other. Beyond that, whether they know it or not, we have both entered into a humane, sustainable and synergistic partnership with the animals and the land. This in itself is huge.

We couldn't help but compare this to our previous experience in corporate America where we'd occasionally hear "Good job." Rarely did anyone at work earnestly shake your hand, look you in the eye, and in a warm, heartfelt manner tell you how much they appreciated what you're doing. Envision your boss coming up to you when you complete a task or meet an important deadline. Imagine him or her telling you that your efforts have added to the quality of his life, his family's lives and his friends' lives.

Right.

In a profit driven, corporate industrial model, employees are encouraged to value profit, volume and efficiency over emotions. Keep your private life private and stay focused on the bottom line.

And while we receive expressions of appreciation on a regular basis, we are amazed to find that eight years later, it's still like hearing it for the first time. When we started, we had no idea that this was waiting. Seeing that it often means as much to those who express it as it does to us, only expands the gift.

Being acknowledged and appreciated for contributing to someone's quality of life may be a basic human need that many of us are missing. For Ken and me, this void is filled and our spirits renewed by authentically caring customers. It is these people who seek us out at the farmers' markets, in an effort to get to know the producer of the food they feed to themselves and their family. Together, we are community.

Disconnect #8: Commercial producer: invisible feedlots and processors

Most commercial meat producers sell their animals at auction, collect their money and go home. They are done. Their animals, however, go on to feedlots where they are crowded into confined areas with hundreds or thousands of other animals to be fattened on grain that makes them sick. These producers have little to no connection with the meat packers who slaughter and process their animals, with the meat that is produced, or with those who eat it.

Reconnect #8: Small producer + meat processor = community

Not long ago, Dale, one of our meat processors, accepted an invitation for lunch at the ranch after mentioning that he'd never had a bison ribeye steak. We asked him to bring the steaks from the animals he had just recently harvested. Joe, who often helps Dale, joined us with his new wife and baby. We had all worked together over the past three years but this was the first time we'd been together in a non-work environment.

As usual, it was windy, so our first-ever social event at the ranch was held inside a three-sided shelter Ken had built from fence posts, shade cloth and steel roofing. We had gathered lawn chairs and used a flat board on two buckets to make a table. Outside the shelter, the wind gusted strongly. Inside, while the baby slept peacefully, the adults grabbed a chance to relax.

We had long talked about someday being able to serve our own meat, from our own herd, on our own ranch. My vision had resembled a scene from the early TV show *Bonanza* with the Cartwrights gathering on the Ponderosa with family and friends. Instead, here we all were tucked inside our snug three-sided shelter. It was great.

Half way through the meal, Dale paid us perhaps the highest compliment a rancher can receive from a meat processor.

"You know, Joe," he said looking across the table at his co-worker, "I think that's about the best ribeye steak I have ever had in my entire life."

Unbeknownst to Dale, Joe had just apologetically said to me that the steak was fine, but that he prefers a little more fat in his meat.

"What do you think?" Dale asked, looking at him.

Caught off guard, Joe, looked almost comically back at him and repeated, "Well, I like a little more fat in my meat."

Ignoring him, Dale pressed, "Yes, but still, don't you think that's just about the best flavor you've ever had?"

Joe may have agreed to be polite, but it didn't matter. Dale's a good meat cutter and we knew he'd eaten plenty of meat in his day. We frankly didn't expect such praise. For us, just having him enjoy the meat would have been enough. But coming from an experienced meat processor to us as new bison producers, his compliment was of the highest order.

Talking about it after they left, Ken looked at me and said, "And you know what the best part of it is, honey? This meat is from our animals we raised on our own place. Right here! With our very own grass!"

His beaming face before me gave way to visions of him covered in dust in our open-air Polaris Ranger ATV with two makeshift plastic seeders obediently bouncing along behind. Back and forth, back and forth, across the quarter-mile-wide pasture, six feet at a time. Ken had persevered for days, in spite of his asthma, allergies and rashes, wearing a scarf across his nose, and often eye goggles to keep out the dust. His determination inspired Kat to keep going ahead of him with the spiking, using discarded equipment that he had retrofitted so that it could be pulled by a finicky ATV.

He got choked up for a moment. That's when I realized that because of his wonderful stubbornness, commitment, and tenacity, we had reached another milestone. Someone had told us what we had believed in our hearts to be true—that ours was the best meat they had ever had. Not the best bison meat, but the best meat, period.

As we often do when we are so full we can't speak, I put my hand in his and we fell silent. We didn't know it would mean so much.

"It's the bison," Ken said looking out at the herd. "It's the bison."

Disconnect #9: Foodservice food

Another place where I often feel a lack of connection with how and where my food—especially meat—is produced, is when I am eating out.

When I eat at a catered event, restaurant, drive-through or theme park, or grab something from the prepared food section of a supermarket, I've just entered the massive and lucrative world of foodservice. Unless a menu or label says that the meat is *100 percent Grassfed*, the likelihood is extremely high that the ruminant animal that provided that meat spent much of its life in a feedlot where it was fed corn, grain, hormones, antibiotics, and even such unlikely ingredients and animal byproducts as stale bread, chewing gum, or chicken feathers. Then the meat was processed, portion cut (fabricated), packaged, transported, distributed and cold-stored. By the time the chef, cook or microwave attendant gets involved, additional human layers have been added. Then, depending on whether someone else serves me or I serve myself, there is another disconnect layer.

Since most menus don't provide information about a food's nutritional value, where the meat animal came from or how it was raised, eating out is not at the top of my to-do list. However, whether the foodservice industry distributes to restaurants, supermarkets or catering companies, it hasn't escaped their attention that I, and many like me, want more of a direct connection to the producers of our food. To accommodate this desire, for the past decade or more, they have increasingly used nebulous promotional words such as "farm-to-fork" or "field-to-plate." Perhaps I'm not supposed to notice that this food is actually being provided by a chain restaurant, a food broker or a huge food corporation.

Reconnect #9: Food prepared by sustainable chefs

There are a number of caring and sustainable chefs emerging as part of the food movement and the effort to reconnect people with the source of their food. The two who caught and held my attention are both from Great Britain, the country that first identified mad cow disease as early as 1985.

In 2010, British chef Jaime Oliver collaborated with TV celebrity and producer Ryan Seacrest to produce the Emmy-winning television series *Food Revolution*. Jaime has chosen to care not only about food sources, but also the obesity epidemic in America, especially among our nation's children. Is our food system in the U.S. really that bad? Watch the *Food Revolution* segment that features double-wide human caskets built for the morbidly obese, and draw your own conclusions. In spite of resistance he has encountered while filming in Los Angeles, he continues to strive to reconnect adults and children with their food sources through education, awareness, gardening and cooking.

In 2006, I learned through a farmers' market couple about the British activist, chef and farmer, Hugh Fearnley-Whittingstall.

"You've *got* to read this cookbook about meat," they said enthusiastically after hearing me describe our sustainable methods and the humane harvest of our bison. "It's called *The River Cottage Meat Book*. In it, the author describes the harvest process for his animals and it even has pictures!"

I was aghast. I had never heard of a cookbook having any kind of pictures showing the harvest process. How had he been able to do it and retain the support of these concerned meat eaters? When the book was delivered a week later, I had my answer. This chef articulates his humane regard for meat animals unlike anyone else. We've never read a more eloquent, straight-forward approach, or more strongly felt a respect for meat animals than exhibited by him. His unique cookbook contains reasonable pictures of the harvest process, as well as explanations. It's in this book that we first read the phrase "carnivores with a conscience." It described us and our customers and we adopted this tagline for one of our handouts.

Hugh has won our hearts for aligning his passion for food with his respect for where the food comes from and then sharing this by teaching others. For him, for Lindner Bison, and for other ethical meat producers and eaters, it's about more than meat. It's about the quality of an animal's life as well as the quality of its death.

His cookbook contains nose-to-tail recipes and his on-farm restaurant is truly farm-to-fork—a secret dream of many of today's chefs. Hugh combines culinary skills with a caring chef's heart. For restaurant dining, it just doesn't get any better than this.

Also worth mentioning is his PBS segment that aired in early 2010. Learning about commercial chicken production, Hugh organized a two-part experiment on his farm. The first part was to raise 3,000 chickens using commercial production techniques. Then he invited local volunteers to his farm for what he called, *The Chicken-Out Challenge*. After seeing his on-site commercial chicken experiment, the volunteers agreed to raise their very own free-range chicken from birth to harvest on his farm.

For those of us who have no farm experience, it was easy to identify with the learning curve of the newbie chicken producers. Many of the volunteers experienced conflicted emotional feelings, much as we had, when it came time to harvest their birds. However, despite the initial discomfort involved with killing, cleaning, cooking and eating the chickens they had raised from hatchlings, most said they would do it again. They learned that humanely raising and humanely harvesting their own chicken was not only better for the birds, but the meat had more flavor than what they purchased in the stores.

Disconnect #10: Industrial hijacking of terms

Some years ago, I became aware of a growing confusion about food terminology and claims. Creating relationships with our farmers' market customers confirmed that they were similarly confused. Not much had changed over the years really. We thought we knew what a word or claim meant, only to find out later that it meant something else. I had to make a choice. Either be guided by what I had learned to be true or continue to put my faith in changing promotional and advertising claims used to describe food.

Reconnect #10: Create personal standards and definitions

These days it takes an enlightened customer to navigate the food world's terms and claims. To help eliminate some of the confusion, we created our own chart which we ended up using as a handout. Because it's hard to keep up with new terms emerging every year, we encourage others to create their own chart.

In the meantime, use the *What's in a Word?* chart to help make better buying decisions. And be aware that claims will continue to morph and change on a fairly regular basis. What this means to me is that I may need to ask different questions in order to match my actual food purchase with my intended purchase. If buying from a store and the person behind the counter doesn't know, they can find out. Or they should be willing to provide you with the producer's name and phone number.

Some reasonable questions to ask may include, "Where does your meat come from? Where do your animals come from? Are they born and raised on your farm? What do you feed your animals? Do you give them antibiotics? Hormones? Do your ruminants receive any corn, grain? What else do you feed your animals? How do you harvest your animals? Where is this done? Who processes the meat?"

Have your questions ready and understand that the answers you hear this season may change next season, depending on any variety of factors. So be sure to ask until you are satisfied. And know your humane meat producer.

What's in a Word?

Term or Claim	Consumer Thinks	Reality
100 percent grassfed	100 percent grassfed	100 percent grassfed See AGA & AWA definitions disallowing grain, corn, etc. www.americangrassfed.org & www .animalwelfareapproved.org
100 percent pastured or pasture-fed	100 percent grassfed	All ruminants are basically pastured. It's what's in the pasture that counts. May include mobile feeding tubs of grain, corn or other 'feed.'
100 percent vegetarian fed	100 percent grassfed	Grain & corn may be part of a vegetarian diet, though unnatural for a ruminant.
bison	buffalo, venison, beef, bison	*Bison bison* is the correct species name. Individuals don't have to wonder what they're getting, but may want to ask if the bison are 100 percent grassfed.
buffalo (the animal)	American buffalo, bison bison	May be water buffalo, cape buffalo or American buffalo, a common misnomer for bison

buffalo (the meat or menu item)	American buffalo, bison bison	See above. Food labeling is so loose in this country. In ground meat, it's perfectly legal to add up to 49 percent beef, still call it 'buffalo,' with no legal obligation to tell you. And it is being done by some. May also be water buffalo; order bison to be sure.
beef	meat	An early beef industry advertising strategy which worked. Many use the term 'beef' inter-changeably with the word 'meat'.
feed yard	grass (yard)	fenced area includes 'feed' (usually grain, corn, etc.)
grassfed	100 percent grassfed	All ruminants are basically grassfed. USDA allows grain feeding with this claim.
grass-finished	100 percent grassfed	Some producers may have them on grass, then put them on grain to bulk them up, then back on grass so this claim can be made.
organic	no chemicals or drugs + 100 percent grassfed	You can feed a ruminant the best organic grain or corn in the world and it still isn't their natural diet of 100 percent grass.
ranch/farm raised	100 percent grassfed	Implies no feedlot. This may not be true. All ruminants are basically raised on a farm or ranch of some kind.
sustainable	recyling menus, food bags, abandoning plastic, styrofoam, buying local, supporting 'green', environmentally friendly practices in general. All of this is a good start	Enlightened sustainability includes ethical nose-to-tail meat consumption. For example, choosing only steaks is unsustainable since steaks represent 15 percent of an entire carcass. Sustainable meat consumption is often economical & plays an important role in helping to restore a native-heritage species. And when everything is used, fewer harvests are necessary. You get the idea!

LINDNER BISON

Disconnect #11: Corporate backlash against small farmers

Large food corporations follow the money. It hasn't escaped their attention that food money has increasingly moved into farmers' markets, on-farm direct sales, and community supported agriculture (CSA). Note: A CSA is a community of individuals who pledge support to a farming operation and share the risks and benefits of food production with the grower; they usually have a system of weekly delivery or pick-up of vegetables and fruit and sometimes dairy and meat products.

As food dollars continue to move away from commercially grown products, it's reasonable to expect backlash from Big Food, Big Ag and Big Meat as they seek to recapture eroding market share. These efforts may take various forms, including the enactment of new laws and regulations and attempts to create doubts about small farmers or discredit their authenticity. There have been reports of large "family-owned" mega-corporations applying for market space at farmers' markets. Another threat is that commercial developers may seek to drive out farmers' markets after the markets have revitalized a formerly undesirable urban area, thereby increasing land values for new property owners and local politicians.

These days, it takes enlightened farmers and experienced farmers' market managers to successfully navigate these constantly changing waters.

Reconnect #11: Community support for small farmers

It's an exciting time for small farmers and farmers' markets everywhere. With continued public support and popularity, it's inevitable that the farmers' markets will experience growing pains. How well the markets transition through and survive this "coming of age" will depend on many factors including community supporters, stakeholders, market covenants, the integrity of market managers, and whether or not there is a certification process in place for both market managers and growers.

At the farmers market level, savvy market managers decline applications submitted by large corporations or companies that may present a "small producer" front. Many understand the intent and charter of the farmers' markets as being specifically for small farmers who are frequently denied access to traditional distribution channels; other market managers may need to be reminded. Farmers market managers and boards are not immune to being seduced by the prospect of increased revenue through sales from larger producers with the ability to produce large-scale inventory.

The introduction of new laws or the revision of existing regulations by larger interests often create an uneven playing field for small farmers, in much the same way as was done to small, artisan meat processors. The paragraph below was found online in 2008 on the Certified Farmers' Markets website, but the 2009 webpage revision *excluded* this important statement. Why? No one seems to know.

> "For farmers, the certified farmers' markets provide an outlet especially suited to moving smaller volumes of produce, thus creating a marketing channel outside of the traditional large volume distribution systems."

CHAPTER 21

Disconnect/Reconnect
—FOR THE ANIMALS—

About the same time that we were experiencing a disconnect from the food we eat, a similar disconnect was occurring in the way most meat animals were being raised. Since our book is about our journey into grassfed bison ranching, we speak to our experience here rather than include all meat species, though as omnivores, we acknowledge and include them in spirit.

The animals represent the second leg of our three-legged sustainable stool.

———————

Bison are native to North America and Eastern Europe. At one time there were 40–60 million bison in North America. Today the bison population globally is estimated at 500,000 with herd growth around 20 percent each year. For comparison purposes, it is reported that there are about 1.3 billion domestic cattle in the world and over 800 breeds. There are three species of wild bison: Plains, Wood and Wissent.

Bison, along with other native-heritage species such as elk, deer, antelope and moose, are classified by the USDA as "non-amenable" or wild. Bison's temperament *and* history substantiate the accuracy of this classification. By nature, bison are gregarious and sensitive, strong, yet breakable. They are incredible survivors with a strong herding instinct and they are unpredictable. Caring bison producers demonstrate their regard for these animals by practicing, seeking, encouraging and insisting on appropriate husbandry methods that encourage and respect all elements of bison's uniquely non-amenable spirit.

As newcomers to bison ranching, we benefitted from the experience and wisdom of a handful of early 100 percent grassfed bison pioneers: Art Crowley and David Hump, South Dakota; Dave Hutchinson and T. R. Hughes, Nebraska; Jan and Austin Moseley and Hugh Fitzsimmons,

Texas. There are more now.

Asking questions and visiting a number of ranches, we considered the domestic livestock production model that we saw being applied to wild bison. While some handling equipment had been retrofitted to provide more humane handling methods, other methods reflected a harsh lack of understanding and regard for this native-heritage animal. We have come to regard commercial handling and production methods applied to bison as an effort by two or three large, commercial producers and industrial meat packers to "cattle-ize" bison.

Disconnect #1: Feedlots

For 100 percent grassfed meat producers, the clearest example of what a disconnect for a ruminant looks like, smells like and is like, is a commercial feedlot. This may be especially true for indigenous, migratory bison. Variations of the feedlot term include a Concentrated Animal Feed Operation (CAFO), feedyard, stockyard, livestock hotel, ranch raised, farm raised, free choice and even the word pastured. As one man put it, "It's what's in the pasture that counts," adding his observation of mobile feeding tubs filled with corn and grain and pasture grasses that were either dormant or comprised of dirt. Based on a producer's bank account, variations on this feedlot disconnect theme exist, though may not always describe the questionable items placed inside the yard or pasture for 'free choice.' Consider too that even when buying meat that is certified organic, a ruminant may be fed the best organic corn or grain in the world and it still won't be their natural diet of grass.

I was in my early 50s when the news of Mad Cow Disease was broadcast from England. It was suspected that the cause originated from ingredients added to the feedlot corn and grain, such as blood and meat from dead animals.

A list of other ingredients inappropriately added to animals' diets was made available on the Eatwild.com website. Here, pioneer Jo Robinson researched and listed multiple USDA studies conducted since 1971 to determine the effectiveness of various ingredients in feedlot diets for beef, swine and dairy. Among the feed additives were newspaper, sawdust, chewing gum/packaging material mixture, processed municipal garbage, beer residue, de-inking paper sludge, cement, telephone books, feather meal and swine or poultry fecal waste. (Search eatwild.com, Questionable ingredients in feedlot diets.)

With Jo's permission, we reprinted the list and handed it out. This was motivated by ignorant market goers who on seeing our "Grassfed Bison" tent banner would laughingly ask, "Grassfed? What else would they eat?" Reading the list, their smiles quickly faded. Most people, like us, just didn't know.

While the feedlot concept traveled here with pioneers and dates back many years, as a child it was never explained to me what they were. Passing them from time to time, I only heard the term, which to me meant a place where animals were fed. No one explained what the animals were eating or why. When I looked out at the black or dark brown ground where they stood, naively I believed the cattle were standing on rich earth. Even later, when I was told it was manure, it would take some thinking before I could wrap my brain around the huge amount of manure and number of animals, which in some cases stretched as far as the eye could see.

Another significant piece of my own disconnect continued well into adulthood before I learned that the corn or grain fed to cattle wasn't a natural diet for them. In fact, it makes them sick. I didn't know feedlot animals were being denied access to what Mother Nature designed their stomachs to digest—a diet of grass—and that there were many reasons why I should care about this, especially since I was eating the meat.

Ken and I also learned about artificial lighting erected in feedlots. These extend the photoperiod, or length of the day in order to fool the animal's metabolism, which naturally slows during the winter. Studies indicate that the lights encourage a bigger appetite so that they will eat more and gain weight during the winter rather than lose it as Nature intended.

In my ignorance, acceptance was absolute. In my silence, permission was given. It would be years before I learned that 50 percent of all antibiotics manufactured are used in CAFOs to offset the animals' predictable loss of appetite and manage any variety of debilitating diseases. As more information was made available through documentaries such as *Food Inc.* and *King Corn*, some people admitted they'd heard about the antibiotic use, but didn't want details.

"I'm not sure I want to know," they said. "It's too scary."

> "It may be that when one hands one's responsibilities to an organization, one becomes by that divestiture irresponsible. It may be that responsibility is intransigently a personal matter – that a responsibility can be fulfilled or failed, but cannot be got rid of."
>
> Wendell Berry, *The Unsettling of America*

Reconnect #1: Species-specific diets

"It's only scary when there are no options," we responded. "But you have choices now. Here, take some information with you."

All ruminants, including bison, have multi-chambered stomachs designed to digest grass. A bison's appetite mirrors the natural grass production cycle, increasing or decreasing depending on the length of the days. As the days become shorter during winter months, their appetite falls off and they typically will lose about 15 percent of their weight during this time. It is believed this is Nature's way of making it easier for the cows to calve in May and June.

In the mid-1990s there was a small but growing group of grassfed bison ranchers scattered throughout North America. While commercial bison producers argued loud and long to newcomers on the virtues of feeding grain, this humble group held quietly to their belief in feeding bison the grass they were designed to eat. These caring ranchers remained in the shadows, without fanfare, humanely raising 100 percent grassfed bison and selling their meat to a growing base of customers. We are among the proud who followed their example. Except for a few rare exceptions, all the meat we have sold has been 100 percent grassfed.

But all grass is not created equal. As we and other producers respond to the demand for grassfed meat, many are facing the challenge for the first time of learning how to sustainably grow nourishing grasses year round.

Google the words *grass species* and you'll see that there are from 9,000–10,000 species of grass worldwide. From there, they can generally be divided into two categories: warm season and cool season grasses.

Depending on weather and region of the country, grasses vary further. Some areas may produce what's known as "hard" grasses and some may produce "washy" grasses, the latter affected nutritionally by the high amount of rain the grass receives. Too much rain and the quick growth dilutes the proteins in the grass. Eating this washy grass makes it difficult for a ruminant to gain weight. They'll eat and eat, enlarging their rumens, but put on little weight. Other grasses are devoid of nutritional nourishment, such as medusa head and cheat grass. Again, the ruminant may graze on it, but it has little to offer that is nourishing, so the animal may not thrive or put on weight. To offset this, some ranchers may offer free-choice grain along with grass hay for a few months during the animal's life, returning them to grass pasture at the earliest opportunity. Many grassfed ranchers believe that the flavor of 100 percent grassfed meat depends on the region and types of grasses and forbs (think broadleaf plants) that the animals eat.

Our own knowledge of the thousands of grasses has grown dramatically since we first bought our bison – we now have a much better idea of how much we don't know.

We followed the lead of long-time bison producers. Bison don't do well with a rich diet, such as water hungry alfalfa that may contain up to 25 percent protein. They do better with grasses with 12 percent protein or less, depending on time of year. They will eat alfalfa, but it's too "hot" or rich for them. It can upset their rumen (the first part of their multi-chambered stomach) and we've seen our animals head briskly for relief at the stock tank or eat lower protein grasses to offset the discomfort of the too-rich diet.

When we first relocated our bison into a lush pasture of alfalfa and timothy grass, they seemed to be doing fine. A few weeks later, we were moving hay bales around and accidentally dropped one in the pasture. When our chores were done and we returned to get it, it was gone. This, we learned, was an example of what experienced producers meant when they say bison do not do well on a rich diet. The bison welcomed the hay because it helped cut the richness of the pasture they were in.

Each year we work to slowly diversify our grasses by sub-dividing pastures and, as we can afford it, overseeding with a variety of grasses and forbs. By rotating the bison in and out of the large paddocks, the goal is to keep them happy, the grasses growing and the soil healthy.

Disconnect #2: Applying the industrial cattle model to bison

Some bison producers have followed a commercial cattle model and applied the same husbandry practices to wild bison. This model may frequently result in avoidable injury to the bison. Though docile in appearance, they are wild and have all of their wild instincts intact.

The Animal Welfare Approved (AWA) organization includes in their list of inappropriate production practices for bison such things as feedlot placement, dehorning, branding, use of cattle prods, weaning and the unnatural separation of family groups.

We've added a few more practices to our list: inadequate or inappropriate fencing, high stress handling, selling or raising one or two isolated bison as meat animals or "pets" and the sale or rental of bison calves for quarter horse training. Other questionable practices may include artificial insemination, inappropriate handling equipment, and adding artificial lights during winter months to trick them into gaining rather than naturally losing weight.

Reconnect #2: Honoring the bison-ness of the bison

The non-profit Animal Welfare Approved (AWA) organization was founded in 2006. Headed by Program Director Andrew Gunther, AWA's mission is to eliminate animal suffering, promote the importance of the human-animal bond and improve recognition of the role of animals in the well-being of people. AWA improves farm animal welfare by establishing high animal welfare standards, auditing compliance and promoting family farmers who adhere to the standards. Their audits are free, voluntary and confidential.

We, along with the AWA, support humane production efforts that encourage, respect, honor and therefore preserve bison's natural instincts. Allowing bison to retain their horns, their testicles, self-wean and remain in their family groups contributes to the creation of a natural pecking order established by the herd for the overall health of the herd. It also helps provide effective natural predator protection.

Because of our experience at our ranch, we include another vital reconnect element. We encourage bison producers to strive to provide enough land so the bison may freely express all aspects of their natural behavior, including their love of running.

Disconnect #3: Off-site harvest

Harvesting animals off-site requires that they be corralled, separated, loaded onto a truck and driven to the slaughterhouse or processing plant. Most current meat processing regulations follow the domestic livestock model and require this method; indeed, it may currently be the only option for producers in some areas to process their meat for resale. However, for a wild animal such as a bison, handling is stressful. Separation from the herd often results in anxiety and distress and the potential for injury increases dramatically. At best, most bison become agitated and may tirelessly run or pace the fence trying to rejoin the herd; at worst, they may injure themselves by trying to climb over or go through the fence. If they are in close quarters with other bison, they may injure each other.

Reconnect #3: Field harvest

There is a growing consensus among small producers and caring customers in favor of field harvest of meat animals. This means that a mobile slaughter truck comes to the ranch and a shooter kills the animal in the field. It allows the animal to remain in familiar surroundings and with the herd. Depending on the proximity of the ranch to the processor's plant, it may even be more cost effective. In addition, some believe that because field harvested animals experience less anxiety, there are fewer toxins in the meat than in their commercially processed counterparts.

It is our belief, and one shared by experienced meat processors, that a humane field harvest especially honors a bison's wild nature. When our animals are harvested, when possible, we are right there with them.

In fact, when we started field harvests of our own, unexpectedly another reconnect element emerged. At first I thought it had to do with the reconnect provided by the presence of our bison, then later found it was more. As our emotionally blurred views of field harvests gave way to clarity, this strange new connection provided a bridge, an appreciation for the life and death cycle of all living species on the planet, including our own. Even our bodies will return to the earth as a part of this sustainable life cycle.

As written about earlier, on initially learning that we raise the animals and sell the meat, well-meaning individuals sometimes said, *Oh! I don't know how you do it*, and *I just couldn't do it*. We know what they mean. However, we know too that wanting to stay disconnected from the life and death cycle may well place that which we profess to care so much about into the hands of non-caring individuals.

This failure to care about a meat animal may be what hidden cameras have captured in industrial/commercial meat production facilities, along with a less-than-positive example of corporate values. Because meat animals are often purchased under commercial contracts or through auction barn bids, the corporate owners of the animals may be sheltered in a boardroom hundreds or thousands of miles away. Physically and emotionally removed from the moments of an animal's life and death, to them the animal may be a non-entity, a thing. In their minds, the animal may be every bit the commodity as a manufactured widget.

Today when I hear the question, *How can you do it?* I respond differently than I did in the past.

"If you see what I see, read what I read and know what I know, how can I not do it? The animals deserve better." The words of Larry's elder are still with me, *Who better than one who loves them?*

We believe that as sobering and painful as the harvest may be, this reconnect with our bison as meat animals is important. It provides completion to our cycle of caring. Instead of compartmentalizing our experiences devoid of the harvest, i.e., enjoying them when they're calves, admiring them as adults, or being mildly annoyed when they outsmart us, we also stand by them on their last day.

For caring meat producers, it may never get easier. We agree with Maurice that we're not sure it's supposed to. In fact, if it ever did, it would be time for us to get out of the business. If we don't acknowledge our human caring, how would we be different from disconnected industrial or commodity producers?

While selling in farmers' markets, occasionally an animal activist will visit our booth, spit on our literature and harass our customers. One day, a woman openly hissed, "You're the enemy." Another asked "how many animals have you murdered today?" "All you care about is your wallet," claimed another.

Then as word spread of how we were raising our bison, a new kind of vegan and vegetarian began emerging. Varying in age, they were often emotionally guarded, distrusting and suspicious. We began to realize that they cared as much as we did. Many had no way of knowing that we cared until we told them. We took the time to answer questions and describe how we were different from what they read and saw on TV. Frequently this exchange resulted in hugs and tears, thanking us for caring. "Thank you for doing what you're doing," they told us.

At first I was incredulous: that this new type of animal husbandry would mean so much to so many, that so many people valued what we were doing. So why were we often both crying? Perhaps we were crying because we knew it could be better and there were so few of us doing it. We had found each other. We had reconnected. Here's an example.

ALLIE'S STORY

One bright Saturday morning a young woman and her boyfriend approached my booth at the farmers' market. Unbeknownst to me, she had come with a single mission and that was to learn about how we harvest our bison.

"We have some questions," she said soberly, not looking at me. "How do you . . . " Suddenly, she burst into tears.

Immediately I joined her in front of the table and put my arms around her, as her supportive boyfriend stood close by. "We love them too," I said and then repeated, "We love them too."

"How do you kill them?" she sobbed.

"We use a rife. A single shot."

"Are the others there when you do it?" she asked.

"Yes, the others are there," I said.

"Are they scared?" In her caring, she was determined. She wanted to know.

"Well, they are startled when they first hear the gun and then some come back out of curiosity," I said. "But it's so much better that they are there all together. It's the best way."

Helplessly I glanced at her boyfriend who was holding her arm now and passed her a tissue. I wasn't sure if my answers were helping or not, but I wanted her to know that we cared too. We were trying to make a difference. As she wiped her eyes, I noticed a crowd of our customers had gathered and were patiently waiting while we finished.

"Thank you for what you are doing," she said, unexpectedly reaching forward to hug me. "Thank you," she whispered again in my ear.

"Thank you for caring enough to ask the question," I said as they began to leave. We both were wiping away tears. A quick glance at the faces of our waiting customers told me that they understood and I was touched by their kindness.

This story is typical of other exchanges we've had with our animal-loving customers. We aren't the hired help behind the meat counter in a supermarket. We're the actual producers. Most small family producers care about the animals they raise, or they wouldn't raise them in the first place.

We still cry, but because we know that our full support of the small processor is critical to the humane harvest we keep it to ourselves. He cares too, by the way. It's important to him that he does a good job, and he does.

"We're all here to serve and that includes the animals," a loving customer named Lyn once said. For me, her comment was well timed as I reviewed and questioned my new role.

Decades earlier, a spiritual teacher had said she believed that the way that we die often reflects the way we live. Given my sphere of influence during my finite existence here, my own sense of completion may best be measured by how well I believe I have used life's moments. Those who use their time wisely and understand well their achievements along with limitations of the journey, may be blessed by reaching the end of their lives with few regrets.

If that's true, then for our bison I believe that to the extent that we can offer them a species-specific quality of life, as close to being a bison as possible, we further express that respect and gratitude by seeing that their death is the most honorable and humane possible.

Accepting the accountability and limitations of my role may be as unique as it is complex. Now when I weep, rather than it being an expression that something bad has happened, I regard it as an expression that life has happened. And a moment of healing follows as I come to terms with what it means to be a caring carnivore in an age of industrialized food production.

Ever the teacher, Ken has an innate ability to clarify things.

"We're no different from other carnivores," he said one day and quickly corrected himself. "Well, I take that back. We're a lot more humane than other predators. The biggest difference between us and other carnivores is that we have a conscience about it."

Yes, indeed. Our small meat processors do too. And customers who find us do too.

Disconnect #4: Control and commercialization of bison genetics

In 2000, someone from Texas A&M University contacted us to take part in a study. They had developed a DNA test to determine if bison carried "cattle markers" (cattle DNA) and wanted to know if we wanted to have our bison tested free of charge.

"Better to do it now," the man said. "Later will cost money."

Respectfully we declined. To us, it was and still is a miracle that bison are even with us on the planet. We aren't breeders, nor could we see needlessly handling our bison and causing them stress to test for something that held little value or application. As grassfed bison meat producers focused on using humane methods to raise bison on chemical-free grasses and introducing their meat to others, we asked ourselves "Will a DNA test change the flavor or nutritional value of the meat or the bison's life on our ranch?" The answer was easy.

A few years passed. Articles began to appear in the media citing reports from Texas A&M that nearly all remaining bison were genetically contaminated with cattle markers. As a result of these reports, a few customers began to ask if our animals were *pure* bison. Initially we laughed it off, saying "We aren't interested in becoming the Nazi bison police." As more Texas A&M testing was done and reported on, the tone changed and included an element of alarm. Perhaps only the Yellowstone National Park herd was a *pure* herd, they suggested. Again we were asked if our bison were really *authentic* bison, or part cow.

Finally our curiosity was piqued, so we paid $20 and sent in hair follicles from an animal we had previously harvested. The results came back showing no cattle markers, but other than our now having an answer for a few customers, the test held little value.

While it still makes no difference to us whether or not our bison's DNA contains cattle markers, the issue has since taken on a far greater meaning. In fact, it has the potential to significantly impact not only our herd, but the species as a whole.

In 2010, we learned of an attempt by commercial bison producers and breeders to use this DNA testing to divide today's bison into two categories: "pure" bison (those with no cattle markers) and "impure" (those with cattle markers). Under current laws, this division could create irreversible ripple effects of seismic proportions. Some reason that "pure" bison could be declared an "endangered" species. If that happened— and the push is underway to do so—there's a chance that bison owners would no longer be able to legally sell their "endangered" bison or their offspring—if private ownership was allowed at all. Under the Endangered Species Act, "trafficking" in endangered species is subject to a $50,000 fine and not less than one year in prison—per charge.

The flip side of this equation is equally disastrous. Bison with the Texas A&M cattle markers may lose their legal status as bison and fall under the same classification as domestic cattle. As mentioned earlier, this would remove many of the protections they enjoy today as "non-amenable" animals under USDA regulations.

And it gets worse. The efforts to arbitrarily cleanse or purify this prehistoric species are in fact based on questionable testing protocols. If there are cattle genes in bison, it is possible that these genes originated tens of thousands of years ago, rather than through inter-breeding with domestic cattle over the last few hundred years. If this is so, rather than indicating "impurity," the cattle markers may be a natural and integral part of what bison genetically are.

Current testing methods cannot determine this one way or the other. Efforts are now underway to sequence the entire bison genome. Meanwhile, any attempted incorrect reclassification of bison as cattle may introduce a new kind of extermination by setting in motion the means to legally allow the destruction of a natural genetic diversity that may date back million of years. (For details, please visit News/Articles at lindnerbison.com. "Bison Genetics – The New War Against Bison," written by bison producer/authors W. Michael Gear and Kathleen O'Neil Gear of Wyoming.)

Reconnect #4: Honoring the natural bio-diversity of bison

> "Biodiversity is the degree of variation of life forms within a given ecosystem, biome or an entire plant. Biodiversity is a measure of the health of ecosystems. Greater biodiversity implies greater health. . . . The period since the emergence of humans has displayed an ongoing biodiversity reduction and an accompanying loss of genetic diversity. . . ." The United Nations designated 2011-2020 as the UN Decade on Biodiversity.
>
> Wikipedia, *the free encyclopedia*

Whether we are bison producers, bison meat eaters, Native Americans, conservationists, or individuals concerned about animal welfare, we all share a connection with bison and with the earth. Each one of us must step forward and accept our responsibility for demonstrating the highest level of caring and commitment to this amazing species.

In the 19th century, bison nearly became extinct due to commercial hunting and slaughter. We dare not fail them again. To learn how you can help, please see Chapter 26, Societal Call to Action.

CHAPTER 22

Disconnect/Reconnect
—FOR THE EARTH—

*In the end, sustainability is basically bringing ourselves into
balance with other living systems of the earth, our source of all real wealth.*
—DAVID C. KORTEN—

*As a child I was taught to be respectful and not throw anything out the
car window or leave trash behind at campsites. Admittedly, that was about the
extent of my regard for the earth, though I loved growing up in Montana. I loved
everything about its mountains, rivers, forests, winters, clear air and beautiful
clear night skies. And the people.*

 *Even as a child, with limited awareness of the rest of the world, I knew the
value of what I had and believed it would never change. By the time I reached
high school, my dad began talking about the Yellowstone River being fished out.
He was angry, discouraged and frustrated about losing this source of food. Each
summer saw more river rafters and tourists. By fall, they were gone and with
them, the trout. Even though restocking efforts were well publicized, I didn't fully
understand just how much we were losing. And not just in Montana.*

 The earth is the third leg of our three-legged sustainability stool.

———◆———

 I have lived in cities or suburbs of cities all of my adult life. That
fact, coupled with my being busy and preoccupied with surviving, kept
me insulated me from many environmental issues and concerns.

 This all changed after we bought our land in northeastern California
and moved our bison there. Now there is an undeniable sense of completion
and wonder. As imperfect as it still is, my new home is a classroom.

 While the seasonal cycles of life unfold through my observations of
insects, birds, and other inhabitants, I am increasingly aware that I, too,

am a visitor here. As participants of a shared ecosystem, we each want to be here and we all belong.

As a guest, it's right and good that I behave respectfully toward the other guests and most especially to my host, the land.

∽

Disconnect #1: Weed-free, bug-free monocrops

One of my first disconnects from the earth was learning to not only accept, but value the uniformity of monocropping, the high-yield agricultural practice of growing a single crop year after year on the same land. From grass lawns to golf courses, from orchards to row crops of any one tree or plant species, little did I know that the only way to maintain such weed-free uniformity was through the use of herbicides, insecticides, and chemical applications of nutrients. When an area is planted with just one kind of plant or tree the soil does not get the balance of nutrients that occurs in a more diverse natural setting.

A prerequisite to my admiration of monocrops was accepting that weeds have no value. This carried over to my first season at the ranch when I overwhelmed myself trying to pull all the weeds that didn't look like the grass I had envisioned for our bison. Despite my best efforts, a few months later a new variety would present itself, and by the next spring, others. Uninvited, they kept showing up anyway. Clearly I needed to revise my approach and that was to educate myself.

I started with our biggest weed concerns: mustard, foxtail, tumbleweed, Canadian thistle and whitetop.

The mustard is edible by bison and it can be baled, too. In the winter, the stemmy stalks of mustard provide roughage and therefore rumen warmth, which helps against the cold.

Foxtail is a grass. Our bison love it when it's tender and green, and they keep it in check by eating it. They stop eating it after it matures and goes to seed, which is when it develops sharp bristle-like "awns" which can cause all kinds of trouble, including death in some animals if it enters an orifice and keeps traveling. I once had a foxtail land in my ear when we were tarping some hay. Not knowing what it was, I attempted to remove it but succeeded only in pushing it further into my ear canal. Even Ken couldn't see what it was. The doctor who removed it that afternoon congratulated us on not waiting to come in as it could have punctured my eardrum. We now respect foxtail in a guarded way.

Tumbleweed makes itself at home every year in a back area at the ranch which has no irrigation. An invasive species from Asia, its real name is Russian thistle. The bison don't like it and neither do we, but back it comes every year. Until we get water to that area, which will encourage competition from more desirable species, we plow it into piles in fall, winter, and spring and burn it. Ken remarked once that the early song about "*Rollin' along with the tumblin' tumbleweed*" takes on new meaning now that we know it came over with European settlers and it is not native to our country.

Canadian thistle has nasty thorns on all leaves, purple flowers and, as you might guess, comes from up north. Though we've read articles about how cows can be trained to eat thistle, having dealt with it now for five years, it is not something we would ask our bison to eat. We remove it by digging, cutting and spraying it with vinegar before it goes to flower. Then we physically remove it from the pastures wearing thick gloves. If left in place, thistle will reseed as it dries out, making the entire exercise pointless.

Whitetop (*Cardaria draba*), also known as hoary cress, whiteweed and peppergrass, is considered noxious. After our experience with it, we've added an "ob" in front of that classification and that pretty well sums up our feelings about it. Over a five-year period, our multiple labor intensive, chemical-free approaches to remove it proved all but futile. (See details below, subtitled *Whitetop*.) Whitetop quickly spreads by seeds and rhizomes, prospering with grazing, irrigation and cultivation—though we didn't learn this until much later. If ignored, it will take over entire areas so nothing else can grow. We saw this happen about five miles away so the first sign of whitetop gets our full attention.

Reconnect #1: Encouraging plant and insect biodiversity

Farmer-author-activist Joel Salatin was instrumental in introducing us to Nature's basic sustainability rules. In particular, he pointed out how Mother Nature actually prefers biodiversity and how unnatural monocropping is. Now that we have our own ranch and we see the variety of grasses emerging as food for our bison, our views on what is welcome there has undergone dramatic reassessment.

For years, the ranch was mostly an alfalfa hay ranch. The previous owners were in the hay business and their customers preferred weed-free alfalfa hay. Since alfalfa is too rich for bison, as we could afford to, we bought a variety of grass seeds to overplant. Then we bought two inexpensive non-agricultural seeders, which Ken retrofitted and ganged together. With chains attached and dragging behind to lightly cover the seed after it dropped, he spent days overseeding both the hay pasture and the grazing pastures.

We watered, we weeded and we waited. Sometimes what we planted grew and sometimes it didn't. What we could always count on coming up though, were weeds. They were happy to out-compete the fledgling grass seed. But here's a change: we now leave any dandelions that emerge. They are good bison food and provide excellent coverage for the soil until more grass can fill in.

Once we have more grass coverage and improved soil health, we expect to increasingly see less weed activity. In the meantime, these plants provide diversity. Bison are known to eat things that cattle will not, so they teach us what works for them and we deal with the weeds on that basis. When they prove to be inedible, we encourage them to leave by sowing new grass seed instead.

After planting the new grass seed, rather than pull new weeds as they emerge, we work now to time their departure. While the new grass is still becoming established, we allow some weeds to remain in place, acting as a nursery crop. This means the desired plants or grass can grow nearby or underneath it, shaded from sun and protected from wind. Later the weeds are mowed off allowing in more sunlight and the grass continues grow to fill in the spot. But weeds will always be there in some form or another, some more aggressive than others. Here's an example.

1. WHITETOP

Our education for different management approaches for invasive weeds began with whitetop. Insistent on not using chemicals, Ken and I became willing students of weed extraction methods. Whitetop has proven to be a worthy adversary.

The first year, I gleefully cut the whitetop. In a few months, it had grown back, spread and asked for more. Year two, I sprayed it with a heavy mix of vinegar and water. It looked and smelled like a growing green salad. Some of it wilted, but because we weren't there to regularly reapply the vinegar, it came back. Year three, we bought a torch device and blasted the whitetop with fire. It shriveled up in the spring and grew back in the fall. We read that rye grass has a natural chemical that retards weed growth and could sometimes outcompete weeds, so that fall we overseeded with rye grass. The rye barely came up among the robust whitetop plants.

Then we discovered an article online saying that solarization can kill weeds. Year four we located a 200 pound roll of the kind of clear plastic used by Big Ag, made a 60 mile detour and took it with us to the ranch. For days, we unrolled, cut, and anchored sheets of plastic over the largest patch of whitetop. As the strong winds tore it loose, we stubbornly fastened it back into place. Finally we were getting somewhere. Each trip we noticed the whitetop under the plastic shriveling up and dying from the magnification of heat from the sun. It was great. We started talking about putting more grass seed in once it had died all the way back.

That winter we left the plastic over the whitetop to make sure it continued to cook. Unfortunately, we learned too late that the plastic had acted like a greenhouse and protected it from the cold. The following spring, back it came, green and happy, aided by the plastic cover which the season before had been its demise, or so we thought.

Year five, I telephoned our local weed expert. He said that in stubborn cases, some farmers actually dig whitetop up with a tractor. We had just purchased a used tractor with an unexpected early inheritance from Ken's mother, Betty. That spring, Ken and Kat spent a half day and dug up the patch of whitetop which had easily doubled in size from the first year. While Ken scooped and dumped tractor buckets of plants and dirt, Kat sorted and pulled the leaves and rhizomes, bagging them both in a large plastic garbage bag. They removed all the bags from the pasture and smoothed the dirt back in place.

This certainly slowed things down. A month later though, Ken saw tiny whitetop leaves beginning to reappear. By mid-summer, the patch was back. It turned out that our tractor could only dig down one or two feet, instead of the recommended three feet to dig up all the rhizomes.

Ken was exasperated and then furious. I agonized for days before agreeing to our only remaining option. We simply could do no more. For the first time since buying the ranch, we went to the hardware store shrouded in defeat and with premeditated criminal intent. I watched sadly as Ken picked out a bottle of chemical weed killer. When we returned, without a word he immediately went out and spot-sprayed the whitetop patch. Within an hour it showed wilting. Two months later the whitetop continued to struggle. Later that summer, he sparingly resprayed regrowth.

We told customers that we had applied the weed killer to approximately .000072 percent of our land. In response, we found that most customers were reasonable once they understood what we're doing and why. In this case, we wanted to be completely chemical-free, but if we didn't eradicate the whitetop before it became further established, it could literally have taken over the entire pasture. And then what would our bison have to eat?

"Everything in moderation," my dad used to say.

2. BENEFICIAL BUGS AND OTHER CRITTERS

In addition to plant biodiversity, the presence of beneficial insects and micro-organisms may be encouraged by such farming practices as not tilling or plowing the soil and abstaining from artificial fertilizers or applications of herbicides. In the future, we hope to be able to control the less beneficial insects such as fly larvae through rotational grazing by the bison, followed by natural bug predators such as chickens or turkeys. Until then, we welcome the variety of area birds that have discovered the many delicious inhabitants of bison pies.

Armed with decades of city living, initially the thought of not having bugs around didn't seem to be a big loss. Then I began to understand and value not only their contribution to various plants, but also to the other species that may eat them. Without them, where would we find the seemingly tireless contributors to soil building and renewal?

I confess that the depth of my insect appreciation is still undergoing some adjustments. On any given day I may lovingly relocate a spider outside and a moment later, heartlessly dispatch a fly or mosquito with the nearest swatting instrument available. I try to be grateful for them all, but there are still many whose purpose may elude me to the grave. For now, I remind myself of the progress I've made in becoming more aware of these natural interactions and symbiotic relationships, many of which are more delicately balanced than others.

We love the earthworms, beneficial soil microbes and countless other things living in the earth. At every opportunity we nurture, replenish and build our soil, rather than mine it, deplete it and move on. And our bison are helping us, as are the birds, reptiles and bugs that allow us to be on the ranch with them.

In the meantime, the weeds and insects all provide a report card for us on the condition of our pastures and our soil. Regardless of what we think or how we value one over another, when it comes to Mother Nature's wise insistence on bio-diversity, we wouldn't have it any other way.

Disconnect #2: Landfills and kitchen disposals

According to *Waste & Recycling News*, in 2007 Los Angeles County ranked second only to Las Vegas in the top ten largest landfills by tonnage received. What is noteworthy to me is that the more I learn about the good my organic garbage can do for the earth, rather than regard it as disposable garbage, I seek ways to funnel it back productively.

Reconnect #2: Joys of composting

There's little I can do to suppress my joy in discovering the potential treasures in my food waste. Totally new to composting, I see it as yet one more facet in the cycle of life which a short time ago was only a theory which others to put into practice.

At our condo in Southern California, I've begun saving uneaten fruits, vegetables, coffee grounds and egg shells instead of throwing them away or tossing them into the sink for grinding. When we head up to the ranch, much to Ken's consternation, I sometimes take these scraps with me. Placing my organic garbage either into my kitchen disposal or a landfill somewhere strikes me as positively wasteful when it can do so much more good being properly returned to the earth. My only question is, *What took me so long?*

At the ranch, "paunch manure," or partially digested grass, is collected from the rumen or stomach of harvested animals. It is saved as a treasure rather than hauling it away and dumping it. Beneficial microbes turn this a postively wonderful compost, full of phosphorus which helps seeds and seedlings get a good start.

When we burn weeds, wood or brush, the ashes are scooped up and mixed with the paunch, as are dried bison pies which we grind with an old shredding machine. The compostable garbage from Valencia is added to the mix along with a little ranch sand. When winter sets in and adds moisture, the composting process begins. Once we live on the ranch full-time, we will be able to manage it even more effectively.

Do I know what I'm doing? Not fully, but in my mind, it's no reason not to try or at least begin. It feels good to learn something new and to actually apply that learning. At first it seemed inconvenient to save assorted food scraps and remnants. I didn't want to be bothered or give myself yet one more thing to do. But the longer we have our animals and our land, the more connected we feel and the more motivated we are to do these things.

Recycling our waste and making compost now seems incredibly natural. We believe we're honoring and expressing gratitude for our gifts from the earth. We also believe that we're contributing, if only in a small way, to a renewal and rebirth of other living things in the soil just waiting for a chance to respond and make their contribution, too.

Disconnect #3: Industrial agriculture

At the farmers' market one bright Saturday morning, a reserved, sophisticated-looking young blond woman came to our booth. Saying little, she looked at the list of cuts on our board and took the pamphlet I handed her. Beside her were two blond children who looked to be about three and four years old; they were quiet and completely well-behaved. She listened to me talk about our meat, made a small purchase and left.

The next week, she came back and told us how wonderful the meat was. A few feet behind her, an older woman waited for her. She was also reserved, perhaps even more so. My attempt to acknowledge her was ignored while she quietly waited for the young woman to complete her purchase.

This continued for over a month. Then one Saturday I put up a card announcing the movie *Food, Inc.* When I saw the younger woman looking at it, I asked if she had seen the movie. She said no, so I recommended it, briefly summarizing some of what I had learned. One of the things I mentioned is that just four big companies were in control of most of the food supply in this country and I'd rattled off the names: ConAgra, IBP, Tyson and Cargill.

When I mentioned Cargill her eyes widened. She looked at me for a moment and offered the only piece of personal information I ever received from her.

"I know that family!" she quietly exclaimed, holding my gaze. She had made the connection and it clearly hit closer to home than she expected.

I couldn't help but muse out loud while completing the transaction. Putting the change into her hand, I said, "I wonder what they eat."

Without a word, she turned and was gone. I never saw her again.

As Wendell Berry has pointed out in his writing, only a sick or insane animal will befoul its own nest. With that in mind, when I think of Big Ag, Big Food, or Big Meat and how many tons of chemicals and livestock pharmaceuticals they are responsible for, I sometimes think of the individuals who run these corporations. When I wonder about the kind of friends and families they have, whose silence gives permission for them to do what they do, I remember the blond, aristocratic young woman. And I wonder about the world she's helping to create for her two well-behaved children.

Reconnect #3: Sustainable agriculture

Ken and I are small producers of 100 percent grassfed bison. The 100 percent grassfed part of this sentence means that by default, we must build sustainable bio-diverse pastures full of legumes, grasses, weeds, forbs and encourage as many beneficial insects and earthworms as possible to find their way to us.

We start by favoring no-till methods of working the ground.

Basically, no-till is a system of farming without plowing and may exclude applying fertilizers or herbicides. The ultimate goal is reduced soil erosion and preservation of soil nutrients. This in turn supports micro-organisms for ongoing soil health.

The bison part of the sentence relates to treating the earth kindly. It is part of bison's nature to migrate, never staying long in one spot. Well adapted for life in their native habitat, they drink about one-third less water than cattle and will travel to find it; bison are also known to be efficient grazers.

We've recently discovered two ancient and exciting sustainable partners in our effort to rebuild and maintain soil health. One is a fungus called mycorrhizae (my-ko-RY-zah). This is a beneficial fungus that has a symbiotic relationship with the roots of plant. Ongoing mycorrhizae studies have shown promise in helping plants in drought-prone areas, as well as rebuilding soil health on previously fallow ground.

The other partner is called biochar. Biochar is a way of capturing carbon using a type of charcoal created by pyrolysis (burning without oxygen) of biomass. It can be made using a slow burning kiln, or purchased. Once in the soil, biochar is said to remain there for decades if not centuries, increasing fertility and locking in carbon.

This fall, we will be using both together for the first time as we overseed a section of pasture. Watch for progress bulletins on our website next year and in the meantime, google these two for additional information.

Overall, our reconnect efforts include sustainable management of both the land and our bison. Because of variables such as weather, weeds and destructive pests such as gophers, we are constantly reevaluating what we're doing and how we're doing it. We take fierce pride in our efforts and we like to share our experiences—the mistakes as well as the successes. And while we still have an enormous amount to learn about farming, we know that by factoring in natural elements such as beneficial microbes, fungus and earthworms, we are on the right track.

Disconnect #4: Absence of trees

When we bought the ranch, there were two trees and one large stump on the property. For us, the absence of trees, especially combined with frequent high winds, is a distinct disadvantage. It increases our use of irrigation water, while wind erosion redistributes dust and dirt and brings in weed seeds. Our bison love to rub on everything, especially the one small olive tree which had (past tense) thorns on its branches. Even with several street sweeper brushes available to them for rubbing, the animals still gravitate to that defenseless tree. Short of barricading it, we are making every effort to save this little tree which now has the bark rubbed off on one side.

Reconnect #4: Planting trees

Immediately after buying the ranch, we made plans to plant trees and bushes as a windbreak. Budget, travel and labor constraints put these plans on hold. Six years later, constraints or not, we could wait no longer. In 2011, we ordered 300 trees to begin the badly needed windbreak.

Unsure of our ability to get them all physically planted, we sent out a bulletin inviting others to our first ever "tree mobbing" at the ranch. Though several customers expressed willing hearts, the distance proved too great and the weather just wouldn't work for them to participate. Instead, Ken and Mike, our new ranch-hand, formed our tree mob of two. While I stayed behind to sell at the farmers' markets, they fenced off a quarter-mile on the first day to keep the bison out. The second day they planted the newly fenced area with 140 trees; and the third day, they mulched. The next month, I joined them in putting in the second row, potting the rest for the second phase of our tree planting the following spring. Two drip irrigation lines were also installed to distribute water efficiently once pumping season began.

Expenses for this first phase were offset by a welcome grant of $500 from a Santa Monica family business owner and a surprise $100 donation from a San Diego customer who wanted to support our windbreak effort. Neither donor could have any way of knowing how deeply their generosity was appreciated.

This first effort represents about one-quarter of the work to be done. Careful budgeting and planning will be needed over the next three years to complete our goal of one mile of windbreak trees. The trees will also invite a variety of birds that will help with insect control and provide free fertilizer.

Though we hadn't talked about the daunting effort of our first planting of 300 trees, one evening just before he left for the ranch, Ken came across a passage in Wendell Berry's book, *The Unsettling of America* which he read out loud:

"If you want to know whether or not a farm is loved, look for trees."

A Call to Action
—INTRODUCTION—

Before we had an inkling of any kind of cultural shift away from industrial food or the existence of an innovative agricultural concept known as multi-species farming, we had become bison producers. Our original plan was simply to create an active retirement, live on the land and have access to great tasting bison meat, the selling of which would help pay for the land. Unwittingly we found ourselves in middle of a food movement that was gaining momentum. Surrounded by producers of food at farmers' markets made it easy to support other small farmers like ourselves, rather than the large commercial food companies.

This was just the first of many steps toward a new level of awareness.

As time passed, I couldn't help but begin to question my own role as a compliant, convenience-driven consumer. Clearly, my attitude had been one of entitlement and long-held beliefs about my food sources were naïve. Realizing how disconnected I had been from how my food was produced, I wondered what else I didn't know about food production. There was a new sense that the information I needed to make a good decision had somehow become splintered, emotional and contradictory. Increasingly, words used to describe foods, instead created suspicion and doubt. They even had moral implications that I wasn't supporting farmers if I didn't want chemicals in my food, or that people worldwide would starve if these chemicals and genetically modified 'improvements' weren't in place. And it was because I really just didn't understand the issues.

Finally Ken and I broke free from the confusion.

We wanted to contribute in a positive way to feeding ourselves and others, as well as express our caring for meat animals and the earth. Rather than rely on media-saturated inconsistencies, political opinions du jour submitted by PhD counter-points, constantly changing highjacked terms, health claims and advice, we stopped trying to assimilate the diverse information feed. Instead, we created our own word definitions and criteria based on our experiences and common sense. We selected information sources with a history of ethical reporting. When we found non-profits supported by agri-business monoliths, we factored it in. Now we were getting somewhere.

Once our personal standards were in place, our journey became one of trial and error, success and failure, discovery and—most of all—determination. Trying new things for the first time, we joyfully found that the more we did, the more we could do. Progress came, often with an awareness that we had just abandoned beliefs once held dear. Yet a sense of renewal and purpose seemed to always follow. We were finally on the right track.

Our Call to Action seeks to empower those individuals who want to make a measurable positive difference. It answers the questions: what can I do short-term or long-term, part-time or full-time? How much of a factor is my own willed ignorance or denial? What issues can I be aware of so I may navigate without harming others, the animals or the earth? Very few of us are experts on national or global food systems. But we are *all* experts in our own food experience within these systems as well as within our geographic regions and communities.

What follows are chapters listing some of the things we've done or suggest be done. It is our fervent hope that you will come up with many more ideas of your own!

CHAPTER 23

A Call to Action
—FOR INDIVIDUALS—

1. Be willing to do what other people aren't willing to do.

Ken and I understand and appreciate that there are those who believe and take comfort in the "trickle down" approach. It implies that one need take no action at all because eventually things will work out the way we want. For me, the test of this method has always been to ask myself *How long am I willing and able to wait?*

In my case, I waited 10 years for bison meat to become broadly available through mainstream commercial distribution channels. As years passed, I never forgot my experience with that bison burger. Finally I reached the point where I knew that, for some reason, it wasn't going to be made available. At the first opportunity, when Ken and I targeted a new life for ourselves, that plan included making bison meat available first to ourselves, then to others. It included hard work and being willing to be inconvenienced in exchange for a way out of our corporate lives.

The further away we got from the industrial parks and office buildings we'd known, the more clarity we gained. We found that beyond the inconvenience and work are wonders and gifts beyond measure. An extra bonus: it's less crowded.

2. Feed yourself first.

On any airline, one of the instructions given to adults traveling with a child is that in an emergency, they are to put on their own oxygen mask first, then assist the child. It had to be explained to me that if the adult passes out from lack of oxygen, the child is doomed, so it was important that this sequence be followed.

Similarly, once I sustainably learn to feed myself, by example and experience am I better able to encourage and empower others to feed themselves.

3. Remodel your empire.

As gratifying as it is to see the growing demand and appreciation for our 100 percent grassfed bison meat, Ken and I have no interest in empire building—though this was not always the case. When we first started out, there's no question that we had a far more traditional business or greed model approach. At the time, it was the only model we knew.

Now that raising 100 percent grassfed bison has become a small business way of life for us, we have indeed "struck it rich." We are passionate about inspiring and empowering others who know they want something more, but may not know where or how to start. Many people now seek us out because they want better food, better nutrition, and a better life for themselves, their families and for farm animals—while incorporating a gentle caring for the earth. We are happy to help by sharing our experience.

Becoming less dependent upon the commercial food industry ushers in a new form of self-sufficiency. This self-reliance often reflects in a general way how we feel about ourselves and that, in turn, can have a positive halo effect on others and our immediate environment.

4. Grow your own food when you can.

Rather than wait 10 years as I did, a better option may be to partially become your own food source, when and if you can. Instead of settling for questionable flavor and nutrition, produce your own food on a windowsill, apartment balcony, your backyard, or in a community garden. You will save money and know the source of your food.

It is unlikely that you will be able to grow everything you eat or eat everything you grow, especially if you live in a city, but even a small tomato plant on a windowsill is a start. Years ago, when we were renting in Santa Barbara, we planted corn in window boxes out in the patio area that bordered the sidewalk. At the time, I felt more than a little sheepish when I looked across the street at a neighbor's wall-to-wall orchids or patio full of flowers. But the popcorn species yielded a wonderful and tasty experience. Along with the heavenly smells from our kitchen, it also brought a lot of smiles from those walking by.

Some readers, for a variety of reasons, may not be able to take any of these steps. This is okay. If you can't contribute directly, support those who can—even if it is only with a smile, a nod, or a voice that authentically expresses appreciation and says "good job." For many of us, it takes courage to do something totally new and unfamiliar, and even more courage to stick with it through inevitable temporary setbacks.

For those readers who want to take a more active role, as with any remodeling effort, expect a learning curve as well as surprises in the way of weather, weeds, bugs and 'other.' As you convert flowerpots into vegetable pots, lawns into gardens, sunlight and water into food, partner with, support and encourage those who do the same. There's something about growing food that brings people together in positive, new and lasting ways.

5. Know the people who produce your meat.

Unless you are an avid and humane hunter, knowing the producer of your meat may require a little more thought, knowledge and effort. We found it was interesting, easier than we thought and absolutely worth the effort. For those who live in cities, Meat CSAs and buying clubs continue to grow in popularity. Join one to contract with a livestock producer or farmer and to secure ethically raised meat from a caring producer. If you buy where the farmer or rancher isn't available, get the phone number and call them to respectfully ask the questions you need answers for. Some individuals, even in cities, now raise their own chickens for eggs and meat. Others may do a partial barter or exchange of goods or services for meat.

6. Create a sustainable in-home menu.

In creating a meat menu and budget, apply the "Carnivore with a Conscience" nose-to-tail principle. Find new recipes and experiment with less-familiar cuts. This kind of menu honors all the gifts of the animal, not just steaks and burger. When everything is used, it means fewer animals are harvested and there is less waste. (See *Lindner Bison's 15 percent Steak Rule* in the Appendix.)

7. Create sustainable standards for out-of-home eating.

When dining out, support single location (as opposed to chain) restaurants that practice sustainability in some of these visible ways: nose to tail meat selections; seasonal selections of locally grown vegetables and fruit; menus which identify by name, farmers and ranchers who provide the food being served. Also look for restaurants that have proudly educated their food servers about where the restaurant sources the foods on the menu.

Meat items should honor species-specific guidelines created by organizations such as Animal Welfare Approved, the American Grassfed Association and Eatwild.com. If you can't get clear information from the menu, ask questions. If the restaurants in your area do not provide this information, respectfully suggest that they do.

If local restaurants are unable or unwilling to provide sustainable menu options, consider treating yourself, your food-growing friends and family to a sustainable potluck with vegetables from organic gardens or vegetable plots and meat from a humane producer you know. To reinforce the sustainable menu concept, have each person proudly tape a 3x5-inch card to the dish they bring. For vegetables, the card should have their name, the name of the food item, dates planted/harvested and a brief description of the non-toxic methods of weed and bug control. For meats, include the species and breed, where it lived, what it was fed, age at harvest and the cut used.

You will all have the satisfaction of knowing that the vegetables are fresh and healthy and that the meat came from a humanely treated, non-CAFO animal. By the end of the meal, you and your dinner companions will feel loved, cared for and respected on a new, contagious level.

8. Buy locally and regionally grown native-heritage food.

Be aware that not all locally grown food is produced by small farms or farmers. Some chain stores now post signs featuring locally grown products. While a step in the right direction, it's wise to keep in mind that many industrial food corporations share the wisdom of having their products grown near major metropolitan areas. This provides them with convenient access and distribution into a large urban population, though the likelihood may remain that the food is commercially or factory-farmed.

Caveat: Decoupling from a commodity based food system may mean going beyond the ideal 50-mile local radius while new farmers can get a better foot hold. As a general rule, all land near cities is often very expensive. This fact alone often prohibits sustainable small farmers and ranchers from getting started. In supporting the humane restoration of a native-heritage meat animal such as 100 percent grassfed bison, or the revival of a non-GMO heritage food species, be willing to buy *regionally* to encourage and support small new producers. Where, when and how we spend our food dollars encourages more of the same food to be produced.

9. Buy from and support small farmers in farmers' markets.

It's an exciting time for small farmers and farmers' markets everywhere. With continued public support and popularity, it's inevitable that the farmers' markets may experience growing pains and a kind of coming of age, depending on community supporters, stakeholders, market covenants, the integrity of those who manage them and whether or not they have a certification process for both market managers and growers.

As food dollars continue to move away from commercial food, it's reasonable to expect Big Food/Big Ag/Big Meat backlash to recapture eroding market share. These efforts may take various forms involving enforcement of new laws, regulations, and attempts to create doubt or discredit authentically small farmers. In addition there have been reports of large 'family-owned' mega-corporations with access to traditional commercial distribution applying for market space at farmers' markets. These days, it takes an experienced farmers' market manager to navigate these self-defining waters.

If a market is over 10 years old, it clearly has earned the support of the community and small farmers who sell there. However, there is a metamorphosis occurring for market goers and farmers both, and all farmers' markets are not created equal. Support those that meet your personal standards and criteria.

10. Support small farmers without compromising their sustainable efforts.

Now that the food movement has reached critical mass and the demand for food from farmers' markets continues to grow, one unexpected side effect may be inadvertently placing pressure on small farmers to produce or sell more. The reason that most small farmers are in farmers' markets in the first place is because they couldn't produce enough volume to be granted access to traditional mainstream distribution outlets.

In some areas, this has also resulted in what we refer to as market self-cannibalism, i.e., too many farmers' markets within a small area resulting in them feeding on one another's customer base and eroding the efforts of the small farmers who sell there. When visiting with small farmers who have sold in farmers' markets for a decade or more, many say the same thing. "Yes, we used to sell at markets two or three times a week and we could make enough money to pay our bills. Now we have to sell at five or six markets every week to make the same amount of money." Others have witnessed the arrival of commercial sellers in some markets, i.e., those with duplicate access to commercial channels.

All of this has occurred as the success and popularity of farmers' markets continues. Because small farmers deal in smaller volumes, they often provide higher quality products and better stewardship of the land, factors that make their products valuable and sought after. If the same small farmers are encouraged to get too big too fast, they may compromise and lose this sustainable edge.

We suggest the following to support small farmers who sell in farmers' markets:

(1) Rather than pressure small farmers to produce more and/or sell more often, encourage community leaders and regulating bodies to exercise wisdom and restraint in granting new applications for farmers' markets within areas already well served.

(2) Educate others on the value of supporting small farmers by shopping at farmers' markets one or two days of the week, rather than demanding access to them seven days per week. Farmers must have time to farm.

(3) Invite and encourage community residents to grow their own food. We believe that self-sustaining home gardens, community gardens and edible landscapes are a more attractive alternative than asking small farmers to become the very high-volume commercial food producers that many wish to avoid.

Most small farmers are content to remain small and/or expand at a reasonable rate to maintain product quality and integrity. They haven't succumbed to the chemical- and profit-driven models that promise production abundance at the expense of flavor and nutrition. However, because large commercial 'family' food interests are knocking on farmers' market doors, eager to pick up any slack or shortfall, the success of authentically small farmers may require our devotion and a commitment to *in*convenience as we distance ourselves from a commodity mindset spanning multiple generations.

11. Become informed and active; join food organizations.

Acquaint yourself with and support organizations that promote and support sustainable food production. This includes such online resources as Eatwild (www.eatwild.com), Animal Welfare Approved (www.animalwelfareapproved.org), Eat Well (www.eatwell.com) and others. Consider joining local chapters of the Weston A. Price Foundation or Slow Food. Seek out or organize Community Supported Agriculture (CSA) groups and meat CSAs. All of them provide a great start for connecting with like-minded individuals while you learn. More groups are emerging all the time.

To help you decide which organization(s) to join, check who they sponsor or endorse, and who sponsors or endorses them. For example, does the group acknowledge donations from a company or industry you would prefer not to support? Check their mission statement or goals and objectives to see how well their core values align with yours. And be prepared that your core values and/or theirs may change over time. Be willing to reassess and adjust your affiliations and choices as new information becomes available.

12. Attend a butchery class.

The shortage of qualified meat cutters for small food producers has had a large impact on consumers' ability to select and purchase meat from other than factory farms. You can help turn this around by supporting small local meat processors. One way to do this is to enroll in an artisan butchery class from an experienced old-time meat cutter. If one isn't available, track down a small butcher or small meat processor and offer to help organize a class. If they are like most of us, they would love to share what they know and empower others who are truly interested in learning. They simply may not have the time to organize such an event.

Like other endangered species, small, excellent meat cutters and true artisan butchers may be hard to find. Once you see the difference in the art of their meat cutting compared to commercial meat "fabricators," you'll understand our unbridled enthusiasm to preserve, protect and restore their numbers.

13. Offer hands-on help to your favorite small farmer.

"Crop-mobbing" is one way to help your small farmer with seasonal crop harvests. On February 24, 2010, *the New York Times Magazine* featured a terrific article online called *Field Report: Plow Shares.* Here's an excerpt:

"The Crop Mob, a monthly word-of-mouth (and Web) event in which landless farmers and the agricurious descend on a farm for an afternoon, has taken its traveling work party to 15 small, sustainable farms. Together, volunteers have contributed more than 2,000 person-hours, doing tasks like mulching, building greenhouses and pulling rocks out of fields."

"The more tedious the work we have, the better," Jones said, smiling. "Because part of Crop Mob is about community and camaraderie, you find there's nothing like picking rocks out of fields to bring people together."

You may also plan a working vacation on a ranch or farm. A

quick check online of an organization called WWOOF (World Wide Opportunities on Organic Farms, or Willing Workers on Organic Farms) will give you an idea of how this may work. While you're at it, you may want to take a look at a few of these randomly selected non-profit examples: pickyourown.org; growfood.org; farmtrails.org; caretakerfarm. org; terrafirmafarm.org; brookfieldfarm.org; and maryjanesfarm.org.

NOTE: Because we have no personal experience with these organizations, we do not endorse any of them. They are listed only as examples. Always research any organization thoroughly before you join and make sure you understand and are completely comfortable with their requirements before proceeding.

There may be nothing quite like directly approaching a small farmer you already know and support via your local farmers' market. Your interest conveys respect and your desire to reconnect. Chances are, after you've spent time on their farm or ranch, you may have such a newfound appreciation for that which nurtures the body, mind and spirit, that you may never look at food in the same way again. And that's the whole idea, isn't it?

14. Influence your peers.

Remember that silence often implies endorsement, agreement or permission. When someone casually mentions that they don't really care whether the meat they eat is grassfed or grainfed, consider that a ruminant in a feedlot somewhere may need your voice. Respectfully suggest that perhaps they should care. Caring may be the single most important ingredient missing in today's commercial production of food.

Many who say they don't care may be unaware of how this kind of mindset may unwittingly contribute to the quality of life for a meat animal. Given the opportunity, it's our experience that most people want to be reasonable and do the right thing. Though they may not know how to respond in the moment, your kind and respectful comment may plant a seed that will sprout later.

CHAPTER 24

A Call to Action
—FOR FOODSERVICE—

Foodservice as an industry expands far beyond the walls of restaurants. To name a few examples, it includes small food vendors, small and large event caterers, and massive distribution of ready-to-eat or near ready-to-eat assorted foods in shopping malls, supermarkets, hospitals, conventions, theme parks, sports arena, airlines and cruise lines. Pretty much where ever human beings congregate, foodservice will be there.

As an industry, perhaps the greatest potential for disconnect exists here. Most producers of commodity foods are as invisible as are the methods used to produce the food.

———◆———

We are proud to sell our 100 percent grassfed bison burger to a single location sustainable restaurant in Santa Monica called The Library Alehouse. With the exception of burger also sold to Lassen's Health Food in Ventura, our meat is sold directly to customers. In all cases, everyone pays the same amount. We do this for three reasons. We want (1) to avoid placing our customers into an unwittingly competitive position with restaurants or stores for our meat; (2) the price to reflect the value of the meat as a gift rather than a commodity, and (3) to encourage an equally shared, new awareness and respect for the work done by small farmers and ranchers.

While the items below are primarily addressed to caring chefs, we acknowledge that unless a restaurant is run by a chef/owner, the chef's influence and involvement may be controlled, managed and limited by those in the accounting office. Here the profit margin dictates.

Regardless of this fact, we've been inspired by chefs we've met and those we've read about, including the two British chefs mentioned earlier.

We share the belief that an active and caring interest by those involved in the preparation of meals may contribute in a positive way to how a meat animal is humanely and sustainably raised.

And we're all for that.

1. Meet your meat.

If you professionally cook, prepare, design and/or serve meat, be willing to learn about the meat animal's life. Get to know the producer of your meat with the goal of making a conscious and honorable connection. Welcome an opportunity to visit your meat while it is a living animal. See the environment where the animal lives. Does the same person raise it from birth to harvest? Is the animal's diet appropriate for the species? (For species-specific diets, visit animalwelfareapproved.org.)

NOTE: Be prepared that not all small farmers or ranchers are set up for on demand farm visits. Also, some may want to screen you in order to validate your request before allowing a visit. It is reasonable that they would want to do this. Remember, this is still new for most of us. Mutual patience, courtesy and respect as we forge new connections and shared new awareness are all elements in building a foundation of trust. If you aren't genuinely enlightened and positively moved by your farm or ranch visit, keep trying. The animals are worth this reconnect effort. You and your customers are worth it too, with the earth as the ultimate benefactor.

2. Make a living connection.

Learn the animal's number, name and harvest date. Hold a moment of silence long distance when that date arrives and consider offering a silent blessing when you cook and serve it to others. When appropriate, let others know this is your new practice. If you find yourself asking *Why*, considering asking yourself, *Why not?*

3. Develop a sustainable menu and cuisine.

Create a nose-to-tail menu featuring wonderful innovative dishes and new dining choices based on carcass yields. This helps create and expand value beyond the traditional price-point.

4. Honor seasonal variations and biodiversity of species.

Nature insists on biodiversity in plants and animals. Passionate and creative chefs celebrate this difference by adjusting their menus to reflect these seasonal variations. This will wisely expand to include variations in humanely raised meat animals harvested within seasonal timeframes. Pork that is raised in the spring may taste different than one raised during the fall. It may also depend on regions. A pork roast from a winter pig in the south will taste different from one raised in the fall in the northern states. Based on regional differences, similar variations in flavor and "mouthfeel" will apply to other meats as well, all a reason for celebration

The value of the sustainable meal lies within diversity, rather than consistency. To create a cuisine that not only changes from season to season, but year to year, requires a special kind of chef, someone as passionate about humane and ethical sustainability as he/she is about cooking. This chef's passion includes a willingness to educate dining patrons, food servers and culinary stakeholders.

5. Be a visible chef. Empower others.

Educate through printed words on menus and boards. Encourage, budget and allow for time with patrons. Be willing to provide a reconnect between where and how their meal was sustainably and humanely grown. Acknowledge by name, those who produced it. This means moving from the kitchen into the dining room. So there isn't a bottleneck of learning, educate food servers so they may reflect the same level of caring involvement and commitment to sustainably and humanely raised food.

6. Enroll in a butchery class.

The combination of chef and butchery professions may provide an authentic reconnect experience far beyond any flavor combinations ever conceived or taught. It may even inspire a new regard and perception for your profession. Ask yourself, "If the meat is humanely raised, authentically sustainable, with a unique regional or local species-specific flavor, how can I best honor and encourage that?"

SPECIAL CALL FOR
SMALL MEAT PROCESSORS AND
ARTISAN BUTCHERS

Your profession is a valuable and nearly lost art! More of you are needed, invited and welcome throughout our North American communities. As we all move toward a sustainable food system, many new farmers and meat producers are beginning by raising a variety of small meat species such as chickens, rabbits, turkeys; medium sized species such as pigs, goats, sheep and larger ruminants such as bison, elk, deer and cattle.

Small meat processors with humane mobile slaughter capability are especially in demand!

Not only are more small meat processors and butchers needed, many carnivores with a conscience want to reconnect with their meat by learning how to butcher. This demand creates ongoing opportunities to host a group class for a reasonable fee and teach the basics of nose-to-tail butchery. By helping others respectfully reconnect in this way, all the gifts from the animals are honored and sustainable menu planning is encouraged by wasting nothing.

You may want to consider approaching talented class participants and see if they are open to a partial barter. Perhaps they are willing to help part-time during your busy seasons. We are all interested and vested in making sure you stay in business — we have so much to learn and there are so few of you to learn it from!

CHAPTER 25

A Call To Action
—FOR BISON PRODUCERS—

This section is included with the respectful understanding that first and foremost, it is not to tell bison producers how to run their businesses. Instead, we speak as advocates for the animals. Based on our experience and the history of the species, we believe bison deserve basic husbandry considerations that fully recognize "the bison-ness of the bison."

———◆———

1. If you can, raise 100 percent grassfed bison.

We've described our journey into grassfed bison ranching as the food movement was just beginning to develop momentum. During this same time, a parallel cultural shift was occurring having to do specifically with avoiding meat from ruminants that had been placed in feedlots.

Within the few largest commercial producer and packer circles of the bison industry, little has changed over the past two decades. Despite overwhelming demand for 100 percent grassfed, bison feedlots and commodity pricing are encouraged, competition and trophies awarded based on carcass weight and size, all symptoms of what is now commonly regarded as a broken and unsustainable food system.

In contrast, demand for grassfed meats has moved to center stage. A 100 percent grassfed bison meat business humanely honors this native-heritage meat animal, as well as the earth and other inhabitants of the eco-system.

2. If you can, sell your meat directly to those who will eat it.

Directly interacting with customers on a regular basis gave us far more than a way to pay our bills. It provided a connection to and a value beyond anything we would have known to expect or ask for. A few years ago, we began to realize that our experiences selling meat directly to customers was something many bison producers may have no way of knowing unless we told them. So while writing the book, when we could, we sent out a few emails to 100 percent grassfed bison producers we knew. Below are two of those emails.

They represent only a small sample of our reconnect experience over the years. We encourage and invite other 100 percent grassfed bison producers to pursue, experience and fully understand this kind of customer impact in appreciation for their efforts. For us, it made all the difference in defining and reinforcing what we are doing, how we are doing it and why.

EMAIL 1.

We just wanted to send you a special note because we are so moved by our customers that we want you to know too. People are so appreciative of the 100 percent grassfed bison meat we sell them. This has been going on for years and for some reason is renewed again in 2011. They understand so much more now about the animals and commercially grainfed meats. It's not uncommon for customers of every shape and size imaginable to emotionally thank us for doing what we're doing.

And we in turn want to thank you for what you're doing.

Though we are very careful to make no health claims, our customers make it a point to seek us out and provide testimonials. Last week, a customer described how a family member with stage 4 cancer couldn't digest other meat, but could digest ours. A mother of a 12-year old with leukemia reported back that her son loved the bone stock she made for him and was back for more. A husband told us his Ukrainian wife burst into tears after she tasted our meat because it reminded her of her homeland – meat here had been difficult for her to eat. A man stood for five minutes waiting for Ken to be free in a farmers' market. When Ken finally turned to him, the man said, "I just want to shake your hand. That was absolutely the best roast I've had in my entire life. Thank you for what you're doing."

The list is nearly endless and we could go on, but we wanted you to know that we believe the significance of what you are doing cannot be overstated. For us, for the animals and for the earth. There is trust building in not only 100 percent grassfed bison meat, but also and perhaps most especially in those who produce 100 percent grassfed bison.

We receive expressions of gratitude and esteem for our efforts. Please know we share this sense of gratitude and esteem for your efforts.

Thank you for what you're doing and continue to do.

Email 2.

I'm stealing a minute when I should be doing other things, but I just got a call from a customer who wanted to order for tomorrow. This is a good example of what we mentioned earlier, and it's important to Ken and I that you and other grassfed bison producers start hearing these stories. It's more now than about empire building. The empire is pretty much in shambles, so this is about empire remodeling. But before that can happen, here's where we start, one customer at a time.

B. is a woman who is probably in her early 50s though she easily looks to be in her mid-60s. Looking at her, she would be easy to miss in a crowd. Somewhat dowdy, bright orange lipstick and dated clothes, she looks angry and tired as if she had the weight of the world on her shoulders. A few weeks ago she bought our meat. It was a short conversation about cooking. As she left I thought what a sad, lonely and sour person, certainly unhappy and unimpressed with anything I had to say about the meat.

The next week she came back. She wanted to know if I remembered her, that she had bought some neck bones and osso buco the week before. I remembered her lipstick first, then her. Then I waited – we never know how people cook the meat, so I braced myself. She began to talk and after saying just a few words, she stopped unable to talk and struggling to regain her composure. As I reached out and touched her arm, she began to tearfully describe that she had lost one son who had died the year before. Now she was in Los Angeles to visit her other son, 35 yrs. old who was also sick and couldn't eat. She said she took the meat home and cooked it up for him that night. She said he ate it all up and then said to her, "You know mom, that tasted so good, I just have to have a glass of wine." She apologized for crying and still couldn't speak, so I just smiled and said, "So you're here for some more?" She laughed and nodded gratefully and together we pulled more items for her to take. Two weeks later, she's now calling to order the items for pickup tomorrow and thanked me several times again over the phone.

This is part of the reconnect process in this food movement that we unexpectedly found ourselves part of. People who find us often need something to trust and believe in, and meat is such a basic part of that. I have no idea what her son suffers from, but I will ask tomorrow if I can. In the meantime, it's our privilege to be able to share the ongoing journey with you so you have an opportunity to see that this is a different time from what any of us have experienced or known in the past. We're working hard to use the moments wisely and well, and we thank you for all you're doing too. It matters in more ways than many of us could've ever imagined and probably in other ways that we may never know. But what we do know, is that it's all good.

NOTE: We since found out both sons seemed to have food allergies of some kind that are mystifying doctors.

Selling our meat directly to those who eat it has provided perspective, meaning and value far beyond raising the animals and receiving a reasonable price.

3. Understand that the bison meat market is changing.

The new meat market reflects a cultural shift in values that includes 100 percent grassfed meat production of ruminants as a synergistic part of sustainable ranching and farming.

Whether buying at a supermarket, farmers' market or eating in a restaurant, meat customers want to reconnect with their humane meat producers. As they move away from a commodity system that has insulated customers and producers from each other, and confused them by using unregulated terms and claims, many have created their own standards. Families want to know if the money they spend for food supports a sustainable or unsustainable system. And they tell their friends via social media networks.

Large or small, most bison producers by their very nature, are conservationists. The species itself insures this. They are efficient graziers, requiring less water, little if any handling, no calving help, have lower protein requirements in grass and hay, and an innate ability to withstand the weather extremes of the North American continent as well as protect themselves against natural predators.

Until recent years, customers tended to hold bison producers in high esteem because they believed that the producers reflected the same sustainable values exhibited in the species they choose to raise. Many believed that all bison were fed only grass. They now understand that this is not true and they need to specifically ask. They do ask.

In addition, customers have learned that most large bison producers not only feedlot their bison, but some dehorn them as well. In fact one man said, "They treat them just like cattle. They raise them like cattle, they make them look like cattle – if they want cattle so bad, why don't they just raise cattle?"

Customers increasingly understand that most bison meat sold in supermarkets, health food stores and restaurants is grainfed, a practice well documented and recognized as not only unsustainable, but an ecological disaster. Some tell us that given a choice between 100 percent grassfed bison and 100 percent grassfed beef, they choose bison. Given the choice between grainfed bison and 100 percent grassfed beef, they choose beef. Given only a choice of grainfed, feedlot meat, many prefer to remove red meat from their menu and buy elsewhere online rather than support that which they regard as inhumane and unsustainable. When eating out, if the menu doesn't say 100 percent grassfed and/or provide the producer's name, they choose another item.

This is no longer a niche or elitist customer, this is an educated Main Street customer. Because of what they've learned, they tell us they are interested in only buying 100 percent grassfed bison from producers they can trust.

4. Disconnect from a mainframe mindset

The more we thought about it, the more the feedlot system reminded us of our earlier years in corporate America. In the old days of huge, centralized computers, only a select few individuals had access to the mainframe. They alone had the control. If you wanted to have anything computed, you had to que up, go through them and play by their rules.

A feedlot is a centralized function accessible only to only a few who have the funds to run such a place. Everyone else has to play by their rules, pay their prices, conform to their standards. These standards are, of course designed to benefit the feedlot operator and the meat packer – no one else.

In the 1980s, it seemed that almost overnight, employees began bringing their strange looking, small personal computers to the office. They had begun decoupling from the mainframe. Today we all have distributed computer systems – everyone has their own computer autonomy. The increase in creativity and productivity exploded with more people involved. And 'distributed computer systems' does not necessarily mean anarchy either. Some of the most complex problems are being solved by wide area networks made up of small computers.

Grass feeding must ultimately be done by a distributed system. It will involve many small ranches and need many more people to get it done. (Think more jobs!) The creativity and productivity will also explode when more people are empowered to finish animals on grass using their own methods and standards, adapted to their own ranch's environment.

And here too, grass feeding will not necessarily lead to anarchy of meat standards or quality. Producers may choose to join a network or cooperative to sell their products, adapting the same general standards that humanely recognize the bison-ness of the bison.

The opportunities to proudly and uniquely trumpet forth regional differences are just beginning to be understood, as well as the paths that will take us there. For example,

(1) Consider ways that may naturally extend your growing season, such as using warm and cool season grasses and rotational grazing. Exciting

new information is also surfacing regularly on new ways to enhance pasture growth and improve drought resistance without chemicals. Mychorrizae and biochar fall into these categories and we encourage you to learn more about both. They are natural tools to enhance grass yields, enrich the soil and retain water.

(2) Be open to new possibilities with old information. Research done years before, but ignored because of the quick fixes promised by industrial agriculture, is now resurfacing and is being looked at again. One particular article had to do with using carbon to sequester and hold onto nitrogen in the soil. Another mentioned a study using minerals to successfully treat brucellosis. A source for much of this information is *Acres USA, The Voice of Eco-Agriculture,* based for the past 40 years in Austin, Texas. There are multiple other sources online. Our interest is not to confirm or deny, but simply offer these as examples of just a few ways to begin decoupling from the mainframe system.

(3) Explore grass farming methods that pertain to the uniqueness of your area. Our place, for example, has irrigation. Though expensive, we're glad to have it. Other bison producers may have no irrigation, instead doing dryland farming dependent on what falls out of the sky. Still others may have washy grasses from too much rain. New information and support from sustainable organizations increasingly invite us all to readdress these issues in an ecologically friendly way.

(4) Develop new questions. (a) For some time, we've heard that it takes longer to get an animal to harvestable weight on grass. Is this a problem? Two years or three years to reach harvestable weight makes no difference as long as each year the next group of animals is ready. (b) We've also heard that feeding grass and/or hay is more expensive than feeding grain or corn. Is this true? It is true that a grassfed animal may be lighter in weight compared to a fat laden, feedlot animal. But feedlot fat is not what we want for our bison, nor do our customers want it. Also, not all meat processors/packers penalize producers for 100 percent grassfed carcasses that fail to reach weight levels of their feedlot counterparts.

(5) Is there a way to improve the soil through affordable and biologically sound approaches? If not, perhaps a professional grass finisher could help. These are people who make their living by managing ruminants on grass and are paid based on the weight an animal gains while in their care. While some systems were originally designed for domestic livestock, the sustainable premise of rotational grazing is duplicatable with bison. (See Resources/Jim Gerrish and Greg Judy books.)

5. Join or create a regional 100 percent grassfed bison cooperative with other small producers.

Decoupling from a mainframe mindset may include finding another way to process and market your grassfed meat. Based on our experience the past eight years, we believe that not only is this possible, it is exactly what customers are hoping for. For those who aren't able to fill their own orders and ship meat, joining with other small bison producers who share the same core values may offer the additional opportunity to experience first-hand the positive and sustainable differences you are making as a humane producer of 100 percent grassfed bison meat.

6. Honor the bison-ness of the bison.

As outlined in Chapter 21, Bison producers may find they have issues unique to raising a wild or non-amenable species. We believe this uniqueness is a profound strength rather than a weakness. Addressing the issues in a way that honors the nature of bison may surpass your greatest expectations.

We believe bison's ancient and finely tuned systems are ill-equipped to withstand human intervention or artificial 'improvement' ala the domestic cattle model. Humanely unaltered and given their natural diet of grass, they are not only fine the way they are, but superior in many ways, far beyond any commodity or domestic livestock model in existence.

By honoring them, they in turn, honor us.

CHAPTER 26

Societal Call to Action

Our experiences with bison propelled us into a new world and encouraged us to share what we've learned. The suggestions offered here acknowledge our belief that bison belong to more than just those of us who are fortunate enough to raise them.

They belong to all of us.

———◆———

Bison are meat animals and a living symbol that crosses cultures. Rather than a global commodity item to make investment bankers rich, bison are a living symbol that crosses cultures. No other species in North America can make this claim. Therefore, we invite a new awareness, connection and involvement from all Americans who are drawn to bison as we and many producers have been drawn.

Because of strides made by emerging science and technology, bison have recently become a potential genetic treasure-trove dating back millions of years. While this new technology may be understandably exciting for some, it is equally alarming for others. Science and technology press us ever forward before we are able to understand the strengths and frailties of that technology. We ask that reasonable and measured caution be exercised by policy makers, community stakeholders, bison producers and the public, until the results and implications of the technology are fully understood.

In other words, what is tested for today may omit significant elements vital to meaningful interpretation tomorrow. It is in this spirit, that we respectfully make the following societal calls to action.

1. Scrutinize any bison conservation plans that could lead to reclassification of bison either as an endangered species or as a commodity.

Since the USDA was asked to add and track bison pricing in 2004, much has been learned about the commodity markets and more is still being learned about the investment banking community in general. Business for them has not changed much since the 2008 collapse, but we note with interest the presence of former Goldman Sachs executives at the 2011 bison "conservation" discussion table in Tulsa. (See item #4.)

In the wake of information reported following the 2010 gulf oil spill and The Nature Conservancy (TNC) Leadership Council (comprised of agri-business companies such as Altria, British Petroleum, Chevron, Dow Chemical, ExxonMobil, Monsanto and Nestle), it is reasonable to consider that non-profit based "conservation" may the new cookie jar for investment bankers and agri-business. In response to critics, TNC president/CEO and former Goldman Sachs executive Mark Tercek said he accepted the billions of dollars " . . . from these companies, so they are not just part of the problem but so they can be part of the effort to restore . . ." If someone causes a problem aren't they legally and morally obliged to fix it anyway? Regardless of the answer, the affiliations may not bode well for massive land conservation and restoration activities that may involve bison.

2. Preserve the non-amenable species classification of bison in perpetuity.

Currently, the USDA has two classifications for meat animals. The classification "amenable" applies to domestic species such as cattle, swine and poultry; while the classification "non-amenable" applies to non-domestic or wild species such as bison, elk, deer and antelope.

Motivated by profit, some high volume commercial bison producers have led efforts to change the classification of bison from a "non-amenable" to an "amenable" species. The significance of these two classifications has been the subject of discontent between commercial bison producers and small bison producers for decades, certainly since we can remember. Now it's time to share what we know.

Federal law mandates that amenable species must be processed only at USDA-inspected plants. Inspections conducted there are funded by tax dollars. In contrast, and depending on the availability of the meat processor, non-amenable species may be voluntarily processed at either a USDA-inspected facility, or a small meat processing plant controlled by the state or county. (As to practical safety concerns, USDA ultimately oversees state and county processors as well, assuring that appropriate safety standards are in place. If they aren't, they have the power to shut the processor's business down until corrective action has been taken.)

All producers requesting voluntary USDA inspection for their non-amenable bison pay an out-of-pocket fee for these services, whereas amenable inspection is mandatory and paid for by tax dollars. Therefore many large-scale bison producers, more likely to use the larger USDA-inspected facilities, would like to see bison reclassified as "amenable" in order to exempt them from inspection fees.

It's not that simple though and there are corresponding negative consequences for the animal. Reclassification would also exempt bison from protections that the non-amenable designation confers. As mentioned earlier, these risks are clearly outlined in an article published in the Western Bison Association's October, 2010 *Bison Review* and posted online at lindnerbison.com.

The article, written by small bison producers W. Michael and Kathleen O'Neil Gear, is entitled "Bison Genetics - The New War Against Bison." It describes the recent DNA test developed by Texas A&M University for the purpose of detecting cattle markers in bison. Concluding that any cattle markers in bison resulted from breeding with cattle in the last several hundred years, some individuals are prematurely pushing to reclassify these bison as cattle. As the Gears point out, this may not only be incorrect, it may also incorrectly reclassify some bison as amenable.

With the Gears' permission, we posted their article on our website and called it to the attention of those who receive our annual newsletter. The following is Lindner Bison's introduction to this article, which can also be found on our website.

> *Though written for a bison producers' Winter 2010 newsletter, the importance of the Gears' article concerning the status of bison as a non-amenable species and perhaps even as meat animals cannot be overstated. For consumers, if some bison are scientifically reclassified as cattle, this may automatically place them in the USDA data bank as an amenable, rather than a non-amenable, species. Based on current U.S. production standards and meat processing laws, the significance of this is three-fold:*
>
> *1. Production methods of amenable species (such as currently done with cattle, sheep, goats and swine) may include elements of dehorning, confinement, castration, artificial insemination, feedlotting, cross-breeding, cloning and patent ownership.*

2. *Meat processing standards for amenable species may actually encourage feedlotting (some meat processors financially penalize producers for lighter carcasses from nongrainfed animals), mandatory inspection, where and how the meat may be stored, sold and/or distributed.*

3. *Amenable species and brucellosis. Other than what we all read in the papers and see in the news, many are unaware of the history of brucellosis and bison. Occasionally we read about Yellowstone National Park and cattle ranchers being upset because bison carry a disease called brucellosis. They are concerned their cattle will become infected with brucellosis when bison migrate out of the park every winter in search of food. Some interesting brucellosis points are rarely mentioned:*

a. Elk are also carriers of brucellosis and are allowed to enter and leave the park freely;

b. Cattle originated the disease, bringing it with them from Europe. Bison developed a tolerance for it in order to survive. The cattle basically can become reinfected from other animals that have developed the ability to carry the disease without becoming sick.

c. Brucellosis control methods:

(1) Amenable species. Currently, the law for controlling brucellosis in amenable cattle is to slaughter the entire herd of cattle.

(2) Non-amenable species. Because bison are non-amenable, they are tested to confirm the presence of the disease. Culling is based on individual test results. Should bison ever become reclassified as cattle and brucellosis discovered, the entire Yellowstone and other herds could be required by law to be slaughtered rather than individually culled.

Amenable meat classification has long been favored by commercial meat producers and commercial distribution channels, since mandatory USDA inspection costs are paid by taxpayers. For at least a decade, commercial bison interests lobbied heavily in Washington to reclassify bison as amenable, while the majority of small ranchers and producers have been against it.

The non-amenable meat classification of bison benefits small producers and ranchers, as well as the bison. Though small ranchers pay USDA inspection fees out of pocket, we do this based on our individual choice, uniqueness of our markets and access to small meat processors, rather than on a mandated or regulated basis.

Through their research, the Gears have introduced critical new information and thinking concerning issues of bison species purity. We are proud to share this timely information as we move ever forward to produce and honor this native-heritage species. In these days of testing, cloning and patenting, Lindner Bison favors reasonableness, thoughtfulness, vigilance and caution. And sharing new information as it becomes available.

Kathy & Ken Lindner, Lindner Bison

Because we believe there is more at stake than taxpayer paid inspection fees, it is time that the public be given an opportunity to become familiar with the issues at hand. Should reclassification attempts for bison progress, it may trigger a time period for receiving public comment. This is when people from all walks of life are given a chance to voice any concerns they may have about a proposed new policy. Unless these issues become clear before that time occurs, it is unlikely the public would understand the importance of maintaining species classification of bison as non-amenable, in perpetuity.

3. Exempt non-amenable bison from genetic modification and cloning, in perpetuity.

We can all proactively work to protect bison as a non-amenable species *exempt* from genetic manipulation, modification, patent ownership and cloning. Until we do, we may be sentencing them to a future of unknown science experiments, disguised as conservation, but designed for the financial gain of a select few. As has already happened with genetically engineered seed and cloned meat animals, cloning and patenting may indeed submit bison to corporate ownership, subject to national and international patent laws.

In today's age of cloning, patenting and Genetically Modified Organisms (GMOs), to the best of our knowledge, bison DNA is still intact. In other words, bison genetics haven't been artificially manipulated by humans.

Going forward, it will be up to all of us, as well as future generations, to decide whether or not to preserve the species regardless of the capabilities science and technology tempt us with. Ownership of the bison genome belongs to generations of all Americans, past, present and future. We will all need to proactively partner together to ask our government officials and representatives to take the necessary protective steps to put these exemptions into law.

"We are all one now," said the Native American drum maker.

We agree. Whether private individuals or ranchers, bison belong to all of us. They deserve our sacred and honorable best.

4. Assure that conservation efforts recognize the humane production of bison for meat.

Based on new information received during the finishing of this book, there is reason to believe there may be an effort by commercial bison producers and land conservancies to bring a new "conservation" matter before the public concerning bison. This may be anchored in part on questionable DNA test results of a small segment of the tested bison population, declaring some bison 'pure' and others 'impure.' The full bison genome is currently being sequenced by the University of Iowa, but at last report, excludes prehistoric genetic sequencing. This omission must be remedied before the full picture may be realized.

Regardless of the bison genome sequencing outcome and because most commercial bison producers involved in the conservation effort are known to feedlot their bison and some dehorn, Lindner Bison's position is that in order for this conservation effort to achieve viable and authentic sustainability, it cannot separate the conservation process from the humane production of bison meat animals from birth to death. This includes diet, while on or off any conservation properties. We believe that the feedlotting of bison and conservation of bison are mutually exclusive. Together they make no sense.

Before conservation synergy can occur, intended husbandry practices by participating producer/ranchers should be disclosed, factoring in all participants of the ecosystem, namely, us, the animals and the earth. Without these three elements identified and appropriately addressed including a 100 percent grass diet, the entire conservation effort may be regarded as unsustainable and therefore, unjustifiable.

SUMMARY

We need to learn how to feed ourselves, given reasonable limitations of our location, seasons, weather, acts of God, culture and/or other influencing elements. While lobbying for an overhaul of our existing food system, rather than wait for it to happen, instead start your own family garden if you can. Each day, become just a little less dependent on industrialized, commercial food. Stand into this storm because it may not pass for generations. The storm is really about who we are, what we value and how we define both.

Ken and I were no different from the young men and women we see today, finding their voice, seeing what their elders have done and are doing. Trying to do it better, knowing that it can be better. We are those village elders now. We stepped out on faith and traveled our path, similar to those paths many are just beginning to find.

As a child of and mostly distant observer of the 60s, I learned that being idealistic often didn't mean being realistic. My moments, which may differ from yours, I will uniquely use. Perhaps I'll take more risk, such as writing this book. If just one person is empowered in a positive way, telling our story may be the only light we can offer in the hope that others may more clearly find their own path, and with it, their way home.

This book, this call to action is meant to be such a light. For those who read it and are touched by it, it is for you. You are touched because you care, as we have cared. You perhaps are ready for change, the way we were ready for change. You may be afraid, the way we were afraid. And perhaps you know too, above all your fears and insecurities, that what we do affects other people. It affects animals, the earth and all that we call home. Perhaps you too have faith that it can be better.

Because faith without works is dead, we share with you this closing riddle:

Q: Three birds were sitting on a fence. One decided to fly away. How many are left?

A: Three. One only *decided* to fly away.

May you fly far.

ACKNOWLEDGMENTS

1. A Special Thanks to Farmers' Markets

As Ken and I began visiting the various farmers' markets for the first time, we found market managers and customers who genuinely wanted us and our meat there—unlike the commercial channels we had tried for years. They seemed to want to see us to succeed. Today, eight years later, we are still selling at some of these same markets.

Gretchen in Pasadena was the first to give us a spot Saturday mornings in the non-certified section (a section reserved for agricultural products that have been processed in some way like our meat, or jam or juice made from fruit the farmer grew). A strong, striking 50-plus-year-old blond, her deep bond with the farmers there is apparent. Some farmers have been with her since the market opened in 1984. When we started we had little meat to sell, so we alternated with another farmer and sold there every other week. Though we don't sell there now, we are forever grateful for her willingness to give us a chance, as well as for her counsel, advice and support. The same goes for the wonderful Pasadena market-goers who supported and encouraged us. Pasadena is where we started.

Torrance was the second market to let us sell our meat. Mary Lou warmly welcomed us and in a no-nonsense Mother Hen fashion, clucked after us with curiosity and interest. She seemed to appreciate our fledgling efforts and we felt well supported by her and her volunteers. We still do after all these years.

But it was Jane, the personable market manager of the Sunday Encino farmers' market who we first met and talked with about selling in farmers' markets. An astute businesswoman, Jane had a down to earth manner and warmth that quickly drew us to her. She helped direct our thinking, and provided endless people to call so we could learn from their experience. She seemed to always have time for us and to want to see us succeed. It was perhaps in Encino where we learned the most. Customers recognized us as the awkward, middle-aged newcomers that we were and volunteered invaluable suggestions. One senior businesswoman in particular sternly pointed out that we needed a better system so that customers weren't asked to wait while we determined what each item cost. She was right. Because of her, we created a spreadsheet system that we still use today.

Despite our love for the Encino market and community, eventually the time came when we had to let it go. We were selling in two other markets and needed to consolidate our efforts. Eventually Jane moved on too, but not before endearing herself to us and many others.

On the recommendation of several customers, we applied to sell in the Hollywood Farmers' Market on Sundays and were excited when a spot opened up. By now, we had fliers and recipe handouts and were better able to answer questions from equally excited and enthusiastic new customers. Most farmers and market goers agree that there is an amazing energy in Hollywood. Attendees come in variety of local and long-distance shapes and sizes. They all seem to love, nurture, support, protect and promote the Hollywood community as well as the small farmers who have gathered there for 20 years. The market originated in the hope that the historic area could be resurrected and reclaimed from the unfortunate slum area it had become. Through the farmers' weekly presence and attendance by market goers, today the market may embody the best of what any community can hope to achieve: support, hope, acceptance, warmth, caring and a general feeling of good will.

Pompea, the market manager, enlists the help of several volunteers and staff to keep the place humming. A gifted, capable woman she recently ushered into existence *The Hollywood Farmers' Kitchen,* located a short half block from the Sunday market. I honestly don't know how she does what she does at her age, but I swear she can dance circles around me on a regular basis. We admire and respect her, as do many.

Finally, the historic and large Santa Monica Farmers' Market added us on Wednesdays and shortly thereafter we were given space in the Saturday market as well. Laura, the Wednesday market manager, is a handsome, fit blond woman with an infectious enthusiasm and passion. One sharp cookie and excellent promoter, she is actively involved with the local KCRW *Good Food* show, hosted by Evan Kleiman. Laura somehow manages to snag time for farmers and introduce their seasonal products to market-goers as well as the local culinary community. We're among the many who seem to thrive on her upbeat presence and support.

Mort, manager of Santa Monica's Saturday Market has endeared himself to me as a beloved curmudgeon of sorts, who fastidiously looks after farmers and patrons and quickly responds to the market's changing needs.

In his mid-fifties, sporting a trim physique and trademark moustache, he takes on the persona of the stern, caring father with a soft underbelly. In spite of the stricter time allowance for the market's operations, Mort regularly makes time to stop by and ask how things are going. And that always feels good.

The last market to enthusiastically add us, was the Sunday Long Beach Marina market. Last only because Dale, the manager, confessed he had somehow misplaced our phone number. Grateful that we called back, we were equally glad to be offered an opportunity there. In fact, he was the very first to visit our ranch and allow us to proudly show him around. A semi-retired minister, Dale is passionate for sustainable food and regularly elevates awareness and appreciation for the small farmers who produce it. As another early pioneer, Dale is widely respected in the Southern California farmers' market community.

2. Pioneering Storm Standers

As much as our love energizes and empowers us, Ken and I could never have realized our ongoing dream without information and inspiration from others. The following list recognizes some of the people who stood at the forefront of the storm before most of us even knew there was one. Most of these people had to struggle to be heard over the din of complacency, convenience and greed, but they remained firm in their vision, hope and purpose, encouraging, strengthening. There may never be enough words to thank them for their integrity, their courage and their caring.

Jo Robinson, author of *Why Grassfed is Best* (1999) and founder of the website Eatwild.com made herself available by phone during the creation of her book and website. Through Jo, we learned for the first time that raising ruminant animals 100 percent on pasture was not only better for our health, but for the health of the animals and the earth as well. Jo's research provided us with the first solid evidence of what grassfed bison producers had believed for years. She provided information in a way we could understand and champion for ourselves and our herd. We have never looked back.

Joel Salatin, a farmer-activist-writer, was the subject of the July 2000 *Smithsonian* magazine article entitled "Down on This Farm the Times They Are A-changin'." Given to us by a neighbor, the article motivated us to make a five-hour winter pilgrimage from Pittsburgh to Salatin's Polyface Farms in Virginia to buy chicken and to learn. We followed Joel, who wisely insisted we help with chores around the farm, asking questions and getting answers. Because of him, we included multi-species farming and rotational grazing in our plans and learned what respect for the animals and the earth looked like. His refusal to ship his meat to customers was our first introduction to this non-barcode empire-remodeler who sought to encourage others to ethically farm or ranch within their own regional communities. We've read many of his books listed on the Resources page.

Michael Pollan's March 31, 2002 *New York Times* article "Power Steer" provided riveting clarity to a broad scale of feedlot-related issues that had troubled us for years. His writing style and perspective gave us courage to continue on the road less traveled and move beyond what bison industry leaders were touting. This article secured the foundation provided by Jo Robinson as we continued to build our fledgling business and find our way.

The bricks and mortar came next: Michael Pollan's *The Omnivore's Dilemma* and *In Defense of Food*; the Slow Food organization founded in Italy by Carlos Petrini; the Weston A. Price Foundation, Los Angeles chapter; the documentaries *Food, Inc.*, *SuperSize Me* and *King Korn*; *Fast Food Nation* by Eric Schlosser; subscription magazines *Acres USA*, *Mother Earth News*, and *The Stockman Grass Farmer*; *The River Cottage Meat Book: For Carnivores with a Conscience* by Hugh Fearnley-Whittingstall; Jamie Oliver's TV series *Food Revolution*; and last, but not least, the article "Putting Bison on Feedlots: Unnatural, Unnecessary, Unsafe," by Andrew Gunther, director, Animal Welfare Approved.

We recognize two other authors. Though we discovered them only recently, their work actually pre-dates the efforts of the above-mentioned pioneers. The first is Wendell Berry, teacher, activist, and author of *The Unsettling of America*, first published in 1977 and reissued in 1996. Berry has written and spoken tirelessly about the importance of choosing community over industry and land ownership over agribusiness contracts. Berry, according to fellow-writer Michael Pollan, is "an American treasure" and "one of our greatest dot-connectors." The second is Wes Jackson, president of The Land Institute and author of *Becoming Native to This Place* (1996). In his book, he advocates the notion that agriculture – not agri-business, is the source of a healthy culture. Also, he believes resettlement will continue to see intelligent and knowledgeable pioneers with staying power and that economic development has not only led to ecological destruction, but ". . . has been destructive of our relationships with people and with place."

New storm-standers are emerging all the time. Among the most recent are bison producers Kathleen O'Neal Gear and W. Michael Gear of Wyoming. Through their pioneering article "Bison Genetics, The New War Against Bison," we became aware of this critical issue and the potential hijacking of the species by industrial and commercial interests. Despite backlash, it is this article that inspired the current bison genome sequencing by the University of Iowa.

Accidental discovery of a short youtube.com video with Joanna Macy described three revolutions in U.S. history—agricultural, industrial and now, ecological—which led us to David Korten's 2006 book called *The Great Turning*. The last sentence in his book provided the title for Part IV of our book. Author of several other books, Korten's premise put into words what many of us have felt and experienced: No one will fix it for us. We as individuals may be our best hope going forward.

If there is a Great Turning, may it begin here with the listed individuals and continue with those from all walks of life who are called to become the first generation of eco-pioneers as they forge authentic and sustainable reconnects between us and other living species on the earth.

3. Professional/Personal

I don't know about other first time authors, but there is no way you'd be reading this without editing and design help from these key people.

Connie Jacobs quickly grasped the essence in the cover design as well as the overall book design and it's been an absolute pleasure working with her.

Stacia and Robert Guzzo, a young Tehachapi couple, agreed to wade through the very first rough draft and provide meaningful comments and insights. My first draft was awful, but they provided loving counsel and patience as I found my way.

Jess Taylor pretty much threw a big bucket of ice cold water on my ego and then handed me a towel. Because of his keen insight and perspective, I worked harder to unpeel story layers that were waiting to emerge. They are here now because of him – thanks Jess.

Frances Robinson, intimately knowledgeable about many of the food movement issues gently and methodically waded through the final draft line by line, revising, smoothing, rearranging and providing a readability I simply could not summon forth. The book has been enriched by her caring, intellectual and moral involvement.

Ken Lindner, of course, my first always reader, editor, deleter, thrower-awayer. Thank you for your love and best-friendship, your clarity, commitment, support and for sharing the vision and wonder of the journey. The best is yet to come.

APPENDIX

Lindner Bison's 15 percent Steak Rule™
Sustainable Menu & Budget Planning
for Carnivores with a Conscience

The adage "You get what you pay for" may never apply more than it does today concerning U.S. food production and 100 percent grassfed bison meat. We continue to appreciate that *what* we choose to eat defines, in large part, how food is produced and how that food production affects us, the animals and the earth.

As new customers discover humanely raised 100 percent grassfed bison meat and a new price structure, we enjoy teaching that it's not necessary to spend a lot of money for this meat if you don't want to. Proudly and sustainably, we practice *nose-to-tail eating* and our product list reflects this. Lindner Bison seeks to honor the gifts of each animal by wasting nothing. In this way we show respect, appreciation and gratitude.

Though Lindner Bison has unlimited access to steaks, we generally eat them on a quarterly basis or about every 3-4 months. How can we ask our customers to eat sustainably if we don't? When hungry for a steak experience, we enjoy our wonderful cubed steaks (aka minute steaks), kabob or top round cuts, as well as other choices from roast, ribs or burger categories. All are delicious & have higher yields. Typically the higher the yield, the lower the price, so this may be an added benefit to move off the steaks.

Our 15 percent Steak Rule is this: On average, about 15 percent of the carcass is steak. *When we practice sustainable eating, this means our menu is generally planned in similar proportion as carcass yield percentages.* So for steaks, as an example, with 365 days/year, 15 percent = 55 days. When we practice *Meatless Mondays*, the year becomes 313 days, and the 15 percent rule equals 47 days. Consider an average meat portion is around 1/2 lb. or 8 oz., and go from there. It's a good start for sustainable and affordable menu planning.

Planning a sustainable menu based on carcass yield creates a shared new connection between us, the animals and the earth. When everything is used, there is less waste and fewer harvests are necessary!

A naturally nutritiously-dense meat, 100 percent grassfed bison has more protein & iron, with less fat and cholesterol, so it takes less to satisfy an appetite. Another plus is that sustainable menu planning supports and encourages small producers like Lindner Bison, and the small meat processors who help them stay in business. With customer support, together we can all make a positive difference!

RESOURCES

ARTICLES, BOOKS, DOCUMENTARIES

Achbar, Mark and Abbott, Jennifer, directors "The Corporation"

Berry, Wendell, "The Unsettling of America"

Fearnley-Whittingstall, Hugh, "River Cottage Meat Book for Carnivores with a Conscience," and "The Chicken Out Challenge"

Gear, Kathleen O'Neal and W. Michael, "Bison Genetics-The New War Against Bison," and "A Brief History of the Evolution of Bison"

Gerrish, Jim, "Kick the Hay Habit," and "Management Intensive Grazing"

Henderson, Fergus and Justin Piers Gellatly, "Beyond Nose to Tail"

Henderson, Fergus, "The Whole Beast Nose to Tail Eating"

Henderson, George, "Farmer's Progress, A Guide to Farming"

Jackson, Wes, "Becoming Native to this Place"

Judy, Greg, "No Risk Ranching, Custom Grazing on Leased Land," and "Comeback Farms"

Kaufman, Frederick, "How Goldman Sachs Created the Food Crisis" April 27, 2011

Keith, Lierre, "Vegetarian Myth"

Kenner, Robert, director "Food, Inc."

Korten, David C., "The Great Turning"

Moore, Michael, director "Capitalism: A Love Story"

Morgan, Dan, "Merchants of Grain"

Oliver, Jaime, "Food Revolution"

Pate, J'Nell L., "Livestock Hotels, America's Historic Stockyards"

Pollen, Michael, "Omnivore's Dilemma," "In Defense of Food," "Food Rules," "Power Steer"

Robinson, Jo, "Why Grassfed is Best," "Pasture Perfect"

Quilty, David, "Greenwash of the Week: The Nature Conservancy and Corporate Donors" September 29, 2010

Salatin, Joel, "$alad Bar Beef," "Pastured Poultry Profit$," "Everything I want to do is Illegal," and "The Sheer Ecstasy of being a Lunatic Farmer"

Spurlock, Morgan, director "Super Size Me"

Welch, Brian, "Beautiful and Abundant"

Woolf, Aaron, director "King Korn"

ORGANIZATIONS
American Grassfed Association
Animal Welfare Approved
California Farm Link
Slow Food Organization
Western Bison Association
Weston A. Price Foundation

WEBSITES
Acresusa.com
Americangrassfed.org
Animalwelfareapproved.org
Beginningfarmers.org
Californiafarmlink.org
Eatwild.com
Farmtransition.org
Lindnerbison.com
Michaelpollan.com
Montanahistoricalsociety.org
Motherearthnews.com
Polyfacefarms.com
Stockmangrassfarmer.net
Thegoodhuman.com
Westonaprice.org